Form and Function in Plants

FORM AND FUNCTION
IN PLANTS

John D. Dodd
Professor of Botany
Iowa State University

Drawings by
KATHLEEN THOMAS O'SULLIVAN

The Iowa State University Press
Ames, Iowa, U.S.A.

PROFESSOR JOHN D. DODD, who is in charge of the plant kingdom course at Iowa State University, teaches advanced courses in plant morphology and has developed special research interests in the fresh-water algae. This book is an outgrowth of Dr. Dodd's twenty years' experience and intense devotion to the teaching of general botany. He holds the doctor of philosophy degree from Columbia University and the master's degree from the University of Vermont, following undergraduate work at New York State College of Forestry.

Library of Congress Catalog Card Number 61–10550

*To the memory
of my father*
ERNEST S. DODD

Preface

The present book is an integration of morphological and physiological subject matter begun at the level of the green algae. Discussions of green plants at various levels of the plant kingdom then are used to build an appreciation of the major evolutionary steps leading to the flowering plants. This approach also has a secondary advantage in that it makes unnecessary the cursory surveys of the plant kingdom which, for reasons of time limitations, frequently are squeezed into the last moments of many a one-term course in botany.

Discussions of the fungi are undertaken after completion of the story of the green plants, thus eliminating a traditional interruption in the sequence of topics in which the evolution of higher plants from the green algae is considered. A coherent treatment of the fungi has been achieved through discussions of growth habits, nutrition, and methods of reproduction rather than a class by class analysis. Discussions of the nature of viruses and bacteria are left for separate introductory courses treating these organisms.

During the past few decades the subject matter of general botany at the college level has become so voluminous and complex that it can no longer be covered adequately in a one year series of introductory courses. Throughout this same period, however, there has been constant pressure from curriculum builders favoring the reduction of general botany to a one-term course or the dispersal of its subject matter within a course in biology.

One-term courses in general botany frequently serve in the dual capacity of being terminal for the casual student and introductory for the plant science major. The alternative practice of offering a stringent course for majors and a light course for the rest of the college community renders a disservice to the sizable group of students who do not grasp the potentialities of a career in botanical science until their first exposure to the breadth and depth of the subject matter.

It is also apparent that those students who desire or need well-rounded training in general botany should be encouraged to begin promptly the series of advanced courses which are standard offerings by most botany departments. In this way, stimulating contacts with subject matter specialists follow the introductory course and are appreciated before the engendered interest dissipates.

With respect to the nature of the advanced courses, exact titles and course contents vary among institutions. In general, however, they cover the following topics:

1. The external structure (gross morphology) and internal anatomy of the higher plants.
2. The functions of plants (physiology).
3. An outline of the plant kingdom which includes the morphology of reproductive mechanisms.
4. The classification of plants (taxonomy) and methods of plant identification.
5. The study of biology at the cellular level (cytology).
6. The mechanisms of inheritance (genetics) and their relation to evolution.
7. The relation of plants to their environments (ecology) and the distribution of plants (plant geography).
8. The diseases of plants (plant pathology).
9. The relation of plants to human affairs (economic botany).
10. The history of botany and botanical philosophy.

When an educational program such as the one outlined above is followed, the full year course in introductory botany may be abandoned with some degree of equanimity. If this is done, however, the conduct and content of the one-term introductory course must be subjected periodically to an imaginative reappraisal. A careful selection and integration of topics which can be covered adequately within available class time is vital to the success of such a course. Equally important is a degree of flexibility permitting modifications to fit the interests and personality of the instructor. A widespread standardization of introductory botany courses could not, and perhaps should not, be expected to emerge from such a procedure. Instead, a variety of courses can result with their individual successes being measured, in part, by their effectiveness in furthering the over-all program of botanical training at any given institution.

* * *

My acknowledgments are with deepest appreciation. The skilled pen of Mrs. Kathleen Thomas O'Sullivan has translated the need for pertinent illustrations into a gratifying reality. Working equally well from materials, ideas, and crude sketches by the author, Mrs. O'Sullivan has provided more than 300 graphic interpretations of the subject matter in the text.

Unless otherwise credited, the photographs were taken by the author. However, it is a distinct pleasure to acknowledge professional assistance by the Iowa State University Agricultural Experiment Station Photo Laboratory, under the direction of Mr. Lou Facto, in processing the negatives and prints. The majority of the photomicrographs of stained sections were taken from slides in the departmental collections prepared by, or under the direction of, Dr. John E. Sass.

Several of the author's colleagues have read portions of the manuscript at some stage in its development. Among them are Dr. Joseph C. Gilman, Dr. John E. Sass, Dr. Lois Tiffany, Dr. C. Clark Bowen, and Dr. Frederick G. Smith. Their thoughtful comments have been deeply appreciated. Dr. Harold C. Bold of the Department of Botany, University of Texas, was most kind in agreeing to review and comment on Chapter 8. The aid of the Botany and Plant Pathology department secretarial staff is gratefully acknowledged and the author is indebted to Dr. Wendell H. Bragonier, Head of Botany and Plant Pathology at Iowa State University, for encouraging preparation of the manuscript by making available secretarial services and other facilities of the department.

A special debt is owed various manuscript reviewers, who customarily remain anonymous, for suggesting numerous improvements in the manuscript itself, and to the Iowa State University Press personnel for effectively carrying forth the intent of the writing. The publisher has deferred to the author's wishes, however, in most matters pertaining to the organization of the subject matter. Thus the final product remains a personal responsibility.

JOHN D. DODD

Table of Contents

CHAPTER 1 | Man in the World of Plants

The world of man, in his natural state at least, is a green world. Portions of this world turn yellow and brown with the changing seasons but, sooner or later, the verdancy of plants returns. Otherwise man could not survive.

The greenness of the world existed long before man entered the premises and quite probably will continue to exist long after his departure. Man's evolutionary development, his brief period of recorded history, and his life as an individual are all inescapably intertwined in the pattern of the green world.

Each year man plants seeds in the soil, cares for the resultant plants in various ways, and eventually reaps a harvest. Yet, no individual has any real part in the creation of this harvest on which his own existence as well as the existence of the balance of the world's population depends.

Thus, in an approach toward understanding his place in the universe, man cannot reasonably avoid the study of plants. When carried on in a scientific manner, this study is called botany.

One of the more exciting stories which botanists can tell portrays the evolutionary development of the higher green plants, and portions of this story provide the major themes of this book. The forms and functions of primitive plants such as the green algae will be examined from various aspects. Also, the changes in form and the acquisition of new functions which occurred as plants emerged from the sea will be considered. During this period of drastic change a most important need was the provision of modifications which would allow the cells of the higher plants to carry on their basic functions in nonaquatic environments. But before such modifications can be discussed, it is necessary to consider in some detail the basic nature and functions of plant cells.

| # The Green Cell

The food manufacturing abilities of plants are centered in those cells which contain the green pigment, *chlorophyll*. In some plants all of the cells of the plant body are green while, in others, the green cells are segregated in special tissues. The first plant to be considered in detail is one whose entire body consists of a single, microscopic cell which carries on a wide variety of activities.

THE SINGLE-CELLED GREEN ALGA, CHLAMYDOMONAS

Algae are a familiar sight to most people although they may not know them by this name. The brownish green rockweeds of the seashore; the greenish "frog-spit" on the surface of a pond; the misnamed "moss" in a watering tank; the green discoloration of the water in an aquarium; the green stain on the damp and shaded side of a fence post; all these are examples of algae. Some are green as grass. Others are yellow, brown, red, purple, blue, or blue-green. Literally any color of the rainbow is possible among the algae because other pigments may obscure the green of the ever-present chlorophyll. Here we will be concerned mainly with the grass-green algae to which group *Chlamydomonas* belongs.

Individual *Chlamydomonas* cells are so minute, perhaps 1/500 of an inch diameter, that they appear merely as green dots when observed with low magnification. Yet, when a single individual is introduced into a medium suitable for its growth, it will multiply so rapidly that the solution appears green within a few days' time.

Although *Chlamydomonas* may seem to be a simple structure, it is, in reality, a very complicated organism. Figures 2.1 and 2.2 reveal some of the parts of this cell which can be identified when a living individual is observed through a microscope while parts A and B of Figure 2.3 are electron photomicrographs of ultra-thin sections.

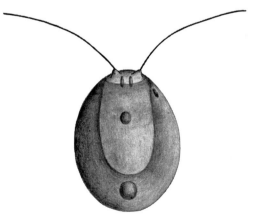

Fig. 2.1. Drawing of an entire cell of **Chlamydomonas,** as seen in the living condition.

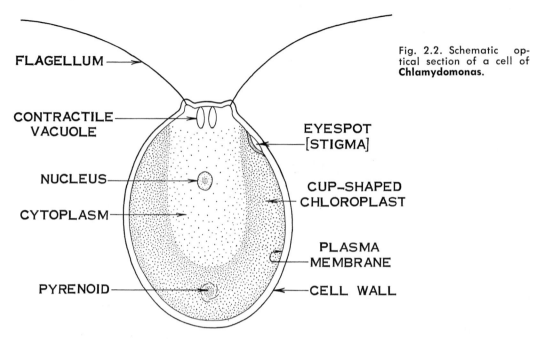

FLAGELLUM →

CONTRACTILE VACUOLE

NUCLEUS

CYTOPLASM

PYRENOID

EYESPOT [STIGMA]

CUP-SHAPED CHLOROPLAST

PLASMA MEMBRANE

CELL WALL

Fig. 2.2. Schematic optical section of a cell of **Chlamydomonas.**

In the living condition *Chlamydomonas* cells move about rapidly but, occasionally, one will become stuck for a moment. With proper lighting the two *flagella* may then be seen thrashing about like whips. It is this whiplike motion of the flagella which moves the cell about. Sometimes, when a cell is oriented correctly, a bright reddish spot may be observed against the green background of the cell. This is the *eye-spot* or *stigma*. Experimental evidence indicates that this structure is light sensitive and, in some way which is not understood, controls the movements of the flagella so that the whole cell may move towards weak light or away from light which is too strong. Occasionally clouds of these green cells congregate in zones of optimum light concentration.

Characteristically the outer surface of plant cells consists of a definite layer in which cellulose is a major component. This layer is called the *cell wall*. In many plants the wall is thick enough to be readily discernible but in *Chlamydomonas* it is thin and difficult to distinguish.

The *protoplasm* within the cell wall has several component parts but not all of them are clearly evident in living cells. The *nucleus*, for instance, is a spherical body which occupies a more or less central position in the cell. But it is often difficult to observe without special staining.

Surrounding the nucleus is the *cytoplasm*, a substance having a consistency similar to that of egg white. Very little evidence of the actual complexity of cytoplasmic structure is obtained by observations with the light microscope.

The green pigments are located in highly modified segments of the cytoplasm which are known as *chloroplasts*. In *Chlamydomonas* each cell has one chloroplast which is a massive, cup-shaped structure larger than any other structure in the cell.

The remaining cytoplasm in which the nucleus is suspended fills the cup of the chloroplast.

Two small bubbles may be apparent in the cytoplasm near the base of the flagella. These appear and disappear in a rhythmic fashion. They are called *contractile vacuoles* and their apparent disappearance is due to a contraction which ejects small drops of fluid from the cell.

A very definite and somewhat spherical spot is observable in the basal portion of the chloroplast. This is called a *pyrenoid*. Tests with iodine demonstrate it to be a center of starch formation.

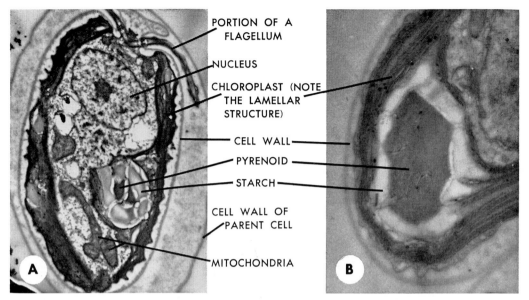

PORTION OF A
FLAGELLUM

NUCLEUS

CHLOROPLAST (NOTE
THE LAMELLAR
STRUCTURE)

CELL WALL

PYRENOID

STARCH

CELL WALL OF
PARENT CELL

MITOCHONDRIA

Fig. 2.3. Cell of **Chlamydomonas** as seen in electron photomicrographs of ultrathin sections. (Courtesy of Stuart Pankratz.) A. Entire section magnified 1,500 diameters. B. Partial section magnified 6,000 diameters.

COMPARISONS WITH OTHER GREEN ALGAE

Among the green algae there are many species which differ greatly from *Chlamydomonas* in appearance. Numerous species have complex plant bodies composed of cells which are permanently united. A large number of green algae lack flagella and are not motile. Furthermore, the cells of many algae are much larger than the cells of *Chlamydomonas*. In some of these the increase in size is due to the development of a large *central vacuole* containing *cell sap* which is a dilute solution of organic and inorganic substances in water. When present the volume of the central vacuole is many times larger than that of any other cell component.

The chloroplasts of many algae (Figs. 2.4, 2.5) differ markedly in shape from the massive cup-shaped form found in *Chlamydomonas*. *Ulothrix*, for example, has a bracelet-shaped chloroplast while *Spirogyra* has a narrow spiral ribbon. The chloroplast of *Oedogonium* is in the form of a finely divided network. The cells of a few green algae contain many small chloroplasts, each of which is shaped like a lens.

The choice of a green alga to illustrate the latter type of chloroplast proved surprisingly difficult. (For many years a very common alga, *Vaucheria*, played varied and useful roles in elementary botany courses, one of its uses being the demonstration of small, lens-shaped chloroplasts. Recently however it was determined that *Vaucheria* should not be classified as a green alga.)

The green alga finally chosen to illustrate the point is a species of *Oocystis* (Fig. 2.4), one of the common inhabitants of the community of microscopic, free-floating, living organisms known as the plankton.

THE GREEN CELLS OF HIGHER PLANTS

It is a point of considerable theoretical interest that the green cells of the vast majority of higher land plants contain chloroplasts of the last-named type. It is generally also true that they have conspicuous central vacuoles and relatively thin cellulose walls. Some of these features are illustrated in (Figs. 2.6A–E) which are drawings of cells from the green tissues of mosses, ferns, pines, corn plants, and apple trees.

This brief introduction to the green cell

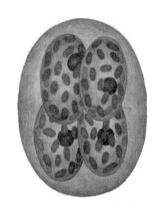

Fig. 2.4. Cells of green algae chosen to illustrate variations in chloroplast structure. (Upper left) **Oedogonium** with a reticulate chloroplast. (Upper right) **Oocystis** with lens-shaped chloroplasts. (Lower left) **Ulothrix** with a bracelet-shaped chloroplast. (Lower right) **Spirogyra** with a spiral chloroplast.

serves to point out the basic similarities between the cells of all green plants. The study of cell structures and functions must now be undertaken in more detail since this is prerequisite to an understanding of the structure and function of many-celled plants.

Figure 2.7 is a diagrammatic representation of a mature cell from the green tissues of a higher plant. The labels indicate most of the parts of such a cell which can be made visible for observation with the light microscope. In the following pages

Fig. 2.6. Green cells from the leaves of various higher plants drawn schematically to illustrate their basic similarities: (A) moss, (B) fern, (C) pine, (D) corn, and (E) apple.

Fig. 2.5. Photomicrograph of a cell of **Spirogyra**.

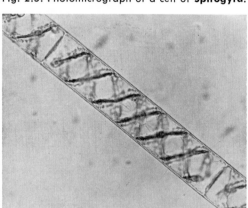

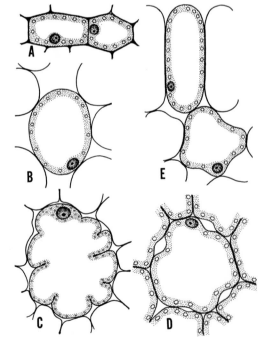

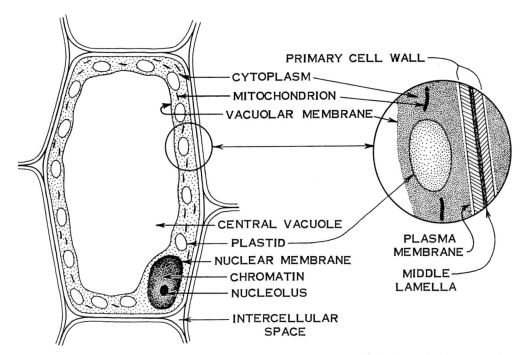

CYTOPLASM

MITOCHONDRION

VACUOLAR MEMBRANE

PRIMARY CELL WALL

CENTRAL VACUOLE

PLASTID

NUCLEAR MEMBRANE

CHROMATIN

NUCLEOLUS

INTERCELLULAR
SPACE

PLASMA
MEMBRANE

MIDDLE
LAMELLA

Fig. 2.7. Diagrammatic representation of a mature green cell (of a higher plant) as seen in a thin section. The inset drawing is an enlargement of a portion of the cell wall and adjoining cytoplasm.

Protoplasm

Protoplasm is the general name for the substance of living matter and the term, *protoplast,* is often used to indicate a unit of protoplasm enclosed within a cell wall. The major subdivisions of protoplasm are the nucleus and the cytoplasm. It is more convenient to describe each of these separately than it is to give a detailed characterization of protoplasm as a whole.

Much of the following discussion is based on information about protoplasm which has accumulated in the past one hundred years through the efforts of numerous workers using the light microscope as a basic research tool. However, the advent of the electron microscope has revitalized this field of study and much new information concerning the so-called fine structure of protoplasm, has become available. Some of this new information

of this chapter each of these parts will be discussed in some detail.

will be included where deemed appropriate to an introductory discussion.

The Cytoplasm

Optically clear cytoplasm, i.e. cytoplasm without granules, is often called *hyaloplasm.* In physical and chemical terms, it is a complex, colloidal system containing various proteins, fats, carbohydrates, mineral salts, and a high percentage of water. Its general consistency has been likened to that of egg white. At times it exists in a fluid or *sol* form while at others it may exist as a semisolid or *gel.* Changes in the physical state of cytoplasm between sols and gels are reversible in the living condition.

One important feature of cytoplasm is the formation of surface membranes wherever it comes in contact with other cell parts. These *cytoplasmic membranes* are not readily visible but they have been proved to exist and to play a vital role in cell functions.

The membrane adjacent to the cell wall is commonly termed the *plasma membrane* while the *vacuolar membrane* separates the cytoplasm from the vacuole. The *nuclear membrane* which separates the cytoplasm from the nucleus is considered to be a part of the nucleus. Evidence from studies with the electron microscope indicates that there are membranes separating each plastid from the cytoplasm. Electron photomicrographs also show that each membrane is, actually, a double layered structure.

In mature plant cells with large central vacuoles, the cytoplasm is spread into a very thin layer which completely lines the cell wall. Occasionally, delicate strands of cytoplasm may cross the vacuole from one side to the other, or from the walls to a centrally suspended mass in which the nucleus is located (Figs. 2.4, 2.5).

When living cells are observed with the compound microscope the top and bottom walls of the cell and the cytoplasm adjacent to them do not absorb enough light

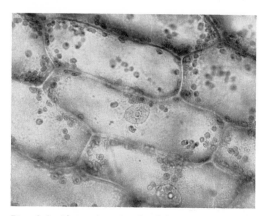

Fig. 2.8. Photomicrograph of living green cells from the leaf of **Elodea.** Nuclei and chloroplasts are evident.

to be readily visible. The side walls and adjacent cytoplasm which are viewed on edge absorb more light and, by contrast, are much more visible. This may result in an optical illusion that cells are two-dimensional unless the fine adjustment of the microscope is manipulated to permit observation of the same cell in several planes.

When cytoplasm is in the fluid or sol condition it may move about the cell in a flowing manner. This process is called *cyclosis.* Often the chloroplasts are moved about by such movements and even the more massive nucleus may be displaced. A standard classroom demonstration involves microscopic examination of the leaf cells of *Elodea* (Fig. 2.8). With magnification on the order of 430 diameters the chloroplasts appear to be moving at a considerable rate of speed. However, if the movement is timed and the distances involved are converted to a macroscopic scale of reference, the rate of movement seems very slow indeed. So slow, in fact, that it would take centuries for a single chloroplast to travel from New York to Chicago at the measured rate.

The Cytoplasmic Enclosures

The basically clear substance of the cytoplasm usually contains a variety of objects which alters its appearance. An attempt could be made to separate these into living and nonliving components but such an attempt has elements of futility which make it undesirable.

Granules — These may be particles of various kinds; stored food, minute crystals, or organic particles of uncertain nature.

Vacuoles — Plant cells tend to accumulate water in small droplets, or vacuoles, within the cytoplasm. As mentioned previously, they are separated from the cytoplasm by vacuolar membranes. Usually the cell sap in the vacuoles contains low concentrations of both soluble inorganic salts and organic substances. Sometimes it may be colored due to the presence of water soluble pigments such as *anthocyanin.*

Much of the visible growth of plants is due to the increasing size of vacuoles as they absorb water. Commonly there is a gradual fusion of many small vacuoles into a few large ones and, eventually, these merge into a single large central vacuole (Fig. 2.9). By the time this happens the cytoplasm has been stretched so thin that it is barely visible.

Vacuoles may contain *crystals* of many sizes and shapes (Fig. 2.10); some of them are large enough to distort the shape of

Fig. 2.9. A series cf drawings illustrating cell enlargement. Note the fusion of vacuoles and the relation between increasing vacuole size and cell enlargement.

the cell. Crystals represent a method of disposal of excess materials which might have a deleterious effect on cell functions. Usually they are salts of organic acids and calcium or magnesium.

Normally, vacuoles tend to absorb more water than they can contain and this results in an outward pressure (turgor) on the cytoplasm and cell wall. This pressure is responsible in large part for increases in cell size and for the maintenance of the shapes of plant structures such as leaves and young stems. The crispness of celery and the firm texture of many other fresh vegetables and fruits result from the interaction of many cells each of which is exerting pressure against its neighbors.

Mitochondria are relatively small rod-shaped structures which occur in the cytoplasm. They are not particularly distinct in living cytoplasm but can be rendered visible through the light microscope by appropriate techniques for killing and staining cells during the process of preparing the cells for examination. Their structure is more apparent in electron photomicrograph (Figs. 2.3, 2.25). Much evidence exists that the mitochondria play

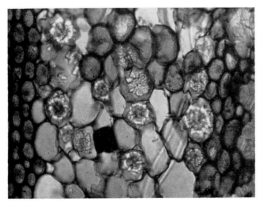

Fig. 2.10. Crystals in cells (as seen in a transverse section of a basswood twig).

a very important role in cell functions. Most of the chemical reactions in living matter involve organic catalysts called enzymes and it is probable that mitochondria are composed of series of enzymes which control certain patterns of chemical reactions in the cytoplasm.

Ribosomes are much smaller particles which are visible only with the electron microscope. Their general nature and significance are discussed subsequently.

Plastids

Plastids are discrete units of cytoplasm which have a denser appearance than undifferentiated cytoplasm. They may be colorless, or variously colored, and perform certain special functions.

One of these functions is the formation of starch from simple sugar (and this is a separate function from the manufacture of simple sugar). As far as the plants which we will study are concerned, this process can occur only in plastids.

The ability to convert sugar to starch is more or less independent of the color of the plastid. It can occur in the green plastids of a leaf cell but it can occur also in the colorless plastids of roots or underground stems such as the potato tuber.

The change from sugar to starch is facilitated by enzymes. In the alga *Chlamydomonas* the enzyme system necessary for this process is located in the pyrenoid (or at its surface) as is indicated by the presence of starch around the pyrenoid (Figs. 2.2, 2.3). Sometimes the plastids of higher plants contain minute protein crystals which may be homologous with pyrenoids of algae since they seem to be centers of starch formation. However, they are not present in plastids of all higher plants. Nor for that matter, are pyrenoids always present in green algae. A further discussion of starch formation is undertaken with the material on building materials and storage products.

The colors of plastids are dependent on the pigments which are present in them. There are three classes of pigments in algae and the higher plants. They are the chlorophylls, carotenes, and xanthophylls.

The three major plastids have colors which are determined by the pigments present.

1. *Chloroplasts* — chlorophylls *a* and *b*, carotenes, and xanthophylls are present and the normal color is grass green.

2. *Chromoplasts* — only carotenes and xanthophylls are present and the normal color is some other color than green.

3. *Leucoplasts* — pigments are present in extemely low concentrations and these plastids appear colorless.

The term *chromatophore* should be mentioned here since it is often used with reference to the plastids of algae particularly those which are not grass green even though they contain chlorophyll *a.* Chromatophore means "color-bearer" and the term has a much wider range of meaning than chloroplast. Chloroplasts are chromatophores, but not all chromatophores are chloroplasts.

The three types of plastids listed above are more or less interconvertible. A chloroplast may become a chromoplast by losing its chlorophyll *a* and *b,* while retaining the more stable carotenes and xanthophylls. This happens commonly in the ripening of fruits and in autumnal leaf coloration. A chloroplast may become a leucoplast by losing most of its pigments. A chromoplast may become a chloroplast, as for example in carrots where "greening" occurs when portions of the root are exposed to light. Leucoplasts may become chloroplasts also, as in the case of the "greening" of potato tubers lying too close to the surface of the soil.

As noted previously, the chloroplasts in the cells of the higher plants are small and numerous having a somewhat flattened shape like a lens. Chromoplasts tend to be somewhat more irregular in shape. The chromatophores of algae exhibit a wide range in shape and structure, an exception being the blue-green algae which lack definitely organized plastids. In this group of plants which is much more primitive than the green algae the pigments are distributed in the outer layer of cytoplasm.

COLORATION IN PLANTS

Green plants are not necessarily green at all times. The spectacular phenomenon of autumn coloration results from a change in the normal green color of the leaves of our common trees. The leaves of certain widely cultivated horticultural varieties of of plants are normally variegated (having a mixture of colors). Parts of such leaves are green while others may be white, red, yellow, etc. The leaves of a few plants appear bright red with no indication that chlorophyll is present at all. Plants grown in poor light, or lacking certain chemical substances may have yellow leaves. The newly formed leaves of some plants may be yellow for some time before they become green. Algae growing at the surface of a pond where they are exposed to intense light may become yellowed while those underneath remain a bright green.

Much can be learned about the nature of pigments from some very simple experiments. For example, if the red leaf of an *Irisene* plant or a *Coleus* plant is placed in boiling water, it will change almost immediately to a bright green color. The slightly pink color of the water indicates that the red color is water soluble. The green on the other hand remains in the leaf indicating that it is not water soluble. The red pigment is an *anthocyanin.* It is dissolved in the cell sap and retained there because of a basic inability to diffuse through living cell membranes. Heating destroys these membranes and the red pigment diffuses out.

Anthocyanins are of considerable interest even though their functions are little understood. Some plants contain them at all times while others manufacture them only under certain conditions. Many plants never form them at all. In the plants which do form them they are an indication of considerable sugar in the cell sap since sugar is essential for their formation.

Their presence in some plants is an indication of an abnormal sugar supply. When tomato leaves turn red for example, there may be a phosphorus deficiency in the soil. The lack of sufficient phosphorus interferes with normal starch formation and the accumulated sugar is used to form anthocyanin.

The anthocyanins are natural indicators of the acidity or alkalinity of the cell sap, being red under acid conditions and blue when basic. Many of the pink, red, purple, and blue flowers owe their colors to anthocyanins. White flowers lack pigments entirely.

The bright red skin of an apple contains abundant anthocyanin. This adds much to the economic eye appeal of the apple but little or nothing to its nutritional value.

The green color of leaves may be extracted by placing leaves in alcohol and heating. Other organic solvents such as acetone will also remove the green pigments. Solutions of extracted pigments from green tissues normally have a bright grass green color. When an equal amount of benzene is added to an alcoholic extract the two solvents mix but, when a few drops of water are added and the mixture is shaken well, a sharp separation occurs between the benzene and the alcohol. The benzene layer is uppermost and appears a darker shade of green while the lower layer of alcohol usually has a yellow color. This crude demonstration shows that there are at least two different pigments in the original extract.

In recent years more refined techniques such as those involving paper chromatography have made it possible to separate the various plastid pigments in relatively simple classroom demonstrations (Fig. 2.11). These methods of pigment separation have shown us also that there are actually several kinds of carotenes and xanthophylls. However, the differences between them are small and their basic structures are similar. The most common carotene is a bright golden yellow while the xanthophylls have various shades of yellow, orange, red, or brown. The carotenoid pigment *lycopene* is responsible for the red color of ripe tomatoes, while a brown xanthophyll gives the characteristic color to a large group of sea weeds.

Many fruits are green while immature and a change in color is an indication of approaching ripeness. This color change is often due to a rapid disintegration of chlorophylls *a* and *b*, which normally mask the carotenes and xanthophylls. When the two green pigments disintegrate, the more stable carotenoid pigments become visible and the fruits take on shades of yellow and orange. In many cases the carotenes and xanthophylls later disintegrate leaving the fruits with a brownish color.

In some mature fruits, anthocyanins may be also present giving tones of bright red, pink, purple, or blue to the fruits. As noted above, the carotenoid pigment, lycopene, is responsible for the red color of ripe tomatoes. This is also true for red peppers. The fruiting structures of algae (see *zygotes*) frequently become brightly colored due to the accumulation of pigments other than chlorophyll.

Fig. 2.11. Separation of chloroplast pigments in a paper chromatogram. The pigments (from top to bottom) are carotene, chlorophyll **a**, and chlorophyll **b**. (The xanthophylls are not evident.)

The colors of autumn leaves are due in part to a similar series of changes. Disintegration of the green pigments permits the yellows and oranges to become visible for a brief period before they also disintegrate and the dead leaf turns brown. The bright reds and scarlets which turn whole hillsides to flame are due largely to the presence of anthocyanins. Degradation products of the various pigments add many subtle shades to the color scheme.

It is evident that the color spectacular of autumn is not due to freezing temperatures since it begins often before the first frost. Changes in the length of days, a gradual lowering of the average temperature, and other related factors are more responsible for the visible changes than is Jack Frost.

As though in preparation for the eventual leaf fall, a special layer of tissue forms across the base of a petiole of a leaf. This abscission layer seals off the normal channels by which food is conducted away from the leaf. In some plants, like the sugar maple, the accumulated products of photosynthesis are utilized in the formation of anthocyanin which turns the leaf red.

As noted previously, the grass green algae contain the same chlorophyll pigments as do the higher plants. This, plus the additional fact that they are able to form starch, are two of the most emphatic arguments in favor of the hypothesis that the higher plants evolved from this group of algae.

All of the other groups of algae contain chlorophyll *a* but most of them lack chlorophyll *b*. Chlorophyll *c* or chlorophyll *d* occur in some of these other groups but the blue-green algae contain only chlorophyll *a* in addition to carotenes and xanthophylls. The additional pigments which occur in some algae have a different chemical nature entirely and will not be discussed here.

Chemical Nature of Plant Pigments

The basic structure of the molecule of chlorophyll *a* has been known reasonably well for a long time. It contains 55 car-

bon atoms, 72 hydrogen atoms, 5 oxygen atoms, 4 nitrogen atoms, and a single atom of magnesium. These atoms are arranged as four *pyrrol* rings centered about the single magnesium atom with a long chain alcohol, *phytol*, attached (Fig. 2.12). The structure of chlorophyll *b* is basically the same, differing merely

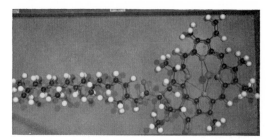

Fig. 2.12. A molecular model of chlorophyll **a**.

by the presence of one more oxygen atom and the absence of two of the hydrogens. The recent laboratory synthesis of chlorophyll is a milestone in scientific history.

It is an interesting commentary that the molecule of *heme,* which is part of the hemoglobin of red blood cells, has a similar structure except that it has an iron atom in the center instead of an atom of magnesium.

The carotene molecule contains 40 carbon atoms and 56 hydrogen atoms. A chemist would describe it as an unsaturated hydrocarbon. As noted previously, the many different kinds of xanthophylls show a wide range of color. Xanthophylls are probably derived from carotene by the addition of one or more oxygen atoms and their color characteristics seem to vary with the number of oxygen atoms present in the molecule.

The anthocyanins are chemically referred to as glycosides. When they are broken down into component parts, one of these parts is always a sugar.

THE MANUFACTURE OF FOOD

It has been emphasized that starch formation is a process by which sugar is converted into a storage product and that it is not a part of the basic food manufacturing process. Both sugar and starch are considered to be foods but the word food has so many variations in meaning that it fails precise definition. For our purposes, a *food* is any substance which can be broken down by living organisms to release energy. However, popular usage of the term *plant food* for various kinds of chemicals required for plant growth has led to a much broader interpretation of the word. Many authorities in the study of plant nutrition now use two terms, *organic nutrients* and *inorganic nutrients*, to distinguish between these basic concepts of the meaning of food.

Organic nutrients fall into three general and familiar categories, *carbohydrates, fats, and proteins*. (Research done during the past decade indicates that a fourth category, that of the *nucleic acids*, should be added to this list. These important compounds are discussed briefly under the material on chromosomes.)

Carbohydrates contain atoms of carbon, hydrogen, and oxygen in the ratio of $1:2:1$. The basic unit of molecular structure of a carbohydrate can be written as CH_2O. In fact the term, carbohydrate, literally means carbon water. CH_2O units are linked together in various ways to give a wide variety of different chemical compounds. For example, the simple sugar, glucose, contains six such units, $C_6H_{12}O_6$.

Fats are similar to carbohydrates in being composed of only carbon, hydrogen, and oxygen atoms but the proportion of oxygen atoms is much less.

All proteins contain carbon, hydrogen, oxygen, and nitrogen. Most of them, in addition, contain sulfur.

Carbon, hydrogen, oxygen, nitrogen, and phosphorus are significant in the structure of nucleic acids.

Organic nutrients, with their available energy, are important to all living organisms, both plant and animal, since living matter requires a constant expenditure of energy in order to remain alive. Without an energy supply, protoplasm shortly becomes disorganized. We eat organic nutrients because we are hungry, but the hunger is part of a complex response to a reduction in the quantity of energy containing substances available to our protoplasm. (The complexity of this hunger response is well evidenced by our national tendency towards overeating.)

Most people are aware that the ultimate source of the energy in organic nutrients is sunlight and that this is stored, somehow or other, by green plants. However, the total amount of such energy storage is little realized. A simple demonstration can be visualized by making a comparison of the size of a fire produced by a single grain of corn with the blaze given off by a single mature corn plant when dry enough to burn. A bushel of corn might be used to plant six acres or to make an adequate fire for broiling hamburgers. But try to imagine the conflagration if all of the dried corn plants from six acres were stacked in one pile and burned. Yet each corn plant grows from but a single grain and all of the energy to provide the imagined fire would have been stored in the plant as a result of the process of photosynthesis.

Or, if the same situation were examined from another angle and the corn were harvested with a yield of 50 bushels per acre, the six acres would yield 300 bushels with a total market value of several hundred dollars. The value of any crop plant depends to a large extent on the amount of energy supplying foods which it contains. From a strictly mercenary point of view, therefore, it may be concluded that green plants have an enviable ability to convert sunlight into money.

When a corn plant, or wood, or any other carbohydrate-containing substance is burned, several events occur simultaneously and rapidly. Gaseous oxygen from the atmosphere is used up. Another gas, carbon dioxide, is released to the atmosphere in equal volume to the oxygen consumed. Water in the form of water vapor is formed, and energy in the form of heat is released. In other words, organic matter and oxygen are combined to form carbon dioxide and water with an accompanying release of energy. If the organic matter burned is a carbohydrate then the reaction may be summarized in the following way:

$$CH_2O + O_2 \longrightarrow CO_2 + H_2O + energy$$

Now suppose that this reaction were reversed:

$$CO_2 + H_2O + energy \longrightarrow CH_2O + O_2$$

This is, basically, the process which green plants are able to perform in sunlight. It is called photosynthesis and is the essential function of the green cell.

The simple sugar *glucose* is one of the products of photosynthesis which accumulates in plant cells and the above reaction can be rewritten in terms of production of glucose by the simple expedient of multiplying everything through by 6:

$$6\ CO_2 + 6\ H_2O \xrightarrow[\substack{\text{living plants} \\ \text{with chlorophyll}}]{\text{energy from light}} C_6H_{12}O_6 + 6\ O_2$$

When written in this way photosynthesis appears to be a very simple process. Actually, however, it occurs as a series of reactions, some of which are well understood while others are still being studied by research workers.

It should be noted that photosynthesis not only produces the basic foods which sustain animal life but also releases molecular oxygen to the atmosphere, oxygen which is essential to the respiration process by which the stored energy in foods is made available for use in most living organisms. The planktonic (free-floating) algae of the ocean have a special significance in this connection. They are more abundant than the plants of the land and their total production of oxygen during photosynthesis is of enormous importance in maintaining the atmospheric balance. A few other natural phenomena result in a release of oxygen but the total amount involved is insignificant in comparison with that released during photosynthesis.

The normal concentration of oxygen in the atmosphere is slightly less than 20 per cent. This must be replaced constantly because the supply is depleted by fires and other oxidative processes including the more common type of respiration carried on by plants and animals at all times.

In this day and age, the necessity of oxygen for life is common knowledge. Yet scarcely two hundred years have elapsed since Priestley demonstrated that a green sprig of mint, when placed in a closed jar containing air unfit to keep a mouse alive, would so affect the air that in slightly more than a week's time, a mouse could live perfectly well in the jar. It is understandable that he failed to appreciate that part of the success of his experiment was due to the fact that the plant was exposed to light.

EXPERIMENTS WITH PHOTOSYNTHESIS

Many simple demonstrations rely on the presence of starch as proof that photosynthesis has occurred under the circumstances of the experiment even though, as mentioned previously, starch is not a direct product of photosynthesis. Starch cannot be formed unless sugar is present and thus the presence of starch means that sugar was there previously. Starch is less mobile, easier to test for, and more revealing of the site of photosynthesis than is sugar.

The Necessity of Carbon Dioxide For Photosynthesis

It is a relatively easy matter to remove carbon dioxide from the atmosphere with sodium hydroxide or barium hydroxide. The plants to be tested should be placed in identical closed chambers, one of which has a normal supply of carbon dioxide while the other is exposed to an atmosphere without carbon dioxide. Preferably there should be a constant flow of atmosphere through both chambers. Also, an avoidance of exposure to direct sunlight is advisable to prevent overheating in the chambers. Both plants should be "light-starved" (i.e., kept in a dark place) for a day or more prior to the experiment so that the leaves are free of stored starch at the start of the experiment. Design of the experiment should take into account the facts that organisms in the soil are producing carbon dioxide all of the time and that the plant itself produces carbon dioxide in respiration. It is perfectly possible to use a green alga which stores starch in this experiment.

The plants are allowed to grow in the two chambers for a reasonable length of time. Afterwards the chlorophyll is removed with a solvent like alcohol or acetone, and the photosynthetic tissue is treated with an iodine solution. The appearance of a typical blue black coloration is evidence that starch is present and, therefore, that photosynthesis has occurred in the atmosphere with carbon dioxide. Its absence in plants grown without carbon dioxide indicates that photosynthesis has not occurred.

The significance of carbon dioxide in photosynthesis and the chemistry of the compounds produced has to do largely with characteristics of the carbon atom which enable it to combine with other carbon atoms as well as other kinds of atoms to form a vast array of natural and synthetic compounds having an infinite variety of energy levels and uses. In fact carbon chemistry is the keynote of much of our modern agricultural, industrial, and medical civilization.

The Necessity of Water in Photosynthesis

There are no simple experiments by which the necessity of water in photosynthesis can be demonstrated. Later in this section there will be a discussion of the technique by which the part that water plays in the process was determined.

The Necessity of Chlorophyll in Photosynthesis

There are many greenhouse and garden plants which have variegated foliage. Some varieties of *Coleus* and geranium have leaves which are partly green and

partly white. If such leaves are removed from plants which have been in sunlight for several hours and tested for starch it will be found that the starch pattern follows faithfully the chlorophyll pattern (Fig. 2.13).

Some varieties of plants produce a certain proportion of seedlings without chlorophyll. These albinos will grow almost

Fig. 2.13. Experiment demonstrating the necessity of chlorophyll in photosynthesis. (A) Living leaf of a variegated **Coleus** with the dark areas containing chlorophyll pigments. (B) The same leaf after pigments were removed and the leaf was treated with an iodine solution. The dark areas contain starch.

normally until the food stored in the seed is used up. Without chlorophyll they are unable to manufacture their own food, and they die shortly after the stored food is exhausted (Fig. 2.14).

The Necessity of Light in Photosynthesis

Two plants of the same kind are first placed in the dark for several days. When tests reveal that their photosynthetic tissues are free of starch, one of the plants

Fig. 2.14. An albino (pigmentless) pea seedling among normal green seedlings.

in the light. When the amount of carbon dioxide in the water of each batch is tested after several hours, it will be found that the carbon dioxide concentration of the one in the light has decreased considerably while that in the dark has increased somewhat due to carbon dioxide from respiration.

The Release of Oxygen During Photosynthesis

Oxygen is soluble to a limited extent in water and there is a natural equilibrium between the oxygen in the atmosphere and that dissolved in the waters of the world. When the oxygen supply in water is increased beyond the equilibrium point the excess passes off into the air as a gas frequently forming bubbles which rise to the surface and burst.

The leafy stems of *Elodea* growing in bright sunlight constantly give off such bubbles of oxygen (Fig. 2.15) and they can be collected in test tubes by water dis-

should be placed in light while the other is kept in the dark. A buildup of starch by the plant in the light when compared to the failure of the dark plant to do so is satisfactory evidence of the necessity of light for photosynthesis. Such experiments should not be too lengthy because light also affects other plant processes than photosynthesis. Abnormal growth effects, or a loss of chlorophyll after long periods in the dark, should not be interpreted as direct results of interference with photosynthesis.

The above experiment is not particularly interesting to perform. Many students enjoy printing pictures on leaves by attaching a negative to a starch free leaf and exposing it to the sun for a day or so. When the print is developed by bleaching the leaf and treating with iodine, the starch-iodine reaction shows up where the negative was light and is absent where the negative was dark.

Algae and other water plants can be used in another type of experiment based upon the utilization of carbon dioxide during photosynthesis. The available water plants are separated into two comparable batches and placed in water with a known concentration of carbon dioxide. One batch is placed in the dark and the other

Fig. 2.15. **Elodea** stem with a bubble of oxygen escaping from the cut end.

placement. A glowing splint inserted into such a test tube will burst into flame indicating that the gas is actually oxygen.

When tangled mats of algae in water are exposed to light the bubbles of oxygen given off are often trapped in the mats and cause them to be lifted to the surface of the pond (Fig. 2.16). A standard chemical test for dissolved oxygen (Winkler reaction) may be used to demonstrate

Fig. 2.16. Mat of filamentous algae with numerous oxygen bubbles entrapped, causing it to rise to the surface.

an increase in the oxygen content of water due to photosynthesis by water plants.

Not all of the oxygen formed in photosynthesis escapes from the plant. Some of it is used in the process of respiration which is carried on by the plant at all times. When light is absent or the light intensity is very low, not enough oxygen is formed to satisfy the respiration requirement and oxygen is absorbed from the environment. Under certain conditions the light may be of such an intensity that the respiration requirements for oxygen are just balanced by the amounts produced in photosynthesis. During periods of maximum photosynthesis, however, the production of oxygen may be as much as twenty times that used in respiration.

THE MECHANISM OF PHOTOSYNTHESIS

The preceding discussion has been quite general and includes much of the background information which has signif-

icance to people with a casual interest in plants. However, the search for knowledge about the mechanism of photosynthesis has been one of the most fascinating pursuits in all of science. The following account indicates some of the highlights of that which has been learned, and some of the problems which are still being investigated.

As noted before, the role of water in photosynthesis is difficult to demonstrate by ordinary laboratory methods. In fact, certain assumptions concerning the role of water led research workers astray for many years. For example, the following is an example of an incorrect hypothesis which was once accepted as being a logical method of sugar formation.

The carbon and the oxygen of carbon dioxide were assumed to be split apart and the carbon attached to a water molecule to form formaldehyde which has the formula, CH_2O. Following this step it was thought that six molecules of formaldehyde were linked together to form one molecule of sugar.

This hypothesis stimulated a great deal of research which yielded much information of importance to science. It was proved to be incorrect eventually by research involving the use of the isotope of oxygen known as heavy oxygen. Plants were grown in one set of experiments with the isotope as part of the carbon dioxide supply. In another set of experiments the isotope was part of the water added to the plants. Chemical analyses showed that heavy oxygen was released during photosynthesis only when it had been part of the water.

The results of these experiments have been interpreted to mean that water is split apart during photosynthesis. Therefore, in order to account for the known volume of oxygen produced it is necessary to assume that at least twice as many water molecules enter into the reaction as had been assumed previously. Furthermore, some water is reformed during the process. On the basis of this information the summary reaction for photosynthesis has been modified as follows:

$$6 \ CO_2 + 12 \ H_2O \xrightarrow[\text{living green plant}]{\text{light energy}} C_6H_{12}O_6 + 6 \ H_2O + 6 \ O_2$$

The splitting of water can be represented for discussion purposes by a simple formula:

$$H_2O \longrightarrow H + OH$$

If the hydrogen released in this reaction were in the atomic state it would have a very high energy level and be so active, chemically, that it would last in this state for only a brief period of time. Atomic hydrogen is such a potent reducing agent that it would combine with some other substance immediately. The hydrogen acceptor would be chemically reduced by the process and, thus, its energy level would be increased.

The question arises naturally as to how the water is split apart in such a way that energy is stored in the active hydrogen. Very probably this is accomplished by the combined action of light and chlorophyll. It represents a conversion of the energy of visible light into chemical energy and, as such, is a key to the maintenance of life as we know it.

Our present knowledge of light permits two apparently dissimilar interpretations of its nature. One is that light behaves as a wave movement. Different colors of light have different wave lengths and different energy values. Red light has a longer wave length and a lower energy value than does blue light which is at the opposite end of the spectrum.

The other theory implies that light consists of definite particles, called photons. Each photon consists of a packet of energy called a quantum. The color of light varies with the energy level of the quanta. Colors at the blue end of the spectrum have a higher energy value per quantum while those at the red end have lower values.

Apparently, a photon of any visible light can be absorbed by chlorophyll and take part in the splitting apart of a water molecule. This suggests that there may be energy left over from the impact of a high energy photon such as that of blue light and that this energy might emerge from chlorophyll as a photon with a lower energy value than the photon which entered the reaction. Such a happening would account for a property of chlorophyll which is called *fluorescence*. When chlorophyll is exposed to sunlight, for instance, and observed from an angle which excludes transmitted light it will fluoresce with a dull red color. When ultraviolet light is used in place of sunlight, chlorophyll glows with a bright red color.

When white light is passed through a prism, or a diffraction grating, the various colors are separated into the familiar spectrum of the rainbow: red, orange, yellow, green, blue, indigo, and violet. If the white light passes through a chlorophyll extract before entering the prism it will be observed that most of the blue light and a large portion of the red light are missing. This indicates an especially large percentage of absorption of blue light and red light by chlorophyll.

Such evidence might be interpreted as meaning that red and blue light were the most effective in photosynthesis. However, the proportion of green light in natural sunlight is higher than the proportion of red and blue light. The percentage absorption of green light by chlorophyll in living plants is admittedly small but a small percentage of a large amount results in a significant total and it is considered that green light is as effective as any other in photosynthesis under natural conditions.

The absorption of red and blue light, however, accentuates the greenness of light which is transmitted through a leaf and, thus, accounts for the normal color of vegetation.

It is not difficult to find statements in

the public press as well as in scientific journals to the effect that the problem of the relation between light and chlorophyll is an outstanding challenge to modern science. It is of interest to chemists and physicists, as well as to botanists. An understanding of this relationship might well lead to a practical method for harnessing the energy of sunlight and this certainly would have a revolutionary effect on our civilization.

The change of carbon dioxide to a carbohydrate is a chemical reduction process and the required energy comes from the hydrogen split off during the photolysis of water. However, carbon dioxide and hydrogen do not react directly with one another. Instead, the hydrogen becomes attached to a hydrogen acceptor while the carbon dioxide becomes attached to a carbon dioxide acceptor. A complex series of reactions eventually results in the reduction to carbohydrate. In the course of these reactions three carbon compounds are formed first and are united in pairs to form six carbon sugars.

It is probable that the dissociation of water occurs within the chloroplast in direct association with the chlorophyll molecules. Evidence favoring this interpretation comes from experiments in which chloroplasts isolated from all other cellular components have been stimulated to give off oxygen when exposed to light. Apparently, the hydroxyl groups (OH) become part of organic peroxides from which oxygen is released by enzymatic breakdown within the plastids.

The mechanism of photosynthesis outlined above has been a working hypothesis for the past two decades and, as is the function of working hypotheses, it has both stimulated and given direction to research in this area. As research progresses, changes in any working hypothesis become necessary and are to be expected, particularly when groups of research workers concentrate their attention on potential weaknesses or inconsistencies in the hypothesis. At present there is dissatisfaction in some scientific circles with the concept that light and chlorophyll act in direct concert to split water apart. Therefore modifications of this concept are being considered.

One of these modifications attempts to relate the following points:

1. It is well known that, under natural conditions, a small percentage of water molecules dissociate into hydrogen and hydroxyl ions. The electron previously shared between any pair of such ions before dissociation remains with the hydroxyl ion and thus the hydrogen ion lacks an electron.
2. Evidence exists suggesting that chlorophyll molecules are excited to emit electrons upon absorption of light energy.
3. It has been demonstrated that cells without chlorophyll may reduce carbon dioxide to carbohydrate provided they are supplied with compounds such as ATP (adenosine triphosphate) and $TPNH_2$ (a reduced form of triphosphopyridine nucleotide). Both of these compounds are extremely important biological reducing agents which supply the energy for many reactions in living organisms.
4. It has been demonstrated experimentally that both ATP and $TPNH_2$ can be formed by isolated chloroplasts exposed to light.

One suggestion for relating these observations is that existing TPN molecules may "accept" the electrons emitted by chlorophyll and, at the same time, take up hydrogen ions. In this way TPN could be reduced to $TPNH_2$. The energy of light which caused the emission of electrons from chlorophyll would thus be stored in the $TPNH_2$.

The final series of reactions in the photosynthetic process would be the reduction of carbon dioxide to carbohydrate with the required energy being supplied by $TPNH_2$.

The chlorophyll molecules which donated the electrons must regain them somehow, i.e., they must act as electron acceptors, before the emission of electrons can be repeated. The source of such electrons could well be the hydroxyl ions resulting from the normal dissociation of water. Their extra electrons could be removed by intermediate compounds and passed along to the chlorophyll molecules.

Hydroxyl ions, when freed of their extra electrons, would be enabled to combine to form peroxides which would then break down to release the oxygen of photosynthesis.

Most of our knowledge concerning the importance of ATP was obtained originally through investigations into the oxidative breakdown of sugar in respiration. In this process ADP (adenosine diphosphate) is converted to ATP by the addition of a third phosphate group. Much of the energy liberated in the breakdown of sugar is used to force this third phosphate group into position. The linkage which holds it in position has been likened to a spring under tension and is known as a high energy phosphate bond. The stored energy becomes available for use in other chemical reactions when the third phosphate group is removed, thus releasing the spring.

The significance of ATP in this present discussion arises from the evidence that ATP may also be formed in chloroplasts exposed to light. It has been suggested that electrons emitted from chlorophyll enter into a series of reactions during which ATP is formed. These reactions occur in a cyclic fashion with the electron eventually returning to the chlorophyll at a much lower energy level. It is significant that water is not required as an electron donor in this cycle of events which is called photophosphorylation rather than photosynthesis.

THE THEORY OF LIMITING FACTORS

This theory is an important biological concept which is well illustrated by the problems of photosynthesis. In its simplest concept the theory implies that when a given reaction is conditioned by several factors it will proceed at a rate determined by that one factor which is momentarily present in a least, or limiting, quantity. An appreciation of this theory is vital to an understanding of the vast interplay of forces which controls biological phenomena.

For example, in midmorning of a typical growing day in the corn belt region, the weather will be bright and warm and the soil will contain sufficient water and nutrients to satisfy the immediate plant requirements. Yet the rate of food formation during the day will follow a certain set pattern, reaching a peak in the morning and often halting long before light intensity diminishes extensively. What limits or holds back the productivity?

Probably in the morning it is the carbon dioxide supply. No matter how far from limiting the other factors might be, the process can go on no faster than the rate at which carbon dioxide enters the plant. Certain greenhouse experiments indicate that an artificial increase of the carbon dioxide concentration actually can result in an immediate increase in photosynthesis. However, the complexities of this approach to increased yields are many and imposing and the student is referred to any of the up-to-date texts on plant physiology for further discussion.

Light intensity is a limiting factor during large parts of each twenty-four hour period. Artificial increases in light intensity, especially as a greenhouse practice during winter months, have resulted in increased production rates in some cases. But the effects of light intensity and of light duration are not limited to photosynthesis alone. Several other functions of plants may be affected by such artificial increases and the total result becomes complex.

The reasons for an early afternoon slowdown in photosynthesis are more difficult to interpret since neither light intensity nor atmospheric supplies of carbon dioxide would be altered significantly from conditions prevailing during the late morning peak of production. Possibly the accumulation of the products of photosynthesis may have an effect on the rate at which the process continues. Also evidence has accumulated in recent years that some of the enzyme systems which control one part of the total photosynthesis reaction may be inactivated by prolonged exposure to high light intensities.

UTILIZATION OF THE PRIMARY PRODUCTS OF PHOTOSYNTHESIS

The simple organic nutrients produced during photosynthesis are used in many ways but these may be grouped together loosely under three general headings:

a. Building materials and storage products

b. Sources of energy

c. Effects on the water relations of cells

Building Materials and Storage Products

Simple sugars such as *glucose* are the basic units from which other carbohydrates are constructed. A *sucrose* molecule, for instance, is formed by the linkage of a glucose molecule with a molecule of another simple sugar, *fructose*.

glucose + fructose $\longrightarrow$ sucrose (+ water)

Sucrose is referred to as a *disaccharide*, a term which implies its chemical nature.

Starch is a storage product which, directly and indirectly, is of extreme importance to man. As a storage product it is of importance to the plants which produce it but another important benefit to plants is that starch formation removes the temporary excess of sugar (formed during photosynthesis) from solution. As will be explained later there is a definite relation between the amount of substances in solution in a cell and the tendency of water to enter the cell. Without the starch storage mechanism a green cell might accumulate so much soluble sugar that the inward movement of water would cause the cell to burst.

The formation of starch is, essentially, a condensation process and starch is a *polysaccharide* since large numbers of glucose molecules are linked together to form each large molecule. The units are arranged in linear series but some kinds of starch molecules are branched. Each time a sugar unit is added to the chain a molecule of water is removed. A summary

of this reaction may be written as follows:

n sugar molecules $\longrightarrow$ 1 starch molecule + (*n* − 1) water molecules

(*n* is a large number but is not always the same.)

This chemical linkage is not a simple process since each sugar molecule must enter into a temporary union with a phosphate group (*phosphorylation*) before it can be added to the chain. In addition, the proper enzymes to catalyze the various reactions involved must be present.

Starch formation is not a continuously uniform process and starch is often deposited in layers of slightly different density which are distinguishable under the microscope. (Figure 2.17 is a photomicrograph of starch grains from a potato tuber.)

Starch grains inside a plastid often become many times larger than the plastid itself. This may be observed clearly in sections of old green stems of a plant called *Pellionia*. In such sections, the chloroplasts appear as small green caps

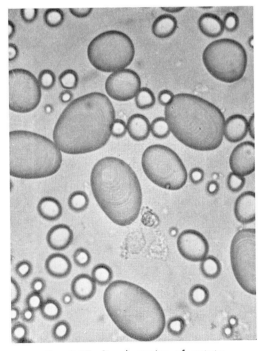

Fig. 2.17. Starch grains of potato.

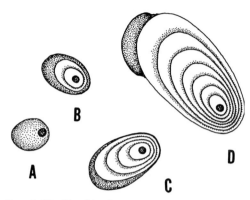

Fig. 2.18. Plastids from stem sections of **Pellionia** containing starch grains in various stages of development. The volume of the starch grain increases from A to D while the volume of the plastid remains relatively unchanged.

attached to the sides of the much larger starch grains which have grown eccentrically within them (Fig. 2.18).

The reversal of starch formation is starch *digestion*. This process is also facilitated by a series of enzymes. Starch digestion is a hydrolytic reaction since a molecule of water must be added each time the linear chain of glucose units is broken.

Cellulose is a major component of the cell wall in the vast majority of green plants and is, thus, a structural product rather than a storage product. It is of direct importance to man in such products as wood, paper pulp, and cellulose derivatives. Man is not able to use cellulose as a food but herbivorous animals have organisms in their digestive tracts which digest cellulose to the simple sugar level and thus make it usable in the animal's diet.

Cellulose is much like starch in that each molecule is made up of a series of glucose units linked together in a linear series. The type of chemical linkage which holds the units together is different, however, so that the physical and chemical characteristics of cellulose differ from those of starch.

The cellulose molecules are bound together in submicroscopic bundles called *micelles* or *microfibrils* which are distributed in a matrix of pectic substances.

Apparently the bundling process is rather untidy in the primary wall and parts of some molecules extend from one microfibril to another. The resulting interconnected framework is both elastic and plastic to a certain extent.

Cellulose has an affinity for water and layers of bound water exist around the microfibrils. This adherent water has a further physical attraction for other molecules of water which are pulled into the spaces between the micelles, thus forcing them apart. Tremendous pressures can be generated when water is absorbed in this way. Rocks can be lifted or split apart by the swelling of dried wooden wedges soaked in water, and warping wood can pull out deeply imbedded spikes. Normally the interior, living cells of plants have walls which are saturated with water, but under certain conditions the replacement of water lost from cell walls can have an important effect on the total functioning of a plant.

The primary cell wall is stretched by cell enlargement to dimensions many times greater than its original area. Undoubtedly cellulose is added to the primary wall during this growth. Later when stretching is complete, secondary wall layers are formed. These are not as plastic as the primary wall and the microfibrils are arranged in a much more orderly fashion. In addition other substances such as *lignin, suberin,* and *cutin* may be deposited in the wall. The nature of such depositions and their effects on cell characteristics will be discussed in a later section.

The individual cells of many-celled plants are cemented together by a chemical derivative of a carbohydrate substance called *pectin*. This is combined with calcium to form a very thin layer between the primary wall layers formed by adjacent cells. This layer is called the *middle lamella*. As is discussed later in this section, its formation is associated with the development of a cell plate which accomplishes the division of the cytoplasm, particularly in higher plants. Some algae, notably *Spirogyra*, form cell plates during cytoplasmic division. Many other algae divide by a process of inward furrowing which pinches the cytoplasm into two parts.

Chlamydomonas divides in the latter manner and the daughter cells separate one from the other immediately. There is no middle lamella in *Chlamydomonas* and the cell wall consists only of a layer of cellulose. However, *Chlamydomonas* may, under certain conditions, secrete abundant quantities of gelatinous substances which "trap" the daughter cells following a division. Many divisions may occur within this matrix and large masses of cells accrue. The significance of this so-called *palmella stage* in the possible evolution of more complex plant bodies is often discussed at length in advanced courses.

Proteins are very complex molecules which are built up as a result of the union of many simpler molecules called *amino acids*. The amino acids are constructed in plant cells from basic units of sugar which are highly modified and then combined with one or more amino groups (NH_2). One simple and important amino acid is *glycine* which has the following molecular structure:

$$H-N-C-C-OH$$

Notice that at one end of this molecule there is an atom of nitrogen which is linked to an atom of carbon. The nitrogen atom and the two hydrogens attached to it constitute an amino group (NH_2). At the other end of the molecule is a carboxyl group which may be written as (COOH).

The various other amino acids have more carbon atoms than the glycine shown above and some of them have amino groups or carboxyl groups attached to other carbons of the chain. Moreover, amino acids can be united (by enzyme action) to form larger molecules. Two molecules of glycine, for instance, may be united to form a molecule of glycyl glycine, which is illustrated below.

$$H-N-C-C-N-C-C-OH$$

Note that the larger, combined, molecule still has a free amino group at one end and a carboxyl at the other, thus making possible the addition of more amino acids. The importance of these observations is that they reveal something of how enormously large protein molecules are constructed by a sort of biological Scrabble game.

There are at least twenty-two naturally occurring amino acids. For the most part they are formed originally in plants. But once formed they may be used over and over again. The protoplasm of both plants and animals constantly builds proteins from amino acids and digests them back to amino acids.

It should be noted again that all proteins contain carbon, hydrogen, oxygen, and nitrogen and that many of them contain sulfur in addition. Certain very important compounds, the nucleoproteins, consist of proteins united with nucleic acids in which phosphorus is a significant element.

Fats consist only of carbon, hydrogen, and oxygen but the proportion of oxygen is much lower than it is in carbohydrates. They are formed by a chemical union between *glycerine* and compounds called *fatty acids*. Glycerine is a three carbon compound, almost like a glucose molecule cut in half. The fatty acids involved are usually long chain hydrocarbon compounds with a carboxyl group attached at one end. When fats are formed, three molecules of fatty acids become attached to each molecule of glycerine. Digestion of fats break the chemical linkages between glycerine and the fatty acids.

Fatty substances are important as storage products, in the normal functioning of protoplasm, and as components of the outer protective layers of stems and leaves.

Carbohydrates as Sources of Energy

One of the major values of a compound like glucose which occurs so commonly in living organisms is that it is a stable, soluble, movable, storage container of energy. Protoplasm is a complex system which requires a continual release of energy within itself in order to maintain its living qualities, and glucose is the most common immediate source of this energy. The process by which it is released is called respiration.

In many respects respiration is similar to burning. Both processes form carbon dioxide and release energy and the more common type of respiration uses up oxygen. In fact the chemical reaction for the burning of a carbohydrate and a summary of the respiration of glucose are identical:

$$C_6H_{12}O_6 + 6\ O_2 \longrightarrow$$
$$6\ CO_2 + 6\ H_2O + 675\ \text{Calories of energy}$$

The relative volumes and weights of materials in this reaction are frequently expressed in terms of the metric system. Although most people understand this system and appreciate its usefulness, many of us continue to visualize such values more readily in terms of ounces and pounds, or quarts and gallons. Since a visual appreciation of the above reaction is deemed important the following comparison is included:

$$C_6H_{12}O_6 \text{ (glucose)}$$

One molecular weight is 180 grams or approximately 0.40 pounds.

plus

$$6\ O_2 \text{ (oxygen)}$$

Six molecular weights equals 192 grams or approximately 0.42 pounds. Since oxygen comprises roughly 20 per cent of the atmosphere, this amount of oxygen would normally occur in about 672 liters, or approximately 177 gallons of air (24 cubic feet).

gives

$$6\ CO_2 \text{ (carbon dioxide)}$$

Six molecular weights equals 264 grams or approximately 0.59 pounds. Since the normal concentration of carbon dioxide in the atmosphere is between .03 and .04 per cent, this amount would normally be diluted into the atmosphere and occupy roughly 400,000 liters or 100,000 gallons of air (13,333 cubic feet). This is, also, the approximate amount of carbon dioxide which could be released from 1.5 pounds of soda in a fire extinguisher.

plus

$$6\ H_2O \text{ (water)}$$

Six molecular weights equals 108 grams or approximately 0.24 pounds (3.8 ounces).

plus

$$675\ \text{Calories energy}$$

675 Calories (675,000 calories) is enough energy to raise the temperature of 6.75 kilograms (15 pints) of water from 0 to 100° C.

However, respiration is a stepwise process during which a great many reactions take place in series, each one controlled by a specific enzyme which acts on the products of the preceding step. Also, at least part of the energy which is released is in the form of usable chemical energy rather than heat. Modern research has revealed the significance to cellular chemistry of the remarkable chemical compound called *adenosine triphosphate* (ATP). This compound is the recipient of most of the energy released during respiration and, by entering into numerous other reactions in living organisms, it releases the energy into these reactions which is necessary to make them go to completion.

Plants are not perfect in transferring all of the energy of glucose to other compounds. Some of the energy does escape as heat and this can be measured with appropriate experiments. Sometimes the escaping heat of respiration of improperly stored grain or silage may accumulate to cause explosions or fires.

In some organisms respiration may occur in the absence of molecular oxygen. This *anaerobic respiration* is a process which releases energy in much smaller amounts than does aerobic respiration. Also, the end products of this reaction are different. *Alcoholic fermentation*, for example, is an anaerobic process which produces alcohol and carbon dioxide instead of water and carbon dioxide:

$$C_6H_{12}O_6 \longrightarrow$$
$$2\ C_2H_5OH + 2\ CO_2 + 25\ \text{Calories energy}$$

In recent years a considerable amount of research work has been done with the biochemistry of respiration. The intermediate steps have been determined and a pattern of cyclic processes involving a series of organic acids has been determined. The first step (*glycolysis*) is a breakdown of a six-carbon sugar to two three-carbon compounds. If molecular oxygen is available, the three-carbon compounds then pass through a cycle of reactions which break them down completely to carbon dioxide and water, with a release of large amounts of energy.

If molecular oxygen is not available, however, the three-carbon compounds pass through a different cycle of reactions in which they are not completely oxidized to carbon dioxide and water. The total amount of energy released is comparatively small and the end products are compounds such as alcohols and organic acids.

The Effects of Sugar Formation
On Water Relations of Plant Cells

In a preceding discussion it was noted that a significant benefit of starch formation to plants is the removal of sugar from solution since the presence of sugar in solution in cells has a direct effect on the tendency of water to enter cells. It is possible to demonstrate that cells with a high concentration of sugar and ready access to water can increase in size to the point of bursting.

In order to understand how this might be it is necessary to consider some of the factors affecting the movements of substances in solution. The first such factor is *diffusion*.

Diffusion

Molecules of substances are constantly in motion. This motion tends to be in a straight line and given molecules travel indefinitely in straight lines providing nothing interferes with the motion. Within the limits of the physical phenomena which concern biology it is unlikely that molecules ever get such an opportunity. Instead, they are deflected repeatedly and move in irregular zig-zag patterns.

Several definitions of diffusion exist,

all of them expressing the idea that molecules can move further in directions where there is the least interference with their motion. One fairly satisfactory definition is that diffusion involves a movement of molecules away from regions of their own greater concentration to regions of their own lesser concentration. Although concentration differences exert a major influence on the direction of diffusion other influences such as temperature and pressure differences have a bearing on the process.

We will be concerned, largely, with the diffusion of gases and of substances in solution in liquids. The following simple demonstration is described in order to illustrate the diffusion of gases. The demonstration (Fig. 2.19) involves the use of a chamber with a volume of several cubic feet. The air in the chamber contains a

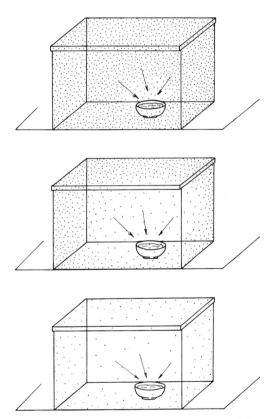

Fig. 2.19. Schematic representation of a diffusion experiment.

known concentration of carbon dioxide. It is assumed that the chamber is sealed to eliminate externally caused air currents and that the temperature is constant to avoid convection currents. Within the chamber a flask containing a concentrated solution of sodium hydroxide in water is uncovered. This solution serves as a carbon dioxide trap since carbon dioxide molecules which enter the solution are retained there because of a chemical reaction with the sodium hydroxide. This means that the concentration of carbon dioxide in the air immediately over the flask is lowered constantly. Molecules of carbon dioxide then move from the surrounding areas in which they are more concentrated to the area of lesser concentration over the flask. As long as the solution continues to absorb carbon dioxide this diffusion toward the flask continues and, in time, most of the carbon dioxide is removed from the air.

The matter of the diffusion of substances in solution is similar. For example, when a cube of sugar is placed in water, the concentration of sugar molecules in solution is greatest immediately around the cube (Fig. 2.20). Their inter-

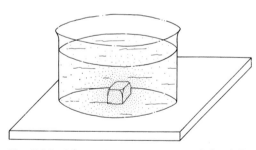

Fig. 2.20. Schematic representation of the diffusion of dissolved sugar molecules away from the immediate vicinity of a sugar cube immersed in water.

ference with each other is greater nearer the cube than farther away and, thus, those on the periphery of the molecular swarm are able to move farther in outward directions before being deflected. Eventually, due to the movements of the sugar molecules themselves, there will be an even distribution of sugar molecules throughout the solution.

Osmosis

When a membrane is placed in the path of diffusing substances the rates of diffusion of the solvent and the individual substances dissolved in it may be altered. Consequently volume changes may occur in the solutions on opposite sides of the membrane. This is particularly true when the membrane is freely permeable to the solvent but only partially permeable or impermeable to the substances which are dissolved in it (solutes). The diffusion of the solvent through such a differentially permeable membrane is called *osmosis*. It is difficult to fix absolute limits to the definition of osmosis and many authorities are inclined to abandon the term entirely. Nonetheless, the concept of osmosis is of distinct biological significance.

Osmosis is usually demonstrated by a simple laboratory experiment (Fig. 2.21). Cellophane tubing (such as that used for sausage casing) makes an excellent demonstration membrane. A piece of the tubing is tied at one end and then filled with a concentrated solution of sugar in water. The open top of the bag is then plugged

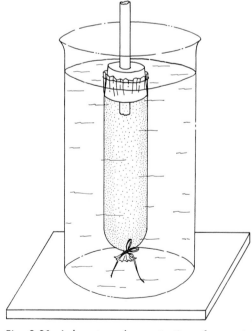

Fig. 2.21. Laboratory demonstration of osmosis.

with a rubber stopper through which a piece of narrow bore glass tubing has been inserted. The glass tube is open at both ends. After tying the cellophane to the stopper carefully so as to avoid leaks, the membrane with the concentrated solution is placed in a beaker of distilled water. In a very short period of time the solution begins to rise in the tubing. It continues to rise for several feet unless leaks develop in the apparatus.

The explanation of the rise is based on certain simple and evident facts:

1. The water in the beaker is 100 per cent water.
2. Due to the presence of the sugar in the internal solution the water inside the membrane has a lower concentration than the external water.
3. The membrane is freely permeable to water.
4. The membrane is not freely permeable to sugar. (Sugar molecules do pass through the membrane but at such a slow rate that the outward diffusion of sugar during a few hours may be ignored.)

According to the definition of diffusion, both the sugar and the water tend to move away from regions of their own greater concentration. The water succeeds in doing this easily but the sugar does not. The inward dffusion of water causes the volume of solution inside the membrane to increase and, thus, the solution rises in the tube. There is an actual hydrostatic pressure devloped in such a situation and it has a considerable magnitude. Pressures in excess of 300 pounds per square inch are well within the range of possibility for laboratory demonstrations of osmosis.

With respect to living cells it is important to note that cell membranes such as the plasma membrane and the vacuolar membrane are differentially permeable. This means that they tend to affect the rates of diffusion of different substances in different ways. In some cases the effect is so slight as to be unmeasurable. In others it amounts to virtual exclusion of particular solutes. In between the extreme cases, the existence of a graded series of effects on diffusion rates is probable.

The term *osmotic pressure* is an expression of the potential maximum pressure which might be generated under ideal conditions when a solution is separated from the pure solvent by a membrane which is permeable only to the solvent. Such ideal conditions do not prevail in living cells and the actual pressures generated as a result of osmosis are always less than the potential maximum. The actual pressure is exerted by the cell sap against the cytoplasm, and through it, against the cell wall. It is called *turgor pressure* and when a positive turgor pressure exists in a cell, the cell is said to be *turgid*. Turgid cells tend to swell and, in growing tissues, this is a factor in cell enlargement. In mature cells, however, the outward pressure is eventually balanced by a resistance of the cell wall to further swelling and by the turgor pressures of adjacent cells.

Plasmolysis

The concentration of soluble materials in the cell sap varies from cell to cell and from plant to plant. Ordinarily it is quite low and may be much less than 5 per cent. This soluble stuff is a mixture of sugars, salts, amino acids, other organic acids, pigments, etc. Some of these are able to pass through the cytoplasmic membranes readily, some pass through slowly, and others are restricted to the cell sap. The water concentration is, conversely, very high, perhaps 95 per cent or more. Thus, when a cell is placed in a solution with a higher solute concentration and, therefore, a lower concentration of water, water diffuses out of the cell. When this happens, the vacuole decreases in volume and the whole protoplast shrinks away from the cell wall. This phenomenon is called *plasmolysis*. It may be defined as the shrinkage in size of the protoplast due to a loss of water by osmosis.

Plasmolysis may be observed readily with water plants such as *Elodea* (Fig. 2.22) or the cells of an alga like *Spirogyra*

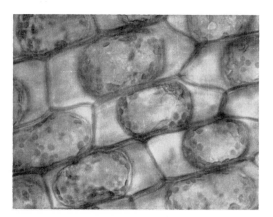

Fig. 2.22. Plasmolyzed leaf cells of **Elodea.**

(Fig. 2.23) which have large central vacuoles. Also, the epidermal cells of *Zebrina* leaves, or beet petioles, show a striking plasmolysis. The latter demonstration is doubly interesting because the cells contain anthocyanin which is restricted to the cell sap. The color intensity is increased as the relative concentration of these pigments is increased by the withdrawal of water.

When a cell has lost so much water by outward diffusion that the cell contents no longer exert a positive pressure on the cell wall, the cell is said to be *flaccid.* This term has a meaning directly opposite to the term turgid mentioned above.

A simple demonstration of how plant form is affected by relative turgidity or flaccidity of cells can be performed with two strips of tissue cut from the same potato (Fig. 2.24). Both strips should be the same length and one should be placed in distilled water while the other is placed in a salt solution. In the distilled water, the cells of the potato tend to become larger due to the inward diffusion of water. The piece of potato becomes slightly longer and crisper. If bent be-

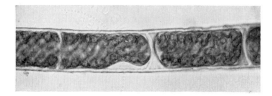

Fig. 2.23. Plasmolyzed cells of the green alga, **Spirogyra.**

tween the fingers it will snap in two rather than bend. The other piece of potato in the salt solution becomes slightly shorter. Each of the cells has decreased in volume slightly due to the loss of water by outward diffusion. The cells no longer push against each other and the strip becomes so limber that it will bend without breaking.

The wilting of leaves when removed from a plant and allowed to dry provides

Fig. 2.24. Two strips of potato, originally of the same length, after immersion in distilled water (above), and in a 3 per cent salt solution (below).

another example. The leaf cells are fully turgid to begin with and their mutual pressures make the leaf appear crisp. Loss of water from the cells makes them less and less turgid until they no longer exert pressures against each other and the leaf wilts.

The Nature of Cytoplasmic Membranes In Relation to Diffusion

Cytoplasm has been described as having a basic protein framework and it is probable that somewhat flattened meshworks of protein molecules form the basic structure of the cytoplasmic membranes. Certain parts of protein molecules are hydrophilic, i.e., they hold a layer of water molecules about them by tenacious adhesive forces. Water molecules held in this way tend to be oriented similarly with similarly charged poles sticking outward. Other water molecules are attracted to these poles and become bound as a second layer. Several layers of oriented water molecules may exist around a protein molecule but there is some unbound water in the microcapillary spaces between the protein molecules. The adhesive forces which attract the water molecules are very powerful but when water is freely available they are soon satisfied.

When water diffuses through a membrane it is unlikely that a single molecule goes all the way through at once. More likely as one molecule escapes from one side of a membrane another molecule is absorbed from the water on the other side to replace it. The direction of diffusion is determined by escape from the membrane into a solution with a lower concentration of water and replacement from a solution with a higher concentration.

The problem of diffusion of solutes through a membrane is more complicated. Certainly the membrane should not be pictured as a sieve which keeps out the larger molecules. Many molecules move through by simple diffusion in the unbound water existing between the protein molecules. If these molecules are non-polarized, their rate of diffusion may depend entirely on concentration differences. If they are polarized, or have polarized groups attached to them, their progress may be greatly affected by electromagnetic forces in the membrane. The same thing applies even more strongly to ionic particles.

One of the complexities of the membrane problem is that certain ions tend to pass through membranes against the normal diffusion gradient and to accumulate in the cell sap in enormous concentrations compared to those in the external solution. It is thought that such accumulations require the expenditure of energy and they have been correlated with high respiration rates.

Another consideration is the diffusion of substances which are fat soluble rather than water soluble. Fatty substances tend to accumulate in membranes where they are dispersed as colloidal droplets in water. Under certain circumstances there may be a change in the membrane which causes the fatty substances to become the continuous phase while the unbound water becomes dispersed as separate drop-

lets of colloidal size. Fat soluble compounds are then able to diffuse in the continuous phase while water soluble substances normally entering by simple diffusion are excluded. The movement of water is not affected particularly since the protein framework continues the process of giving up water molecules to one side and replacing them from the other.

The Fine Structure of Cytoplasm

With the aid of modern research tools such as the electron microscope and the high speed centrifuge, the fine structure of the cytoplasm has become subjected to intense scrutiny. From this work a concept is emerging that the cytoplasm may consist of an elaborate, three-dimensional maze of delicate internal membranous surfaces which are contiguous with the more prominent surface membranes discussed above. This maze is called the *endoplasmic reticulum*. Its enormous total surface area seemingly provides working space for the vast number of chemical reactions which are carried on in living cytoplasm. Although the best known examples of the endoplasmic reticulum occur in certain specialized animal cells, it has been observed in a number of plant cells (Fig. 2.25). Eventually, it may be possible to demonstrate that various modifications of this concept of cytoplasmic structure can be applied to all living cells.

THE NUCLEUS

The nucleus tends to assume a spherical shape, especially in cells which lack conspicuous central vacuoles. In highly vacuolated cells, however, where the cytoplasm becomes stretched into a thin, peripheral layer, the nucleus becomes flattened somewhat into a hemispherical shape. This is due to turgor pressure exerted by the cell sap against the cytoplasm in which the nucleus is always enclosed.

Until recently the nucleus has been studied more intensively than the cytoplasm. Part of the reason for this is that the nucleus becomes a brilliant object when specially stained and is more interesting to observe with the light micro-

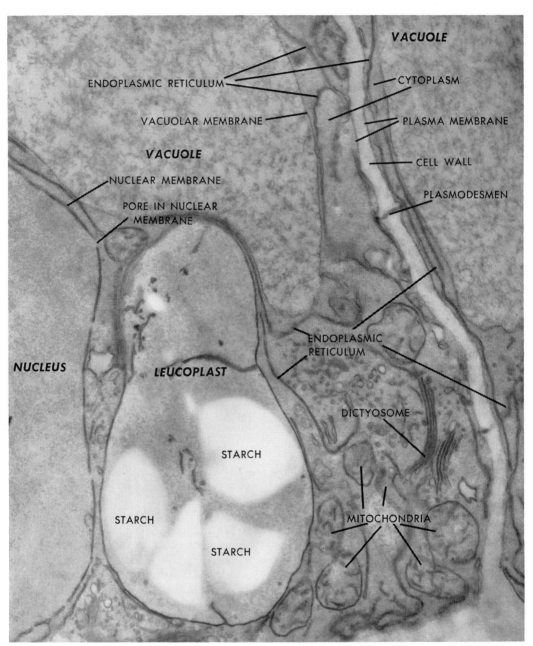

Fig. 2.25. Electron micrograph of a section of portion of a root tip cell of radish. Cell organelles not previously illustrated are the endoplasmic reticulum, dictyosomes, and plasmodesmata (sing., plasmodesma). The first of these is discussed in the text. Dictyosomes are sometimes called Golgi bodies and their function is not well understood. Plasmodesmata are threadlike connections of living cytoplasm which pass through cell walls between adjacent cells. Of interest is the presence of pores in the nuclear membrane. The fixation used in preparing this material for sectioning results in precipitation artifacts in the vacuoles and does not emphasize nuclear details. (Courtesy of Dr. C. C. Bowen.)

scope than is the cytoplasm. The reverse is true for observations with the electron microscope and, currently, more attention is being given the cytoplasm.

The structure of the nucleus seems easily described at first. At the nuclear-cytoplasm boundary is the *nuclear membrane*. Within this there is a large quantity of a fluid substance, the *nuclear sap,* and one or more large, spherical bodies called *nucleoli*. Distributed throughout the nucleus is a three-dimensional network of finely divided material called *chromatin*.

The apparent simplicity vanishes the moment further study of the nucleus is undertaken. The nature and function of the nucleoli, for example, are still not clear. The physical distribution of the chromatin in an undisturbed living nucleus is difficult to determine. Certainly the brightly stained network seen in a prepared slide is not truly characteristic of the living nucleus. When, for instance, the nuclear division process is studied in stained slides it appears as though the chromatin network becomes organized into rod-shaped bodies called *chromosomes*. It is probable, however, that the chromosomes actually exist as discrete bodies in the nondividing nucleus as well, even though the boundaries between them are rarely detectable.

Nuclear and cytoplasmic divisions occur repeatedly in regions which are called meristems and sections through the apical meristem of an onion root (Fig. 2.26) are used extensively in introductory studies of these processes. The roots are killed quickly and with a minimum amount of distortion before the sections are made. This means that the division process in any particular cell is stopped at the stage it had reached at the moment of fixation. By examining many cells stopped in various stages, it is possible to obtain a concept of the entire process of nuclear and cytoplasmic division. However, this method of study may create an impres-

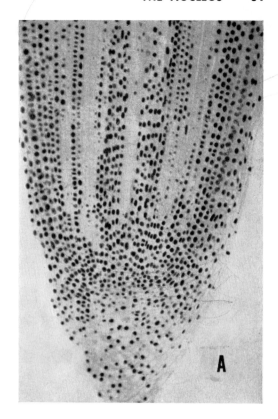

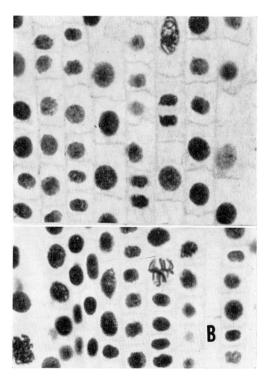

Fig. 2.26. Mitosis in an onion root tip. A. Longitudinal section of an onion root tip. B. Enlarged portions of A showing nuclei in various stages of mitosis.

sion that the cell jumps from stage to stage while actually there is a gradual progression between the more obvious stages which increases in speed from start to finish.

NUCLEAR DIVISION (MITOSIS)

The division of one nucleus to form two is called *mitosis* and, in stained sections, the first evidence that mitosis has begun is an increased brilliance of the stain. In a nondividing nucleus, on the other hand, the chromatin is very finely dispersed and does not stain brightly. The increased stainability is correlated with an aggregation of the chromatin into coarser threads as mitosis begins. The main events in the process of mitosis have been named as phases (Figs. 2.27, 2.28). They will be discussed in order beginning with the early stages which are called the *prophase*.

Prophase

During the early portions of this phase many changes occur:

a. The chromatin becomes more concentrated and takes the shape of long, thin strands called *chromosomes*. These are, at first, tangled together like a ball of yarn. It is known that each chromosome is a double structure and each of the lengthwise parts is called a *chromatid*. The threadlike core (*chromonema*) of each chromatid is loosely coiled at this time. As prophase continues the chromosomes continue to become shorter and thicker and to stain more deeply. These changes are associated with a more pronounced coiling of the chromonemata.

b. The nucleolus gradually disappears. (The significance of this disappearance and the subsequent reappearance of nucleoli at the end of mitosis have long been a minor biological mystery.)

c. When the chromosomes have shortened considerably, the nuclear membrane rather abruptly disappears allowing the chromosomes to lie free in the cytoplasm.

d. At about the time that the nuclear membrane disappears, some very fine threadlike structures called *spindle fibers* appear in the cytoplasm. These occur in two groups at opposite poles of the cell. (Their exact nature is still a matter of dispute.) They converge to indefinite points in the cytoplasm at opposite poles of the cell but they are not attached to any definite structure, i.e., there is no centrosome as in animal cells.

Some of the spindle fibers become attached to the chromosomes at definite points called *kinetochores*. A fiber from one pole attaches to one chromatid of a chromosome while a fiber from the opposite pole attaches to the other chromatid. Other fibers are unattached and pass through the chromosome mass, extending from pole to pole.

Metaphase

The chromosomes soon become rearranged in the cell in such a way that they lie in a flat plane across the cell. This *equatorial plate*, as it is called, lies midway between the two poles of the cell. The movement of the chromosomes is associated with an adjustment of the lengths of the attached spindle fibers, but whether this is cause or effect is difficult to prove. In lengthwise sections of root tips, the equatorial plate is normally seen in edge view only. Research workers, interested in the numbers of chromosomes per cell, cut cross sections so that they can view the equatorial plates from the poles. When seen in this way the chromosomes are spread out evenly in approximately the same plane and, thus, they can be counted readily.

Anaphase

The anaphase is a phase of movement. The two chromatids of each chromosome separate and move toward opposite poles. Some authorities maintain that this is due to a contraction of the attached spindle fibers which causes the chromatids to be pulled apart. The separated chromatids are now called *daughter chromosomes*. It is an important point that the two separated groups of daughter chromosomes are alike with respect to numbers and kinds; and that the number and kind in each group are identical with those of the nucleus which began the division. In this way, the process of mitosis maintains a constant chromosome number in the body cells of a growing organism.

Telophase

Anaphase is completed when all of the chromosomes have reached the poles of the cell. Telophase is the end phase during which daughter nuclei are reconstructed from the clumps of chromosomes at each pole. In each clump the individual chromosomes begin to lose their clearly separate identity and a nuclear membrane is formed around the mass. Then this daughter nucleus begins to swell through the absorption of water and other substances. The chromatin becomes more and more diffuse and loses its brilliant stainability. Sooner or later during this reconstruction process the nucleoli reappear.

CYTOPLASMIC DIVISION (CYTOKINESIS)

While the division of the cytoplasm is not truly a part of mitosis it is a related process. In the cells of the higher plants, it involves a residual part of the mechanism of mitosis and usually begins during telophase. In the higher plants, cytoplasmic division is initiated by a thin, membranous *cell plate* which forms in the approximate position and plane previously occupied by the chromosomes at metaphase. It seems to be the result of the fusion of minute droplets which accumulate at the midportions of the long spindle fibers which extend from pole to pole. The original cell plate does not completely cross the cell. Once it is formed, additional *peripheral fibers* appear in the cytoplasm around the plate. Droplets accumulate on these fibers also and fuse with the existing cell plate. In this way the plate grows and eventually separates the cytoplasm into two units, each one of which contains a daughter nucleus.

There are differences of opinion as to whether or not the cell plate is also the future middle lamella of the cell wall. One school of thought holds that the cell plate splits flatwise to form two cytoplasmic membranes, one for each of the two new cytoplasmic surfaces, and that the middle lamella is then secreted between these two new membranes. However the middle lamella is formed, each of the new protoplasts soon begins to deposit cellulose on its own side of this layer. Thus the primary cell wall is the joint product of two adjacent cells. Secondary wall thickenings will be discussed later since they do not normally begin to form in meristematic tissues.

Interphase

Following nuclear and cytoplasmic divisions the daughter cells grow for some time before they divide again. This growth involves both increase in size due to the absorption of food and water and the assimilation of some of this material into new protoplasm. It is known that the amounts of those chemicals which are significant in the structure of chromosomes are doubled during interphase and from this it has been inferred that chromatid duplication occurs during this phase.

Nature of Chromosomes

Considerable emphasis is placed on discussions of chromosomes in biology courses. This emphasis is justified on the basis of a vast body of scientific information indicating that chromosomal substances control the development of organisms. Not only do they control large scale patterns such as the formation of pine trees from pine seeds and oat plants from oat seeds, but they also control minute details such as the shape of outgrowths of the cell walls of certain algae.

Scientists have been led to the conclusion that chromosomes are made up of large numbers of smaller units called *genes*. The interaction of large numbers of genes insures that a bean seed will give rise to a bean plant but it is probable, also, that a few genes or even a single gene may influence the final expression of a

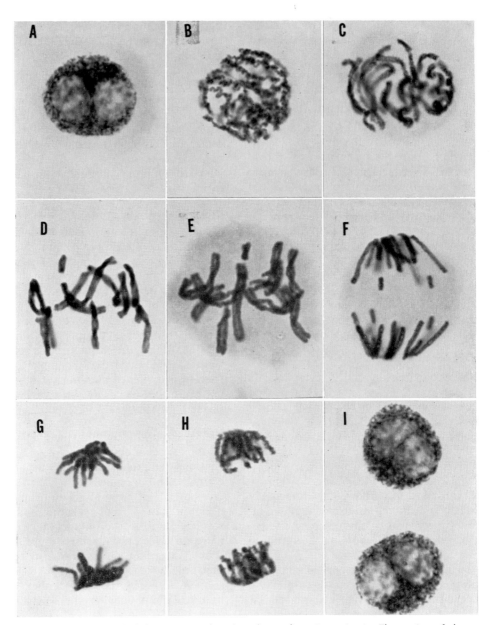

Fig. 2.27. A series of photomicrographs of nuclei undergoing mitosis. The series of drawings in Fig. 2.28 was conceived from these photomicrographs. In preparing the slides from which these pictures were taken a staining technique was used which is specific only for chromosomal substances. (Courtesy of Dr. C. C. Bowen.)

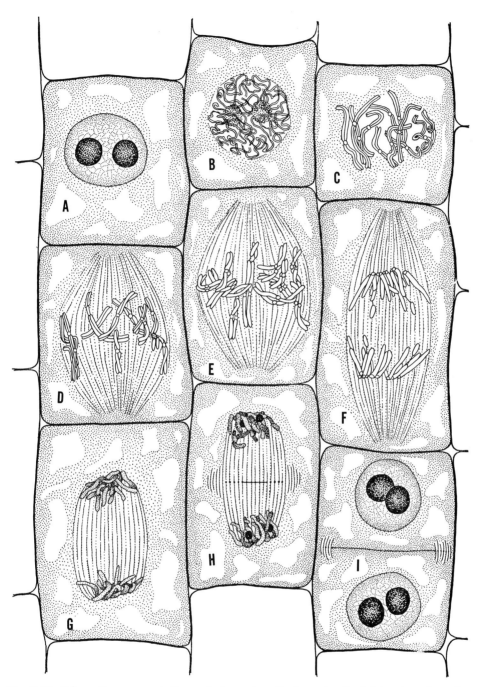

Fig. 2.28. Schematic representations of stages in mitosis and cell division based on the photomicrographs in Fig. 2.27. A. Interphase. B. Early prophase. C. Later prophase. D. Rearrangement of chromosomes just prior to metaphase. E. End of metaphase (chromatids beginning to separate). F. Anaphase. G. Late anaphase. H. Telophase of mitosis and beginning of cytokinesis. I. Daughter nuclei formed, cytokinesis almost complete.

single adult characteristic such as flower color.

As a generality with significant exceptions, it can be stated that all living cells of the body of a plant have the same numbers and kinds of chromosomes. However, when one realizes how many different kinds of cells there are in a plant the question arises as to how cells with the same inheritance can become so vastly different. Some indication of the answer is given by the fact that no two cells in a plant exist in exactly the same environment. Epidermal cells in a leaf are exposed to different conditions than the green cells inside. Cells of a root have different conditions of life than do stem cells. The interplay of large numbers of genes in the control of cell physiology permits an infinite variety of cellular response. Thus, neighboring cells with identical sets of chromosomes and genes may mature into entirely different kinds of cells because their immediate environments are different.

Students of the mechanisms of heredity have learned much about genes in the past two decades. In some organisms investigators can point to an exact spot in a particular chromosome where exists a gene which affects the expression of a single adult character. Yet most of these investigators hesitate to say exactly what a gene is. Many of them are convinced, however, that it is a large, self-duplicating molecule, which is composed of a protein plus a compound called desoxyribose nucleic acid (DNA).

Evidence has accumulated that DNA exists only in the nucleus while a chemically related compound referred to as RNA (ribonucleic acid) becomes abundant in the cytoplasm. It has been suggested that the RNA is manufactured in the nucleus and that it migrates, in an unknown manner, into the cytoplasm.

Further evidence indicates that the RNA molecules are united with proteins to form minute particles of relatively uniform size which are called *RNP granules* or *ribosomes*. These particles are not visible with the light microscope but have been observed with the electron microscope. A theory has been advanced that the ribosomes function as templates in the chemical construction of enzymes, i.e., they attract the appropriate amino acids to their surfaces in proper order and orientation so that chemical bonds between them are readily achieved.

In a sense, therefore, the ribosomes contain a coded system of information concerning the formation of specific enzymes. Since the enzymes present in a cell determine largely how the cell will react within a given microchemical environment, this theory may have opened the door to a fuller understanding of numerous life processes.

CHAPTER 3 | **Reproduction**

Reproduction is basic to perpetuating plant species. As will be seen, many of the major features of reproductive cycles in the higher plants are evident in the lower plants. Hence, a study of reproductive mechanisms in the lower plants is fundamental to an understanding of the life cycles of higher plants.

The *green algae* are used to introduce the relation of cell division to reproduction, the possible origin of gametes, the formation of zygotes, the process of meiosis, and the concept of alternation of generations.

Mosses and *liverworts* illustrate the concepts of the embryo and the wind disseminated spore. Also, in discussions of these plants, the significance of the formation of gametes within multicellular sterile cases will be considered. Furthermore, these groups provide examples of plants with an alternation of generations in which one generation is well adapted to an independent existence on land while the other generation is at least partially dependent.

Ferns are used to introduce the concept of the sporophyll, or spore-bearing leaf, and, also, as examples of plants having two separate and independent generations, both adapted to life on land.

Selaginella illustrates the important concept of heterospory.

The *pine* is used to introduce a discussion of seeds and to illustrate how the evolution of the seed habit is related to the evolution of gametophytes which are completely parasitic on the sporophyte.

The life cycle of *flowering plants* is then discussed in some detail and the reproductive mechanisms described are compared with those of the lower plants.

REPRODUCTION IN THE GREEN ALGAE

The term algae applies to a vast array of plants many of which are only distantly related to one another. They range in size from single-celled structures barely visible under the microscope to ocean giants a hundred feet or more long. Primarily, they are restricted to moist or wet environments. Most of them contain chlorophyll and are photosynthetic although a few species of nonchlorophyllous algae are known. In some groups of algae there are accessory pigments which serve to alter the normal green color due to the complex of chlorophyll pigments. In this section we are to be concerned with the reproduction of only the grass-green algae since they are considered to be the progenitors of the higher green plants. Much of the discussion is based on the reproductive mechanisms of *Chlamydomonas*, a single-celled green alga discussed in some detail early in the second chapter.

The Life Cycle of *Chlamydomonas*

Chlamydomonas plants normally occur in large numbers wherever they are found. As noted previously, one cell placed in a suitable environment can give rise to a vast number of progeny within a few weeks. This is accomplished by the division of one cell to form two, two to form four, four to form eight, etc. (Fig. 3.1). Cells may remain clumped together within the parent cell wall for two or three, or even more divisions but eventually they separate and live as single individuals. The process of new cell formation involves a precise division of the nucleus (*mitosis*), and an equal but not so precise division of the cytoplasm each time cell division occurs. In this plant the division of the cytoplasm is accomplished by an inward furrowing of the cytoplasm rather than by a cell plate. The daughter cells which are formed are identical in appearance with the parent cell as well as with each other. They are somewhat smaller than the parent but are capable of rapid growth. When first released these daughter cells are called *zoospores* (Fig. 3.1) but each one soon becomes a normal sized adult plant.

This type of reproduction is variously called vegetative, asexual, or nongametic. Some authorities feel that the last term is preferred. As long as the environment remains suitable to the growth and division of *Chlamydomonas*, it is probable that reproduction will occur in this manner for indefinite periods and the number of individuals becomes enormous. Careful estimates show that there may be more than 10,000 individuals per milliliter of the culture solution when it has a decided green color.

However, no environment, particularly a fresh-water environment, is likely to remain unaltered indefinitely. A few of the more obvious changes which could occur are as follows:

1. Natural ponds occasionally dry up.
2. Seasonal changes in temperature occur.
3. Many kinds of chemical changes may occur in the water.
4. Other plants compete for light, carbon dioxide, oxygen, mineral salts, space, etc.
5. When overcrowded in the environment, individual cells of *Chlamydomonas* compete among themselves.

As a result of one or more changing factors in the environment (perhaps the most important being a depletion of nitrogen) the cells of *Chlamydomonas* undergo physiological changes which cause them to unite in pairs instead of undergoing further growth and nongametic divisions. Each member of a uniting pair is called a *gamete* and the fusion of gametes is an important step in the gametic reproductive cycle (Fig. 3.2).

In certain species of *Chlamydomonas* the gametes do not differ markedly in appearance from normal vegetative cells. However, in some species of this genus, as well as in many other genera of algae, gamete formation involves the division of adult cells into large numbers of individuals which are much smaller than zoospores. These divisions are like the nongametic divisions in that they involve mitosis and cytoplasmic division but they do not stop at 4, 8, or even 16 individuals. Divisions continue until one cell has been partitioned into a much larger number of cells, the number being on the order of 64 or 128.

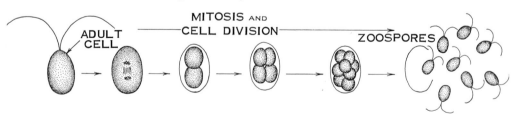

Fig. 3.1. Nongametic reproduction in **Chlamydomonas.** (Mitosis and cell divisions resulting in the production of zoospores.)

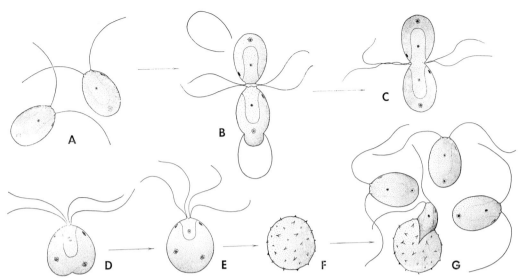

Fig. 3.2. Gametic union in **Chlamydomonas** resulting in the formation of a diploid zygote. Meiosis in the germinating zygote is followed by the release of four haploid zoospores.

The many small individuals are gametes but, except for their smaller size, they are similar in appearance to zoospores. They differ physiologically, however, in that they do not have the ability to grow to the normal size for adult cells. Nor do they have the ability to divide again. Thus, they have no future unless they pair with other gametes and unite to form zygotes.

When two gametes which are capable of fusing come together the cell membranes at the point of contact are dissolved and the cytoplasm of one blends with the cytoplasm of the other. Eventually, the two nuclei fuse to form one nucleus which has, therefore, twice as many chromosomes as does the nucleus of a single gamete (or a zoospore or an adult plant). The fusion process is called *fertilization* or *syngamy* and gametic union is a natural event in the life cycles of all of the plants we will study. The fusion cell itself is called a *zygote*.

In *Chlamydomonas* the zygote soon loses its flagella, increases in size, and becomes a thick-walled resting cell. In this condition, it can survive desiccation and endure a greater range of temperatures than vegetative cells. In a sense, it is a survival mechanism which permits the inactive protoplasm within to remain alive whether frozen in icy mud or carried aloft in a dust storm. When conditions again become favorable germination of the zygote may occur. (A number of research workers are, at present, concerned with the actual conditions which induce zygote germination in various species of algae.)

When a zygote of *Chlamydomonas* germinates, the wall cracks open and four zoospores emerge. These soon grow to normal adult size and each one can initiate a new population. It is an important point that each one of the four zoospores has a haploid nucleus. This is the result of a process called *meiosis* which occurs in the zygote prior to its germination.

Meiosis is sometimes referred to as reduction division and it will be considered in detail in a later chapter. At this point meiosis may be defined simply as a process involving two successive and somewhat specialized nuclear divisions as a result of which four nuclei are formed, each one of them having a chromosome number which is one half that of the parent nucleus. (This definition of meiosis may be compared with a similarly phrased definition of mitosis as a process involving a single nuclear division as a result of which two nuclei are formed, each of them having the same number of chromosomes as the parent nucleus.)

If, for example, the haploid chromosome number of a certain species is eight, the diploid nucleus of the zygote has sixteen chromosomes. During meiosis in the zygote the chromosome number is reduced and the nucleus of each one of the four zoospores has eight chromosomes.

Meiosis plays a significant and necessary role in the gametic life cycle. If the chromosome number were not reduced at some point in the life cycle the number of chromosomes in a nucleus would be doubled by gamete fusion in one generation, redoubled in the next and so on until a vast and unwieldly number of chromosomes accumulated.

Also, as will become apparent later, meiosis accomplishes a reshuffling of the chromosomes and genes which affects the hereditary nature of succeeding generations.

It will be practically impossible for science to fix a time when the evolution of gametic reproduction began. It seems very likely that nongametic methods of reproduction evolved first and were the only mechanisms for a long period of time. Possibly the union of two cells which we recognize as the initiation of the gametic cycle was a successful accident which resulted in a somewhat larger vegetative cell rather than a resting zygote. This may then have given rise to a whole population of similar diploid cells by nongametic reproduction. It is even conceivable that the chromosome number may have doubled several times in this manner (as well as in other ways now well known to research workers). Furthermore, when the chromosome numbers became so large that the normal mechanisms of mitosis became inadequate, the stage would have been set for the evolution of meiosis.

Evolution of Sexual Differences Between Gametes in the Algae

In the most primitive condition, all of the gametes of a species are so alike that any two may fuse even though they come from the same parent cell. However, from this primitive condition a wide range of differences between gametes has evolved. These differences can be summarized by a consideration of three morphological terms: *isogamy*, *anisogamy*, and *oogamy*, and two physiological concepts: *homothallism* and *heterothallism*.

When all the gametes of one species look alike, the condition is termed *isogamy*. Commonly, *isogametes* are small, highly motile, and produced in very large numbers. However, in at least one group of green algae, isogametes are formed which lack flagella entirely and consist of the undivided contents of previously vegetative cells.

Anisogamy is a condition in which the gametes are similar in appearance but differ in size and motility as well as in the numbers produced by the parent cell. Here we see evidences of the beginnings of morphological sexuality. For example, in *Pandorina* (Fig. 3.6) the female gametes are like the male gametes in general shape, number of flagella, and color. But they are larger than the male, less numerous, and move about much more slowly.

Oogamy is a state in which female gametes have become highly modified while male gametes have retained such primitive features as being of small size, highly motile, and very numerous. Female gametes, on the other hand, have become much larger and have completely lost their motility. Usually they accumulate large amounts of reserve food. Female gametes of this type are referred to as *eggs* while the smaller, motile, male gametes are called *sperms*.

Sometimes the eggs may be released from the parent before fertilization but in many algae they are retained within the cell wall in which they are formed. The enclosing wall is referred to as an *oogonium* and, in most algae, the zygotes are released from the oogonium before germination takes place usually by a decay or breakage of the wall.

In summarizing the evolutionary development of morphological sexuality in the algae it is evident that male gametes tend to be smaller than females, are produced in larger numbers, have little reserve food, and usually have some means of locomotion which enables them to reach the female gametes. Many more male gametes are produced than females and, therefore, most of them are doomed to perish. However, the active movements of large numbers of male gametes tend to insure that at least one will make contact with each female gamete.

Female gametes tend to be larger than the males, are produced in fewer numbers, are less motile or completely nonmotile, and have greater food reserves. They may have the added protection of being retained within the parent cell wall. The chief advantage of the egg lies in the fact that it contains a large supply of stored nutrients. It is able to build a heavier wall around the zygote and, when germination occurs, the new haploid plants which emerge will be larger and more vigorous than those emerging from zygotes formed by isogametes. Possibly this advantage outweighs the concomitant disadvantage that they are produced in smaller numbers.

Functional differences in sexuality do not always parallel structural differences between gametes. For example, some isogametes will fuse only with isogametes from different plants of the same species while, on the other hand, some species produce eggs and sperms on the same plant body which are capable of a normal fertilization. Careful analysis of both physiological and morphological expressions of sexuality is necessary in order that the nature of a plant can be correctly interpreted. The basic terms used to describe physiological sexuality of the gamete producing plants are *homothallism* and *heterothallism*. (The word thallus refers to the plant body in the lower plants.) When homothallism exists the gametes produced by the same thallus or in a clonal culture are capable of fusion to form zygotes. (A clonal culture is derived from a single individual by means of nongametic reproduction.) In the heterothallic condition the gametes must come from different thalli or clones in order to fuse.

When the gametes involved are recognizably different as male and female gametes, the thalli which produce them may be called male and female plants. However, when isogametes are involved, there is no basis for determining which of the two strains is male or female. In such cases the different strains are referred to as plus and minus.

Very often the separation of genetic factors which control maleness and femaleness, or plusness and minusness, occurs during meiosis and two of the four resultant nuclei carry the determiners of maleness while the other two carry determiners of femaleness. In such cases the application of the term heterothallism has a clear-cut meaning and its use can lead to no confusion.

In some organisms which produce both male and female gametes on the same thallus these gametes are incapable of uniting with each other and must find appropriate gametes from other thalli in order to accomplish fertilization. Such plants have the appearance of homothallism but are functionally heterothallic.

The genetic factors controlling this type of sexuality are seemingly more complex than those controlling the simple heterothallism described above. Many organisms have been described as being homothallic on morphological evidence only and, in such cases, careful experiments involving clonal cultures may be necessary to determine the actual type of sexuality involved. In cases where such determinations have been made, the species may be described as being either *bisexual and self-fertile* or *bisexual and self-sterile* in order to avoid misunderstandings.

The terms *monoecious* and *dioecious* are often used in place of homothallic and heterothallic. A rough definition of monoecious is one household and it is used to indicate that both gametes are produced by the same plant. Dioecious means two households and implies that one kind of gamete develops in one plant and the other kind in another plant.

These terms are subject to misunderstandings in the same way as described above for homothallic and heterothallic. Furthermore they are used extensively in describing the heterosporous nature of the diploid generations of higher plants (see discussion of heterospory). This is an entirely different matter than sexuality in the haploid generation and it is to be hoped that the usage of monoecious and dioecious will eventually be restricted to discussions of the higher plants.

Specific Examples of Reproduction In the Green Algae

Chlamydomonas has been cited as an alga demonstrating both isogamy and homothallism. However, there are many species in this genus and some of them have highly advanced types of sexuality, ranging from isogamy to oogamy and from homothallism to heterothallism. A considerable amount of research with *Chlamydomonas* is being done in the hope of finding a biochemical basis for sexuality.

As described previously, *Ulothrix* is a green alga with an unbranched, filamentous plant body and bracelet-shaped chloroplasts. Each filament increases in length as a result of vegetative cell division with the new cell walls always forming at right angles to the long axis of the filament.

The number of filaments is increased by a nongametic process involving the production of zoospores (Fig. 3.3). Any cell (except the basal attaching cell) can undergo a series of divisions by which its protoplasm is segmented into several cells. These escape through an opening in the wall and become zoospores. Except for the fact that they have four flagella, these zoospores look remarkably like *Chlamydomonas* cells.

Each zoospore swims about rapidly for some time but eventually attaches itself to an object in the water. A new filament then develops from the attached zoospore as a result of repeated cell divisions with the new walls forming in parallel planes.

Gametic reproduction in *Ulothrix* (Fig. 3.4) begins in the same way as nongametic reproduction. However, the number of divisions within a parent cell is greater than if zoospores were being formed, i.e., gametes are more numerous than zoospores.

Also, the gametes are smaller than the zoospores and have only two flagella apiece instead of four. In appearance, they resemble the gametes of *Chlamydomonas*.

Most species of *Ulothrix* are heterothallic and, therefore, plus and minus strains must be mixed together in order for gametic unions to take place.

The zygote becomes a thick-walled resting cell which may have an extended period of dormancy. Meiosis occurs prior to germination and segregation of plus and minus strains occurs at that time. When the zygote does germinate, four haploid zoospores emerge and each one is capable of giving rise to a new filament. Since the nuclear divisions involved in filament growth are mitotic, all of the cells of a given filament will

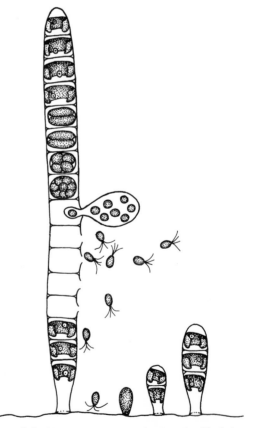

Fig. 3.3. Nongametic reproduction in **Ulothrix**. Contents of cells of the filament are divided and released as zoospores. Each zoospore ultimately gives rise to a new filament.

be plus if the zoospore was plus or minus if the zoospore was minus.

This particular life cycle has been presented in some detail in order that its essential parallelism to the life cycle of *Chlamydomonas* be made clearly evident. It seems a logical speculation, based on this parallelism, that *Ulothrix* evolved from a *Chlamydomonas*-like ancestor. And, since *Ulothrix* is never classified as an animal, one can add this evolutionary relationship to other pertinent arguments favoring the classification of *Chlamydomonas*, and its relatives, *Pandorina*, *Eudorina*, *Volvox*, etc., in the plant kingdom.

Pandorina grows as a motile colony comprised of eight or sixteen cells (Fig. 3.5) each of which is like *Chlamydomonas*. The most widespread species is heterothallic and anisogamous. Both gametes are motile but the female gametes are larger and more sluggish than the male (Fig. 3.6). Otherwise they resemble the gametes of *Chlamydomonas*.

Spirogyra is a green alga with unbranched filaments and ribbonlike, spirally arranged chloroplasts. Most species are

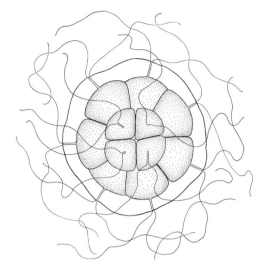

Fig. 3.5. Motile colony of **Pandorina.**

heterothallic but it is impossible to recognize plus and minus strains in the vegetative condition. Normally they both grow tangled together in quiet waters.

When gametic reproduction is initiated (Fig. 3.7), small swellings become evident on each cell. The *papillae* from cells of opposite strains grow towards each other and eventually come into contact. The wall between them at the point of contact dissolves and an open *conjugation tube* is formed between each pair of cells. The gametes comprise entire protoplasts of individual cells. They are nonflagellated but normally show anisogamy since all of the gametes of one strain move through the conjugation tubes to join the gametes of the other strain. Zygotes are formed and develop very thick walls. The walls of the cells containing zygotes break

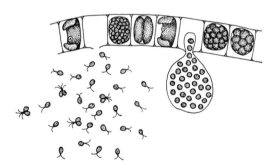

Fig. 3.4. Gametic reproduction in **Ulothrix.** Contents of the cells of the filament are divided into numerous small isogametes. Upon release they unite with gametes of opposite strains to form diploid zygotes. Meiosis occurs in the germinating zygote and each of the four resulting spores is capable of initiating a new filament in the same manner as the zoospores formed nongametically.

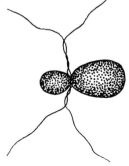

Fig. 3.6. Anisogametes of **Pandorina** at the start of a gametic union.

open eventually and the zygotes fall to the bottom where they undergo several months of rest.

When germination occurs each zygote gives rise to a filament. Prior to germination the zygote nucleus undergoes meiosis to form four haploid nuclei of which three degenerate. The surviving nucleus contains either the gene for plusness or the gene for minusness and thus the emerging filament can be one or the other but not both. This is a matter of chance and, since many zygotes germinate at the same time, the filaments of the new population are a mixture of plus and minus strains.

Oedogonium is a filamentous alga which is recognized by its reticulate chloroplasts and a peculiarity of some of the cell walls which have a series of circular ridges at one end. All of the species of *Oedogonium* are oogamous and the egg is always retained in the oogonium which has a small entrance pore for the convenience of the sperm (Figs. 3.8, 3.10). The sperms are small and produced in pairs in special cells called *antheridia* (Figs. 3.9, 3.10). When released they swim rapidly and are chemically attracted towards oogonia which contain unfertilized eggs.

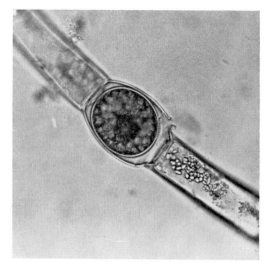

Fig. 3.8. Filament of **Oedogonium** with an oogonium.

The zygotes become resting spores which are released by decay of the oogonium wall. Meiosis occurs prior to germination. After germination each of the four resultant zoospores can initiate a new filament (Fig. 3.11).

Some species are heterothallic; others are bisexual and either self-sterile or self-fertile. Certain species are said to be *nannandrous* meaning that they produce

Fig. 3.7. Gametic reproduction in **Spirogyra**: Formation of conjugation tube; conjugation of non-flagellated gametes; maturation of the zygote; meiosis in the zygote; degeneration of three of the four haploid nuclei; emergence of new filament from the germinating zygote.

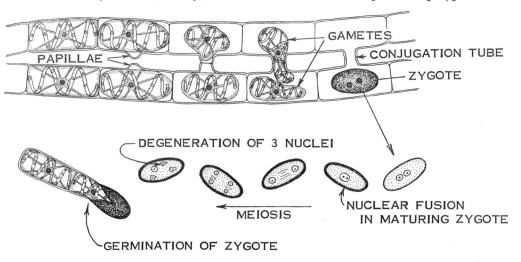

GAMETES

PAPILLAE

CONJUGATION TUBE

ZYGOTE

DEGENERATION OF 3 NUCLEI

NUCLEAR FUSION IN MATURING ZYGOTE

MEIOSIS

GERMINATION OF ZYGOTE

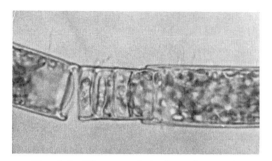

Fig. 3.9. Filament of **Oedogonium** with antheridia.

uals of a particular species. The symbol n is used to designate this fact, i.e., a haploid nucleus has the n chromosome number. By way of contrast the cells of the vegetative plant body of higher plants have *diploid nuclei*, i.e., each nucleus has two identical sets of chromosomes or, more briefly, the $2n$ chromosome number.

In the algae considered so far the nuclear divisions which precede gamete

dwarf male plants. This unusual situation is brought about by the production of modified zoospores which have enough physiological maleness to cause them to swim to female plants. There they attach themselves and germinate to produce dwarf filaments which are capable of producing true sperms.

During the phase of nongametic reproduction in *Oedogonium* the entire contents of individual cells become modified and break out of the cell walls to become zoospores (Fig. 3.12). The zoospores are unusual in that they possess a whorl of flagella rather than two or four (Fig. 3.11).

THE CONCEPT OF ALTERNATION OF GENERATIONS

In all of the algae which have been discussed so far, the cells of the vegetative plant body have contained *haploid nuclei*. This means that each nucleus has one set of chromosomes. The number of chromosomes in a set varies from species to species but is constant for the individ-

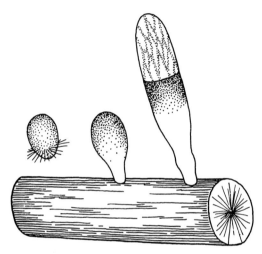

Fig. 3.11. Origin of a new filament of **Oedogonium** from a zoospore. (The zoospore could have been the product of either the gametic or the nongametic cycle.)

formation are mitotic. Thus the gamete nuclei are haploid and have the same chromosome number as do the nuclei of vegetative body cells. With a few notable exceptions, the gametes of plants are produced by plant bodies having haploid chromosomes numbers and this gamete

Fig. 3.10. Filament of **Oedogonium** with sperms released from antheridia swarming about the oogonium.

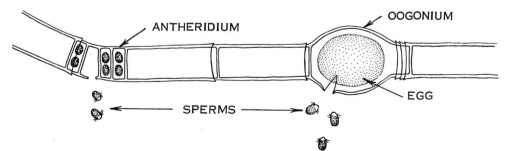

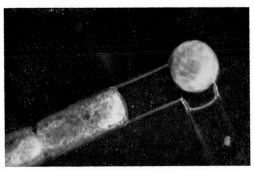

Fig. 3.12. Filament of **Oedogonium** showing the release of a zoospore (nongametic reproduction).

producing generation is called a *gametophyte*. (This point should be considered carefully by students who are familiar with the life cycle of animals because in practically all animals the nuclear divisions which precede gamete formation are meiotic.)

When two gametes fuse and their nuclei unite, the resulting nucleus of the zygote has two sets of identical chromosomes and this is origin of the *diploid* condition. In the algae cosidered above, the zygote is the only cell which is diploid. Meiosis precedes or accompanies germination of the zygote and four haploid nuclei are formed. This marks the beginning of the gametophyte generation.

The gametic life cycle of an alga such as *Ulothrix* can be diagrammed to show these over-all relationships (Fig. 3.13).

It is possible to interpret the zygote as a single-celled diploid plant. Since it frequently gives rise to spores it may be

termed a spore-producing plant or sporophyte. However, this term will be used more frequently in considerations of the diploid generation when it is multicellular.

The use of the term *spore* may be confusing since spores are discussed in relation to nongametic reproduction and also in relation to the cells formed by germinating zygotes. In recent years the proposal has been made that the term *mitospore* be used for spores formed during nongametic reproduction which involves only mitosis and that the term *meiospore* be used for the spores produced as a direct result of meiosis. There is considerable merit in this proposal, yet it does add two more words to an already overburdened vocabulary and these terms do not completely supplant the more familiar ones.

The discussion of algal reproduction up to this point would seem to imply that the zygote always undergoes meiosis. While this is true of a great many algae there are some well known examples of algal species in which the zygote undergoes mitosis instead of meiosis. This results in the formation of a vegetative plant body which contains diploid nuclei instead of haploid nuclei. These diploid plants may look exactly like the haploid plants or may be entirely different in appearance. Often there are mechanisms by which the numbers of diploid plants are increased by nongametic reproduction.

Eventually, however, some or all of the cells of the diploid plant undergo

Fig. 3.13. Diagram of the gametic life cycle of algal species with zygotic meiosis.

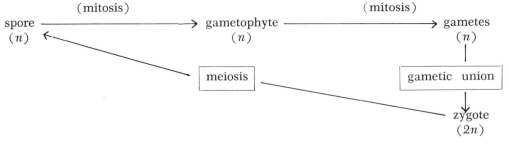

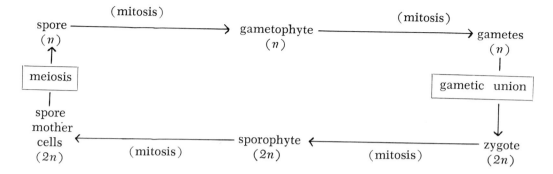

Fig. 3.14. Diagram of a basic life cycle involving alternation of generations.

meiosis. Most commonly, the resultant cells become spores and the particular cells which undergo the meiotic process to produce them are called *spore mother cells* or *sporocytes*. A diploid plant which gives rise to haploid spores is termed the *sporophyte generation*.

As has been emphasized each of the haploid spores gives rise to a new gametophyte generation and, in this process, all of the nuclear divisions are mitotic.

From this discussion it may be seen that many algae have an alternation of a gamete-producing generation, the gametophyte, with a spore-producing generation, the sporophyte. Figure 3.14 illustrates the basic outline of this *alternation of generations*. As will be seen, it applies to seed plants, ferns, mosses, etc., as well as to many of the algae.

LIFE CYCLE OF A MOSS

In mosses and their relatives the liverworts, the alternation of haploid gametophyte generations with diploid sporophyte generations is well established. The gametophyte is wholly self-nourishing and independent but the sporophyte is epiphytic and partially dependent on the gametophyte. Moreover, the gametophytes of many species of mosses and liverworts have evolved the most varied and elaborate modifications for independent life on land of any known gametophytes. This, plus the fact that neither generation has true xylem and phloem tissues, sharply separates the group from all the higher land plants.

Mosses and liverworts have many alga-like features but they are separated from the algae by the following three characteristics in addition to the fact that they are primarily adapted for life on land.

1. The occurrence of a layer of sterile jacket cells around the developing gametes.

2. The occurrence of wind-spread spores.

3. The development of an embryo stage of the sporophyte which is retained within and nourished by the gametophyte tissue.

The *embryo* stage of the sporophyte is the result of the retention of the zygote within the structure in which it is formed. It does not become a resting spore but begins to divide soon after its formation. The divisions involve mitosis instead of meiosis and, as a result, a mass of diploid cells is formed inside gametophyte tissue. This is the *embryo* and, historically speaking, its appearance marks an important highlight in plant evolution.

A convenient point to start the life story of a moss is with the germination of the haploid spore. This is a nonmotile structure which is spread by wind movements rather than by swimming in water. Following transport to a suitable environment the spore wall cracks open and the

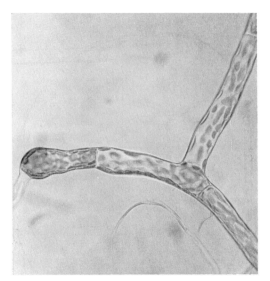

Fig. 3.15. Protonema of moss originating from germination of a moss spore.

contents emerge as a cell containing numerous, lens-shaped chloroplasts. This cell divides again and again in parallel planes to form a row, or filament, of cells which is called a *protonema* (Fig. 3.15). The protonema is distinctly algalike in appearance. It soon begins to branch and does so repeatedly until a green, tangled web is formed in the surface layers of suitably moist soil. Some of its branches lose their chlorophyll and develop a dark color in their walls. These branches of the protonemal system are called *rhizoids*. An odd, unexplained feature of rhizoids is that their cross walls are oblique rather than at right angles as are the cross walls of the green protonema.

After a period of growth in this algalike phase, certain of the cells of the pro-

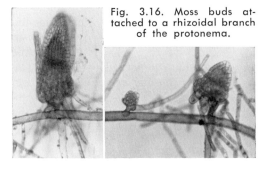

Fig. 3.16. Moss buds attached to a rhizoidal branch of the protonema.

tonema begin to divide in several planes to form small, potato-shaped masses of cells. These masses of cells are called buds (Fig. 3.16). A protonema which covers several square inches of soil may form several hundred or even several thousand buds, scattered more or less uniformly.

The buds may germinate immediately or enter a resting phase. When they do germinate each one becomes one of the leafy moss plants (Fig. 3.17) which are familiar to everyone. The fact that most of

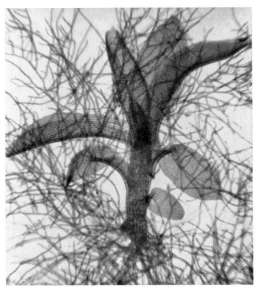

Fig. 3.17. Young leafy moss plant arising from a protonema.

the buds germinate simultaneously accounts for the tendency of mosses to grow in uniform clumps.

The leaves and stems of mosses are not true leaves and stems since they lack highly specialized conducting tissue. Their nature will be discussed subsequently.

When the leafy moss plant reaches maturity it is capable of producing *gametangia* (gamete cases). These are of two kinds, *antheridia* (Fig. 3.17A) and *archegonia* (Fig. 3.17B). An antheridium is a cigar-shaped structure which consists of an outer jacket of sterile cells and an inner mass of cells each one of which eventually gives rise to a sperm.

The archegonium is a flask-shaped structure having a long *neck* and a swollen basal portion called the *venter*. One of the cells within the venter, which is at first no different from any other cell, becomes larger and better nourished than its neighbors. This cell differentiates into the female gamete or egg.

The neck of the archegonium consists of an outer cylinder of cells and a single row of cells in the center of the cylinder. These *neck canal cells*, as they are called, are actually part of the same row of cells as the egg. When the egg is mature the canal cells disintegrate and the disorganized contents dissolve in water leaving a free canal to the egg (Fig. 3.18C).

The gametangia are formed at the tips of the main branches in some mosses (Fig. 3.19) and at the tips of short side branches in others. Usually there are series of protective leaves which overarch the branch tip and there may be a number of sterile hairs (*paraphyses*) between the gametangia. The total number of gametangia is often large (Fig. 3.20).

Fig. 3.19. Leafy moss plant with terminal rosette of leaves partially dissected to show location of gametangia and paraphyses.

Archegonia and antheridia may occur together in the same branch tip, on different branches of the same plant, or on different individuals entirely. When they occur on the same branch, they may

Fig. 3.18. Gametangia of a moss. A. Antheridium B. Archegonium with neck canal cells present C. Archegonium with neck canal cells dissolved and neck canal open D. Archegonium with embryo.

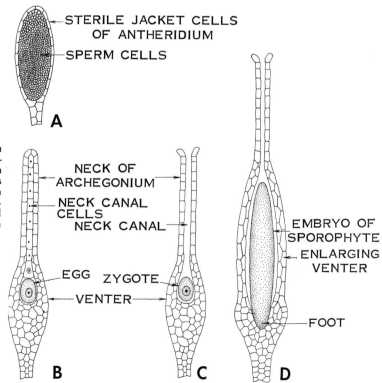

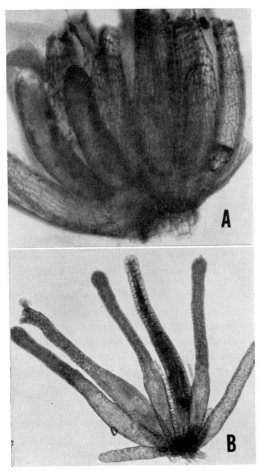

Fig. 3.20. Gametangia of mosses. A. Cluster of living antheridia dissected from a leafy moss plant. B. Cluster of living archegonia dissected from a leafy moss plant.

surface water films where they become actively motile. Frequently sperms are transferred from plant to plant by splashing rain drops. A chemical substance is secreted by mature archegonia which stimulates the sperms to swim in the right direction and, sooner or later, a sperm finds its way down the neck canal of an archegonium. There it fuses with the egg to form the zygote. Only one sperm from the many fuses with each egg.

It is usual that the archegonia do not all mature at once and this is, in a sense, a safety device which spreads the chances of fertilization over a period of time.

Once the zygote is formed it begins to grow immediately into the embryo of the sporophyte generation. Even though there are many archegonia per stem tip, it is normal that only one sporophyte will develop per tip. Apparently the growth of the first successful embryo inhibits the

develop at the same time or one type may mature later than the other. It follows from the above that it is a difficult matter to determine whether or not a moss species is truly heterothallic. Even if the gametangia appear on different leafy plants, both plants might have come from the same protonema. Thus the point would be settled by growing the species from single spores under controlled conditions.

Fertilization depends on the presence of free surface water films on the plants. Dew and light rain create favorable conditions. When mature antheridia absorb water, they swell and burst open at the tip. This discharges the sperms into the

Fig. 3.21. Stem tip of a moss with leaves removed to show enlarged venter of an archegonium enclosing an embryo. (Compare with Fig. 3.18D).

potential growth of any other zygotes that might be formed.

The division of the zygote nucleus and all succeeding divisions of nuclei in the embryo are mitotic and the embryo is, thus, a diploid structure.

The moss embryo is cigar-shaped, and each of the two ends is a growing point (Fig. 3.18D). The basal portion is called the *foot* and it burrows down into the haploid tissue of the stem tip. The foot is an absorbing organ, taking water as well as inorganic and organic nutrients from the gametophyte for the nourishment of the embryo.

The middle portion between the tips of the embryo develops into the stalk or *seta* of the sporophyte while the upper tip portion eventually develops into the *capsule*.

As the embryo gets longer, the tissue of the venter of the archegonium grows, also. In this way a continuous, protective layer is maintained over the embryo (Fig. 3.21). The neck of the archegonium is not affected by the enlargement. Usually it turns brown and withers.

Fig. 3.22. Group of moss plants showing the relation of sporophytes to gametophytes. The capsules of the sporophytes are in various stages of development and each capsule is covered by a calyptra.

Eventually, the stalk portion of the embryo begins to grow so rapidly that the enlarged venter is torn away from its attachment to the stem tip. It is then carried upward as a membranous cap over the tip of the developing capsule of the sporophyte (Figs. 3.22, 3.24, 3.25). At this

Fig. 3.23. Schematic sections of moss capsules: A. Longitudinal section with immature spore tissue (compare with Fig. 3.27A.) B. Median transverse section of immature capsule. C. Longitudinal section after maturation of spores (compare with Fig. 3.27B.)

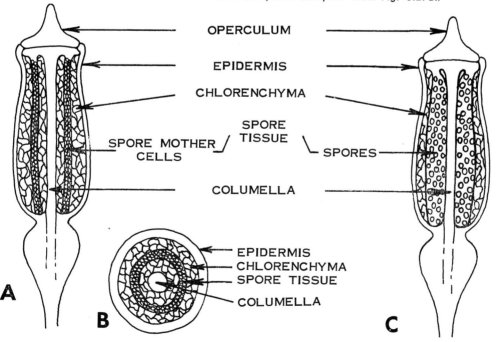

OPERCULUM

EPIDERMIS

CHLORENCHYMA

SPORE TISSUE

SPORE MOTHER CELLS

SPORES

COLUMELLA

EPIDERMIS
CHLORENCHYMA
SPORE TISSUE
COLUMELLA

A

B

C

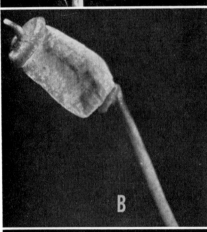

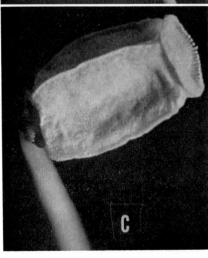

stage, the remnant of the archegonium becomes known as the *calyptra*. It still retains its function of being a protective layer over the developing capsule.

The young sporophyte of a moss usually becomes green and is capable of carrying on photosynthesis and manufacturing its own organic nutrients. However, the sporophyte still is dependent on the gametophyte for most of its water and inorganic nutrients which come from the soil.

The capsule which develops at the upper end of the enlarging sporophyte has, essentially, a cylindrical organization (Fig. 3.23). There is a central core of sterile tissue surrounded by a narrow cylinder of spore-producing tissue. Outside this is a

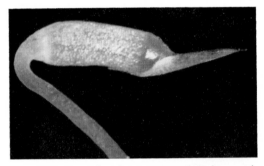

Fig. 3.25. Capsule of a species of **Mnium** with calyptra in place.

wider cylinder of cells which are usually photosynthetic. The outermost cylinder is a cutinized epidermis which often contains functional stomates. The significance of this type of epidermis is discussed in a later chapter.

The open end of the capsule is covered by a circular lid called the *operculum* (Fig. 3.24). When this lid falls off, or is picked off, it reveals a ring of toothlike structures (*peristome teeth*) around the opening (Figs. 3.24, 3.26).

The spore-producing tissue consists, at first, of a large number of spore mother cells (Fig. 3.27). Each one of these undergoes meiosis and thus the total number of

Fig. 3.24. Capsules of the hair-cap moss (**Polytrichum**): A. With calyptra ("hair-cap") in place B. With calyptra removed C. With operculum removed to show peristome teeth.

spores is four times the number of spore mother cells. As the spores mature each one develops an outer layer of waxy material like cutin.

When the spores are mature there is a natural sequence of events by which the capsules are opened. The chief agency in this process is dry air and it is interesting to contrast the requirement of dry air for spore dispersal with the requirement of free surface water for fertilization.

In species of the common moss genus, *Mnium*, for example, the calyptra shrivels and falls off, exposing the capsule which then begins to dry out. As it dries it shrinks and this causes the operculum to be popped off. The teeth around the capsule straighten out as they dry (Fig. 3.26) and this exposes the spores. The teeth are very sensitive to changes in atmospheric

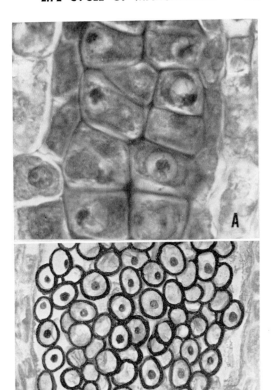

Fig. 3.27. Enlargements of portions of longitudinal sections of the spore tissue of a moss capsule: A. Spore mother cells (at start of meiosis) B. Maturing spores.

Fig. 3.26. Capsule of a species of **Mnium** with operculum removed to show the peristome teeth.

humidity. They tend to close the opening during damp weather and their movements as they dry out may help to loosen up the packed mass of spores within. Once the spores are out of the capsule they are picked up by air currents and may be carried long distances. The presence of the cutinized wall plus their naturally de-

hydrated protoplasm protects them from damage by desication during this voyage. When a spore lodges in a suitably moist place the cell contents swell and cause the spore wall to crack open. This is the beginning of the protonema of the next generation.

LIFE CYCLE OF *MARCHANTIA*

Marchantia belongs to a group of plants known as the liverworts. In this group the basic pattern of the life cycle is similar to that of the mosses and no attempt will be made to discuss the group as a whole. *Marchantia*, however, provides a classical example of heterothallism and, on this basis, warrants a brief discussion in this section.

The haploid plant body of *Marchantia* is a green, ribbonlike thallus which branches periodically in a Y-shaped fashion (Fig. 3.28). It is of fairly common occurrence on soil along stream banks, in moist woods, and on shaded cliffs. Sometimes it becomes extremely abundant in burned over forest areas provided moisture is plentiful. (The nature of the *Marchantia* plant body is discussed in Chapter 5.)

This plant has an especially effective method of nongametic reproduction. Numerous, wafer-shaped vegetative buds called *gemmae* are formed in open cups on the surface of the thallus (Fig. 3.28). When detached, the gemmae (Fig. 3.29) quickly give rise to new plants.

When gametic reproduction occurs in *Marchantia* it becomes evident that there are separate male and female plants (Fig. 3.30). Prior to this time, however, this distinction cannot be made since both plants look alike in the vegetative condition.

The male plants bear antheridia (Fig. 3.31) imbedded in disclike segments of the thallus which are raised into the air on

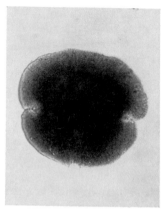

Fig. 3.29. Photomicrograph of a single gemma of **Marchantia.**

slender stalks (Fig. 3.30). When mature, the sperms are discharged into films of water on the surfaces of the discs which act as splash platforms, i.e., the splattering of rain drops when they fall on the discs causes droplets containing sperms to be spread to nearby plants, some of which are female.

The archegonia (Fig. 3.32) are to be

Fig. 3.28. A. Thallus of **Marchantia** with gemmae cups B. Enlargement of a gemmae cup.

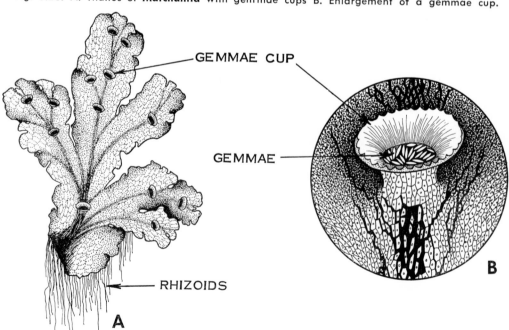

GEMMAE CUP

GEMMAE

RHIZOIDS

A

B

ARCHEGONIAL
BRANCH

ANTHERIDIAL
BRANCH

Fig. 3.30A. A group of male and female plants of **Marchantia** with antheridial branches and archegonial branches.

found on the under surfaces of similar discs which have several fingerlike projections extending outwards (Fig. 3.30). When sperms are transferred to the female plants they swim toward the archegonia in surface water films. Commonly fertilization occurs in several archegonia and embryos begin to form in each of them (Fig. 3.34).

The mature sporophytes which develop from the embryos resemble moss sporophytes in that each one consists of a *foot*, a *stalk*, and a *capsule*. However, they are smaller and less complex struc-

Fig. 3.30B. Photographs of antheridial branch (left) and archegonial branch (right) of **Marchantia.**

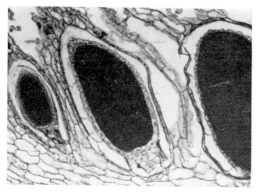

Fig. 3.31. Partial section of an antheridial disc of **Marchantia** with imbedded antheridia.

turally. Also, they are more completely dependent on the gametophyte than are the sporophytes of mosses (Fig. 3.34).

The wall of the capsule is only one layer thick and has no stomates. The whole sporophyte, including the capsule, is retained within the enlarged archegonium until the spores are fully mature. At this time, the stalk elongates rapidly, pushing the capsule downwards until it

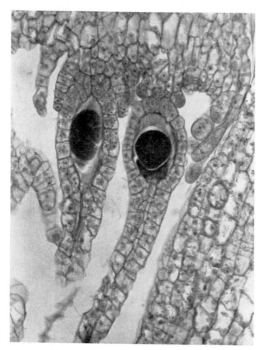

Fig. 3.32. Partial section of an archegonial branch of **Marchantia** with archegonia in position.

emerges from the protective sheaths which had surrounded it (Fig. 3.33).

Dry air then causes a loss of water and the resultant shrinkage tensions tear open the capsule wall allowing the spores to be released.

Mixed with the spores are numerous special structures called *elaters* (Figs. 3.34, 3.35). These are long, pointed, dead cells with spirally thickened walls. As they dry they change shape constantly and their movements help loosen the spore mass so that individual spores can be carried away in air currents.

Experiments with large numbers of plants grown from spores have shown that half of the spores give rise to female

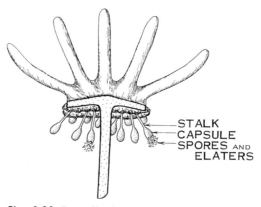

STALK
CAPSULE
SPORES AND
ELATERS

Fig. 3.33. Partially dissected archegonial branch of **Marchantia** showing the attached mature sporophytes.

plants and the other half to male plants. On the other hand, when plants of a given sex are propagated vegetatively (as by gemmae), they always give rise to plants of the same sex. From such experiments it has been concluded that sexuality in *Marchantia* is controlled by genetic factors and that these are separated during meiosis.

This contention was strengthened by experiments with another liverwort (*Sphaerocarpos*) in which tetrads of spores were isolated before they broke apart. When the individual spores of each tetrad were then separated and allowed to grow into mature plants it was always found that two of these plants were female and

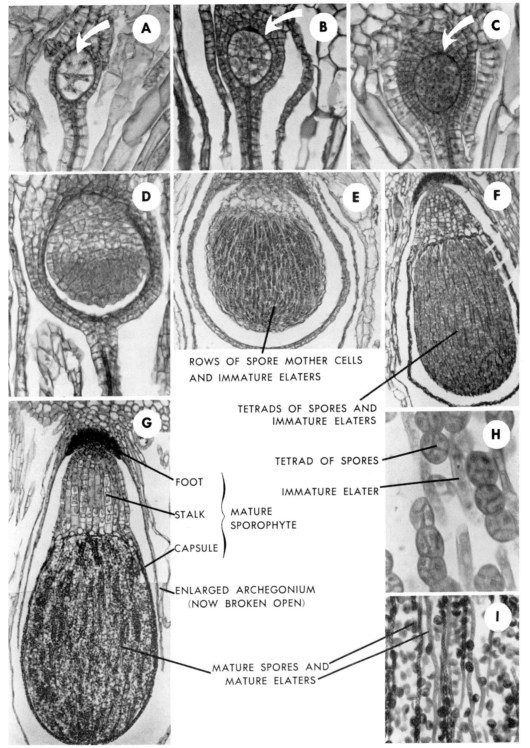

Labels within figure:

ROWS OF SPORE MOTHER CELLS AND IMMATURE ELATERS

TETRADS OF SPORES AND IMMATURE ELATERS

TETRAD OF SPORES

IMMATURE ELATER

FOOT

STALK

CAPSULE

} MATURE SPOROPHYTE

ENLARGED ARCHEGONIUM (NOW BROKEN OPEN)

MATURE SPORES AND MATURE ELATERS

Fig. 3.34. Series of photomicrographs showing development of the **Marchantia** sporophyte:

A, B, C. Arrows point to early stages in the development of the embryo within the enlarging venter of the archegonium.

D. The spherical embryo shows beginnings of differentiation into foot, stalk, and capsule.

E. The cells in linear series within the capsule are spore mother cells. The elongated cells will become elaters.

F. The spore mother cells have undergone meiosis to form tetrads of spores. (See also the enlargement in H.)

G. Mature sporophyte just at the time the stalk begins the rapid elongation which pushes the capsule out of its protective coverings.

H. Tetrads of spores and immature elaters enlarged from F.

I. Mature spores and elaters enlarged from G.

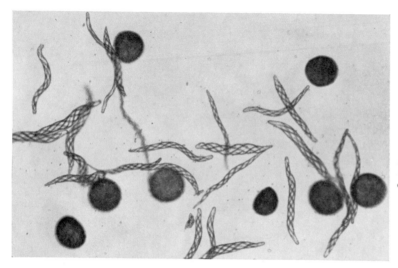

Fig. 3.35. Spores and elaters of **Conocephalum** (a relative of **Marchantia**).

the other two male. The research which led to this discovery is of exceptional interest to science since it further demonstrated that the presence or absence of a particular chromosome was related to the actual expression of sexuality.

FERNS AND THE SPORE-BEARING LEAF

Ferns are plants which have true roots, true leaves, and true stems. They do not produce seeds nor do they have flowers. However, their spores are produced on leaves and it is probable that comparable spore-bearing leaves on the ancestors of the flowering plants became modified into the stamens and pistils of modern flowers. The details of structures and reproductive mechanisms which follow apply mainly to a group of so-called "modern ferns" which includes many of the familiar ferns found in temperate regions.

The Fern Gametophyte

As it was with the mosses, the spore is a convenient point of entry into the life cycle of ferns. The fern spore is wind spread and able to exist in dry air for considerable periods of time. When it lands on moist soil the spore germinates to form a short, algalike filament (Fig. 3.36). One or more cells of this protonemal stage may give rise to tubular rhizoids which are not separated from the parent

cell by cross walls. The protonemal stage is of short duration because the terminal cell soon begins to divide by oblique cell walls to form a roughly triangular apical cell. By dividing alternately to the right and to the left the apical cell causes a flat membrane to be formed (Figs. 3.37, 3.38). The daughter cells formed by this activity continue to divide for some time. The enlargement of all of the cells formed by these divisions causes the membrane to take on the shape of a heart with the apical cell in the notch. This gametophyte of a fern is often called a *prothallus*. As it gets larger it may become somewhat thickened in the middle due to an occasional division of the apical cell in a third plane. Many rhizoids develop from the lower surface of the central midrib region. Their primary function is the anchorage of the prothallus to the ground so that it is in contact with capillary soil water. Although difficult to prove, it is quite possible that the rhizoids have additional significance in the absorp-

Fig. 3.36. Germination of a fern spore resulting in an abbreviated, algalike, protonemal stage of the gametophyte.

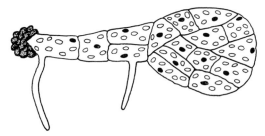

Fig. 3.37. Young fern prothallus (gametophyte) shortly after the apical cell has become active.

tion of mineral nutrients and water from the soil.

The prothallus is green and is completely independent in its nutrition. It is a small structure, rarely reaching the size of a fingernail. All of the nuclei are haploid and all of the divisions are mitotic.

Most ferns produce both antheridia and archegonia on the same gametophyte (Fig. 3.39). The antheridia begin to be formed earlier than the archegonia. They are spherical bodies attached to the lower sur-

face of the prothallus (Fig. 3.40). When the sperms are mature the contents of the antheridium swell and force the outermost wall cell to open like a lid, allowing the sperms to escape. Once in the external film of water the multiciliate sperms begin to swim rapidly.

The archegonia are not formed until the central portion of the gametophyte be-

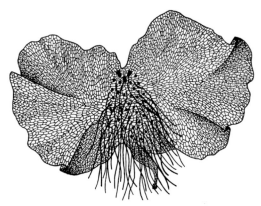

Fig. 3.39. Mature fern prothallus with antheridia, archegonia and rhizoids (ventral surface).

Fig. 3.40. Sectional view of a fern prothallus showing structure of an antheridium with maturing sperms.

comes more than one layer thick and the venter of the archegonium is sunken in the gametophyte tissue (Fig. 3.41). Only the neck protrudes and it has a decided curvature. The neck canal cells disintegrate and dissolve out of the neck canal when the egg is mature. Sperms are attracted to the archegonia and eventually one enters the canal and reaches the egg (Fig. 3.41).

The Fern Embryo

The zygote which results from the fusion of the egg and sperm begins to divide shortly by mitosis and gives rise to a more or less spherical mass of diploid cells (Fig. 3.42). This is the embryo of the

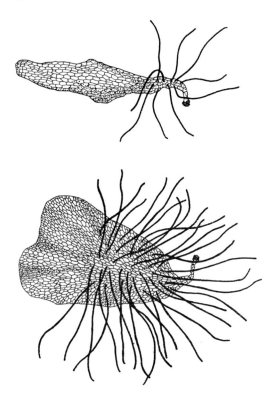

Fig. 3.38. Immature fern prothalli as seen from the ventral surface.

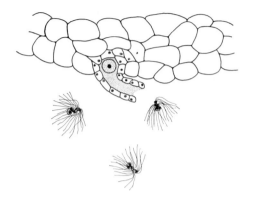

Fig. 3.41. Sectional view of a fern prothallus showing the structure of a mature archegonium. Note the sunken venter with a large egg, the curved neck with the open neck canal, and the motile sperms swarming about the archegonium.

sporophyte generation. Like the moss embryo it is nurtured and protected by the surrounding gametophyte tissue. However, it differs from the moss embryo in that it is spherical rather than cigar-shaped. Furthermore, it develops four regions of meristematic activity rather than two, as in mosses (Fig. 3.42).

One of these regions is a foot which serves to absorb nutrients and water from the gametophyte tissue. Of the rest, one region gives rise to a *primary root* and another to a *primary leaf*. These two structures develop rapidly. Each one has a strand of specialized conductive tissue which is continuous from one to the other. The primary root is a true root and functions as such. The primary leaf pushes up into the air, usually through the apical notch of the gametophyte. It becomes green and is a photosynthetic structure. The primary root and the primary leaf are soon able to take care of all of the nutritional needs of the young sporophyte and it becomes completely independent of the gametophyte (Figs. 3.43, 3.44).

The fourth lobe of the embryo develops slowly until this time. Then it becomes active as a stem tip growing point and gives rise to the type of prostrate stem known as a *rhizome*. As the rhizome

grows it gives rise to more leaves and more roots (Fig. 3.45). These secondary leaves are much bigger than the primary leaf and have a different shape. By the end of the first growing season the primary leaf and the primary root are dead. The only surviving structures are those formed by the rhizome growing point which developed from the fourth lobe of the embryo. All of the succeeding roots and leaves of a mature fern plant come from this structure (Fig. 3.46).

The Fern Sporophyll

The tissues which make up leaves, roots, and stems will be discussed in a later chapter. However, it is necessary to consider something of fern leaves in order to

Fig. 3.42. Early stages in the development of the embryo of a fern sporophyte within the archegonium:
A. First division of the zygote.
B. Second division of the zygote.
C. After many divisions the embryo becomes four-lobed. The lobes give rise to a primary leaf, a primary root, a foot and a rhizome growing point.

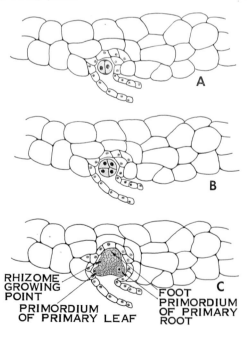

RHIZOME GROWING POINT

FOOT

PRIMORDIUM OF PRIMARY LEAF

PRIMORDIUM OF PRIMARY ROOT

C

Fig. 3.43. Fern prothallus with attached young sporophyte. The primary root and primary leaf are well developed, and the rhizome has begun to grow.

Each spore mother cell undergoes meiosis to form 4 spores and thus the potential total number of spores in a sporangium is 64. Each of the spores is, of course, haploid. As the spores mature they separate from one another and develop heavily cutinized walls.

Dry air plays an important part in the release of the mature spores. First the indusium shrivels up and exposes the spo-

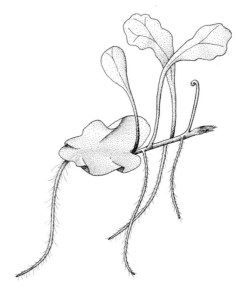

Fig. 3.45. Somewhat older fern sporophyte, still attached to the prothallus but no longer dependent on it. The rhizome has begun to grow rapidly giving rise to secondary leaves and adventitious roots.

complete the story of the fern life cycle. When the leaves of many ferns are mature they develop a large number of rusty-looking spots on their under surfaces (Figs. 3.47, 3.48, 3.49). Each of these spots is called a *sorus* (pl. *sori*) and it consists of a cluster of *sporangia* (spore cases). The sorus may be naked or covered by a protective, membranous flap called an *indusium* (Fig. 3.49). The appropriate term to be applied to the spore-bearing leaf itself is *sporophyll*.

Each sporangium is somewhat flattened and has a slender stalk by which it is attached to the leaf. The sporangium walls are one cell layer in thickness and are transparent except for one row of conspicuous cells extending partially around the edge. This row of cells, which looks something like a zipper, is the *annulus*. Careful examination reveals that all of its walls, except the walls facing outwards, are very thick and rigid (Fig. 3.50).

In many of the modern ferns each sporangium contains 16 spore mother cells. Each of them is diploid as are all of the rest of the cells of the sporophyte.

rangia. Then the cells of the annulus begin to lose water rapidly through evaporation from their thin outer walls. This causes their radial walls to be pulled towards each other, in this way shortening

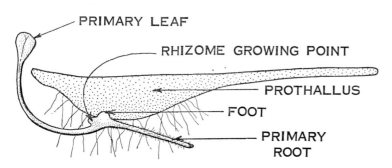

PRIMARY LEAF

RHIZOME GROWING POINT

PROTHALLUS

FOOT

PRIMARY ROOT

Fig. 3.44. Section of a fern prothallus and attached young sporophyte at a comparable stage to the illustration in Fig. 3.43.

Fig. 3.46. Mature fern sporophyte with rhizome, roots, and large, compound leaves.

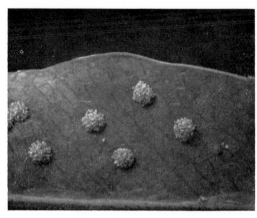

Fig. 3.48. Under surface of a fern leaf showing sori without indusia (naked sori).

Fig. 3.49. Under surface of a fern leaf showing sori with indusia.

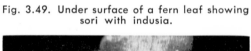

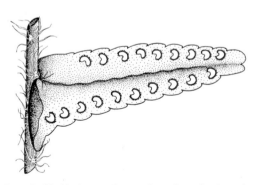

Fig. 3.47. Under surface of a fern leaf with sori.

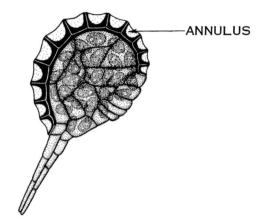

Fig. 3.50. Mature fern sporangium with enclosed spores.

the outer circumference of the annulus. This induces tensions in the lateral walls of the sporangium which eventually cause it to rip open and fold back on itself (Fig. 3.51). This process is very interesting to watch under the microscope. With a little imagination one can see resemblances between an opening sporangium and a baseball player getting ready to throw a ball. When the tension in the annulus cells reaches a peak it is released suddenly and the whole sporangium snaps shut violently. This hurls the spores out into the air where they are distributed by air currents. Each spore is capable of producing a new gametophyte.

The opening of spore cases during dry weather is a consistent feature of land plants in general. It is obvious that spores will travel further when it is dry than when it is wet and they will not be induced to germinate prematurely in an environment which is only temporarily moist.

In the ferns which have been discussed all of the spores produced by a given species have the same appearance and give rise to gametophytes which are basically similar. These ferns are said to be homosporous.

In a few ferns and in most members of the other groups of plants to be considered, the spores produced are of two kinds, *microspores* and *megaspores*. The sporangia which produce them may have different appearances as may, also, the sporophylls themselves. Such plants are said to be heterosporous.

SELAGINELLA — AN INTRODUCTION TO THE CONCEPT OF HETEROSPORY

Selaginella (Fig. 3.52) is one of a group of plants known as the club mosses. A

Fig. 3.52. Branches and vegetative leaves of a species of **Selaginella**.

more familiar genus in this group (to residents of the temperate zones, at least) is *Lycopodium* (Fig. 3.53) which includes plants known commonly as running pine, ground pine, ground cedar, etc. *Selaginella* does grow in the temperate zones but the species which do so are inconspicuous and usually known only to those botanists par-

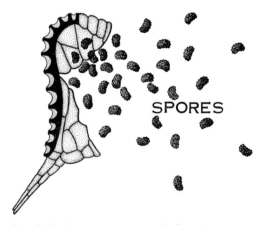

SPORES

Fig. 3.51. Fern sporangium discharging spores.

Fig. 3.53. The branching stem system, vegetative leaves, and terminal cones of a species of **Lycopodium.**

ticularly interested in this group of plants. The tropical and subtropical species are larger and more conspicuous. Many of them are cultivated, particularly in the greenhouses of colleges and botanical gardens. Species of *Selaginella* provide some very interesting clues as to how the seed habit may have developed but their actual relationships to modern seed plants are extremely remote.

All club mosses have true stems and true roots but their leaves have a basically different nature than the leaves of ferns which will be discussed in a later chapter. The name club moss is appropriate since many of them look like overgrown mosses, with clublike structures at the tips of their stems. Each of the clublike structures is a *cone* or *strobilus* (Figs. 3.53, 3.54). It consists of a group of sporophylls attached to a central axis. The sporophylls of most species are separated from the vegetative leaves in this manner. In *Selaginella*, the strobilus consists of four rows of sporophylls. Externally, all of the sporophylls look alike and, also, they are very little different in appearance from the vegetative leaves.

At the base of each sporophyll there is a single, more or less egg-shaped sporangium. Microscopic examination shows that some of the sporangia contain a large number of small reddish-colored spores.

These are called *microspores* and the sporangia containing them are called *microsporangia* (Figs. 3.55, 3.56). The other sporangia contain smaller numbers of light colored spores which are as much as 1,000 times larger in volume than the microspores. They are called *megaspores* and the megaspores in each *megasporangium* look like golf balls in a plastic bag when viewed with appropriate magnification (Figs. 3.55, 3.56).

The condition described above in which two kinds of spores are produced by a given species is called *heterospory*. As will be seen later, the evolution of heterospory

Fig. 3.54. Branches of **Selaginella** with terminal cones.

was an important step in the evolution of seed plants. Apparently this condition developed independently in several evolutionary series.

The question of why some sporangia contain microspores while others on the same plant contain megaspores is a pertinent one and *Selaginella* provides us with some information in answer to this question.

When the sporangia of *Selaginella* are very young they are all alike and each one contains a large number of spore mother cells (Fig. 3.57). In some of the sporangia, all or most of the spore mother cells under-

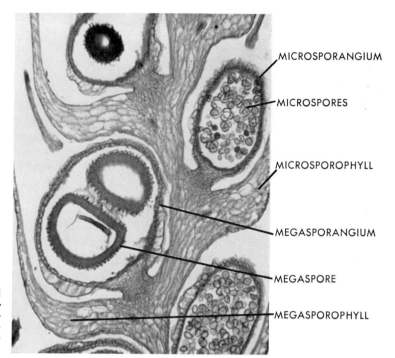

Fig. 3.55. Longitudinal section of a cone of **Sel-aginella** showing micro-spores in a microspo-rangium and megaspores in a megasporangium.

go meiosis to produce spores. This results in the large number of microspores.

In other sporangia most of the spore mother cells disintegrate before meiosis. In many species there is only one surviv-ing spore mother cell and it undergoes meiosis to form four spores. These have the same space in which to develop and the same food supply as do the larger numbers of microspores in neighboring sporangia; and they grow accordingly. Without understanding the basic reason for the disintegration of all but one of the spore mother cells, we can, nonetheless, accredit the differences between micro-spores and megaspores to differences in their nutrition.

The sporophylls which bear microspor-angia are called *microsporophylls* while those which bear megasporangia are called *megasporophylls*. There are several hundred species of *Selaginella* and among them there is considerable variation in the distribution of the two kinds of sporo-phylls in the strobilus. The microsporo-phylls may be segregated from the mega-sporophylls in one of several patterns or

the two types may intermingle indiscrim-inately.

When the spores are mature both kinds of sporangia split open violently due to tensions caused by the drying action of air. In some species this process hurls the spores out and away from the plant. They are relatively heavy and are not spread

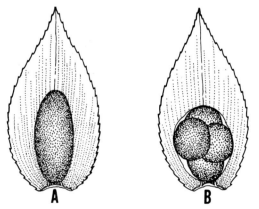

Fig. 3.56. Individual sporophylls from cones of **Selaginella:** A. Microsporophyll with attached microsporangium. B. Megasporophyll with at-tached megasporangium in which the outlines of the four large megaspores are evident.

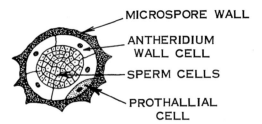

Fig. 3.58. Microspore of **Selaginella** with the enclosed male gametophyte (many times enlarged).

far before they fall to the ground. In other species they never quite escape from the strobilus. In such cases they may lodge in between the sporophylls or remain in the open sporangia completing the life cycle there.

Each microspore develops into a gametophyte which produces sperms only. This male gametophyte is very much reduced in size and is formed completely inside the microspore wall (Fig. 3.58). It consists of a single vegetative cell and one antheridium. When the sperms are mature the microspore wall breaks open and the sperms are released into surface water

films. This entire development is dependent on food stored in the microspore since there is no photosynthetic tissue in the male gametophyte.

The megaspore gives rise to a much larger gametophyte than does the microspore (Fig. 3.59). A mass of haploid cells is formed inside the megaspore wall causing it to crack open. The mass of cells then expands somewhat. In favorable situations it may become faintly green and manufacture a limited amount of food. However, it is dependent, for the most part, on food stored in the megaspore; food which was produced originally by photosynthesis in the sporophyte.

One to several archegonia are formed in this female gametophyte. The venter of each archegonium is sunken in gametophyte tissue and only the very short neck protrudes (Fig. 3.59B). Fertilization occurs sooner or later when a swimming sperm manages to find its way into one of the archegonia. The zygote develops into an embryo which eventually becomes the mature sporophyte. The embryo is nourished by the gametophyte but, as we have seen, the gametophyte itself is largely dependent

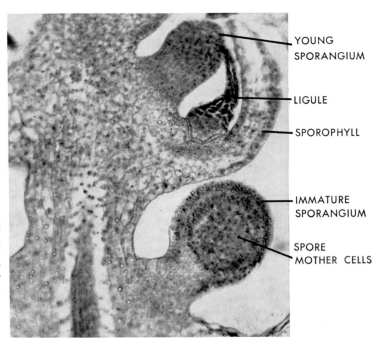

Fig. 3.57. Longitudinal section of a cone of **Selaginella** showing the young sporangia before they become differentiated into either megasporangia or microsporangia.

YOUNG SPORANGIUM

LIGULE

SPOROPHYLL

IMMATURE SPORANGIUM

SPORE MOTHER CELLS

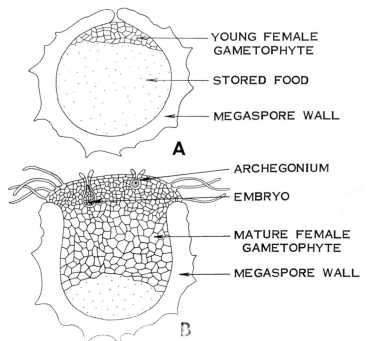

YOUNG FEMALE GAMETOPHYTE

STORED FOOD

MEGASPORE WALL

A

ARCHEGONIUM

EMBRYO

MATURE FEMALE GAMETOPHYTE

MEGASPORE WALL

B

Fig. 3.59. Stages in the development of the female gametophyte of **Selaginella**: A. Early stage within the megaspore wall. B. Mature gametophyte partially protruding from the megaspore.

on food stored in the megaspore by the preceding sporophyte generation.

The following three significant points emerge from this discussion of the life story of *Selaginella*:

1. Genetically similar spore producing tissue may be affected by nutrition in such a way that two different kinds of spores are produced.
2. The microspores, which are produced in large numbers, are small and have only a limited food supply. They produce very much reduced male gametophytes which develop entirely within the microspore wall.

Fig. 3.60. Young sporophyte of **Selaginella**. The foot is embedded in the gametophyte which is still enclosed in the megaspore wall.

3. The megaspores are fewer in number and are provided with larger quantities of stored food. This nourishes the female gametophytes and, through them, the embryos of the next sporophyte generation. This partial adoption of the female gametophyte by the sporophyte of *Selaginella* is to be compared with a complete adoption in plants which produce seeds.

THE LIFE CYCLE OF PINE — A FIRST LOOK AT THE SEED HABIT

Pines belong to a large group of plants called *gymnosperms*. The name means naked seeds and implies that the seeds are developed in an exposed position. This condition contrasts with that of the flowering plants or *angiosperms* in which the seeds develop within a protective tissue. Pines are not closely related to the flowering plants even though plants in both groups produce seeds. Nor are pines closely related to *Selaginella* even though both are heterosporous. Evidence supporting statements such as these will be considered later.

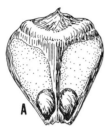 

Fig. 3.61. The ovule-bearing scale of pine. A. Dorsal surface of the scale with two ovules. B. Ventral surface of the scale with small, subtending bract.

Fig. 3.63. Newly emerged female cones of pine at the tips of a developing twig (photo taken in late spring): A. Approximately natural size. B. Much enlarged.

In pines, the two kinds of spore producing structures are segregated, and as a result, there are separate male and female cones. (Technically, it is more proper to call them microsporangiate cones and megasporangiate cones.) Both occur on the same tree and may even be found on the same branch.

Female Cones

The larger and more familiar cones are the mature female cones (Fig. 3.74). Each one consists of a series of overlapping, scalelike structures which have, in the past, been interpreted as being megasporophylls. However, each of these scales has a small bract associated with it in such

a way that the bract might well be considered to be the modified leaf rather than the scale. This fact has been responsible for the modern interpretation that the female pine cone is not a simple strobilus. This is a technical matter and a semantic escape from the terminological quandary is provided by the use of the term *ovule-bearing scale* for the parts of the female cone. Two *ovules* (structures which eventually mature into seeds) are borne at the base of each of these scales (Figs. 3.61, 3.62).

The female cones of many pines take two years to reach maturity. They are very small when they first appear at the tips of newly formed twigs in the spring (Fig. 3.63). Both male and female cones, new leaves, and undeveloped stems are all pre-

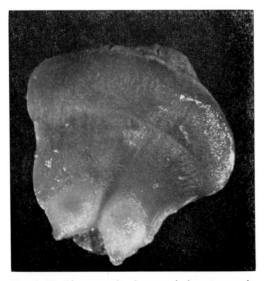

Fig. 3.62. Photograph of an ovule-bearing scale dissected from a one-year-old pine cone.

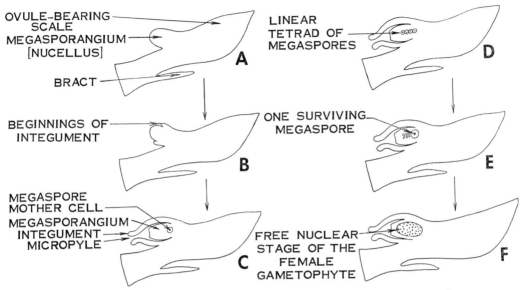

Fig. 3.64. Schematic sections of stages in the development of a pine ovule: A. Early appearance of the megasporangium (nucellus) on the surface of the scale, before the formation of the integument. B. Integument forms as a collar around the mesgasporangium. C. Integument fully developed and micropyle evident; megaspore mother cell in prophase of meiosis. D. Linear tetrad of megaspores in the megasporangium. E. Degeneration of three megaspores and growth of the one surviving megaspore. F. Free nuclear stage of the female gametophyte.

formed in the dormant winter buds. When the buds open in the spring all of these parts begin to grow and expand. Two or three or perhaps more female cones may occur at the tips of the more vigorous branches but they are the last of the pre-formed parts to become evident. During the first year of growth the female cones may become only as large as a small birds' egg. The major volume increase occurs during the second year (Fig. 3.74).

The Ovules of Pines

As noted above the ovules occur in pairs at the base of the upper surface of the ovule-bearing scales. Each ovule begins as a small swelling which has an oval outline (Fig. 3.64). The nature of this swelling indicates that it is a *megasporangium* and this term is gradually replacing an older term, *nucellus*, which was applied to this tissue long before its true nature was understood. As the megasporium grows it develops a ringlike zone of meristematic tissue some distance from its tip. Because of active cell divisions in this zone a collarlike band of tissue begins to overgrow and enclose the megasporangium. This is the *integument*. It serves, presumably, to protect the inner tissue from excessive evaporation and against some predators. In mature seeds the integument forms the major part of the seed coat. The integument does not completely seal over the nucellus, however. A small cavity is left inside and a small opening, the *micropyle*, extends from this cavity through the integument to the outside.

The ovule, thus, consists of two major parts, the megasporangium and the integument.

Deep within the megasporangium one of the cells which was at first no different from any of its neighbors begins to enlarge considerably. This is the *megaspore mother cell*. When it achieves a certain stage of maturity the nucleus of this cell undergoes meiosis giving rise to four haploid nuclei. Cell walls develop between the nuclei and four *megaspores* are formed. They are lined up in a row which is called a *linear tetrad*.

Next, three of the four megaspores begin to disintegrate and gradually disappear. The one surviving megaspore enlarges rapidly and synthesizes a large mass of protoplasm. Then the haploid nucleus of the megaspore begins to divide by mitosis. After several divisions, a large number of haploid nuclei lie free in the cytoplasm without any new cell walls to separate them. Finally cell walls begin to appear between the nuclei, and the mass is partitioned neatly into an organized tissue. This tissue is quite large and it persists into the mature seed. In that portion of the mass which is closest to the micropyle there are developed anywhere from one to several archegonia, each one containing a very large egg cell (Fig. 3.65).

The tissue just described is considered to be a female gametophyte by the following traits:

1. It developed from a haploid cell, the megaspore.
2. It consists only of cells with haploid nuclei.
3. At maturity it produces female gametes.

Note that the gametophyte is completely enclosed in sporophyte tissue and that the megasporangium does not shed the megaspores as in *Selaginella*. Not only has the female gametophyte become completely dependent for its nutrition on the sporophyte generation but it is no longer separated from the source.

In pines the development of the ovule proceeds to the point of egg formation during the first year but fertilization does not occur until the spring of the second year. In most other gymnosperms the ovule completes its entire development

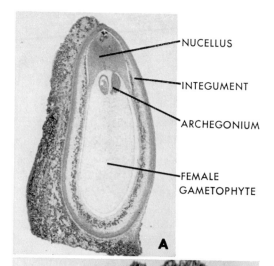

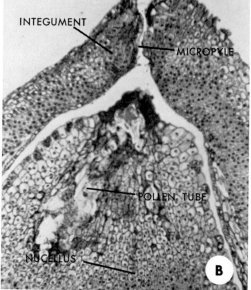

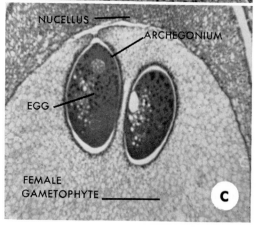

Fig. 3.65. Sections of a pine ovule containing a mature female gametophyte with archegonia. A. Entire section. B. Partial section showing micropyle and irregular growth pattern of the pollen tubes growing through the megasporangium (nucellus). C. Partial section showing details of the archegonia.

during one growing season. Before dis-
cussing fertilization, though, it is necessary to take up the sequence of events
which leads to the formation of the male
gametes.

Male Pine Cones

Male pine cones (Fig. 3.66) differ from
female cones in many respects including
numbers and location. They are borne at
the base of the new year's growth of a twig
rather than at its tip. There are usually
many of them in a tight cluster rather
than two or three. Both types of cones
may appear on the same branch but, in
general, female cones occur only on the
more vigorous branches while male cones
can often be found on more poorly developed twigs.

The male cones are simpler structures
than the female cones and there is little question that the scales of the male
cone are truly microsporophylls. Each one
bears two parallel microsporangia, attached to the lower surface, one on each
side of the midrib (Fig. 3.67). The tip of
each microsporophyll is membranous and
curves upward to overlap the one above. By
this method of overlapping scales all of the
microsporangia of a male cone are protected against premature drying.

Each microsporangium contains a large
number of microspore mother cells and,
as expected, each microspore mother cell
undergoes meiosis to produce four microspores. These are arranged in the form of
a spherical tetrad (Fig. 3.68), rather than
a linear tetrad as are the megaspores. Soon
all the microspores separate, become
rounded in shape, and begin to form a
thickened wall which has at least two
layers.

Fig. 3.66. Male cones of pine. A. Opening of
terminal bud in spring exposing young male
cones at base of the new year's growth. B.
Mature cones just before pollen dispersal. C.
Cones become somewhat elongated at the time
of pollen dispersal. D. Male cone of pine, cut
lengthwise to show arrangement of the microsporophylls.

At two points in the wall of each micro-spore, the inner and outer walls separate in such a way that the outer wall becomes inflated, forming two balloon-like append-ages. This is an interesting adaptation since it increases the total surface area without altering the weight and makes possible a more efficient dispersal in air.

The contents of the microspore divide several times by mitosis (Fig. 3.69A). Two of the cells formed are small and function-less. They are called *prothallial cells* and are thought to be vestigial remnants of the plant body of the male gametophyte. After these divisions the whole structure can no longer be called a microspore. The proper and more familiar name for it is *pollen grain* (Figs. 3.69B, 3.70). When the pollen grain has completed these divisions and developed its cutinized outer wall it is ready for dissemination.

At this time the main axis of the male cone begins to elongate and the micro-sporophylls are separated. In this way the microsporangia are exposed to dry air. Drying causes them to split open, expos-ing the pollen grains which are blown away in air currents. This process occurs in late spring and, when it happens, clouds of yellow pollen dust may be seen drifting among the branches of a pine tree.

Pollination

At the time of pollination (Fig. 3.71) the young female cones stand straight up at the tips of the branches to which they are attached. The ovule-bearing scales are slightly separated so that a space exists between each one and the next. The air is full of pollen and some of the pollen grains drift down between the scales. Each ovule secrets a small drop of sticky fluid through the micropyle. Pollen grains become trapped in this fluid and are drawn through the micropyle into the pol-len chamber when the fluid is reabsorbed. Once pollination is completed the stalk of the cone bends so that it hangs downward and growth of the scales eliminates the spaces between them, effectively sealing the cone.

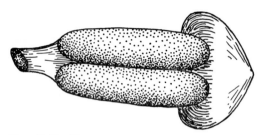

Fig. 3.67. Microsporophyll of pine with two microsporangia.

The Male Gametophyte

Each pollen grain gives rise to a tube-like outgrowth which slowly digests its way through the megasporangium tissue toward the developing female gameto-phyte. This structure is called the *pollen tube*. Several mitotic divisions occur dur-ing the growth of the pollen tube but only the last division is important since this produces two male gametes (Fig. 3.72). These are commonly called sperms yet they lack flagella and cannot swim. The growth of the pollen tube carries them to an archegonium and deposits them in close approximation to the egg.

The first cell in the developmental se-ries leading to pollen tube formation was the microspore. Furthermore, the mature pollen tube contains several haploid nu-clei and produces male gametes. There-

Fig. 3.68. Section through a microsporophyll of pine showing tetrads of microspores formed by meiosis from microspore mother cells in the microsporangium.

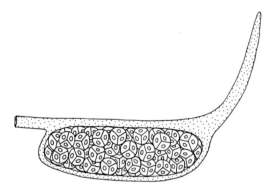

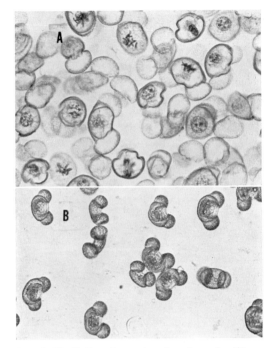

Fig. 3.69. Pollen formation in pine. A. Microspores in the process of becoming pollen grains. (The nuclei shown are haploid and mitosis is evident in some of them.) B. Mature pollen grains (whole mount).

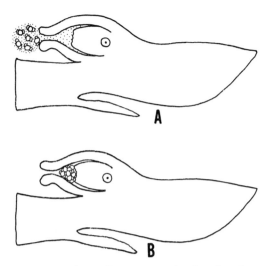

Fig. 3.71. The pollination mechanism in pine. A. The pollination fluid is extruded as a droplet from the micropyle. Note the adherent pollen grains. B. Reabsorption of the pollination fluid draws the pollen grains through the micropyle into the pollen chamber.

Fig. 3.72. Mature pollen tube of pine (male gametophyte). The two prominent nuclei are sperm nuclei.

fore it may be considered, properly, as a male gametophyte in which the plant body of the gametophyte has been diminished to the two insignificant prothallial cells.

Fertilization

In most pines, the egg has been formed and the pollen tube has reached the archegonium by late spring of the second year.

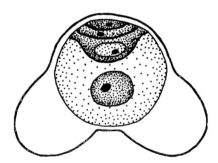

Fig. 3.70. Structure of a mature pollen grain of pine.

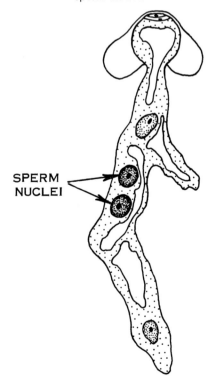

SPERM NUCLEI

The sperms are discharged from the tip of the pollen tube and one of them creeps by amoeboid movements across the few remaining microns of distance separating it from the egg. The resultant zygote promptly begins to divide by mitosis to form the diploid mass of cells which is the embryo stage of the sporophyte. The early stages of embryo formation are complex and will not be discussed here. When the emybryo is mature, it consists of a lengthwise axis with a root tip growing point at one end and a stem tip growing point at the other. Surrounding the stem tip there is a whorl of leaflike appendages called *cotyledons* (Fig. 3.73).

The whole embryo lies lengthwise in the massive tissue of the female gametophyte. This tissue has accumulated much reserve food which is used later by the embryo during germination. The superficial resemblance of the female gametophyte tissue to the endosperm of such seeds as corn was recognized long ago and it has been called endosperm (improperly) for many years.

The Pine Seed

By the time the embryo is mature, the integument of the ovule has become much thicker and very hard. The female gametophyte has expanded enormously. The megasporangium is gone except for a papery membrane at the micropyle end. This matured ovule is now a seed. It can remain alive under dry conditions for long periods of time and then germinate when placed in a suitable environment.

Fig. 3.74. Mature female cones of pine at the end of the second year's growth. A. Before the scales open. B. After the scales open to allow seed dispersal.

Fig. 3.73. Mature seed of pine dissected to show the embryo lying in the massive female gametophyte.

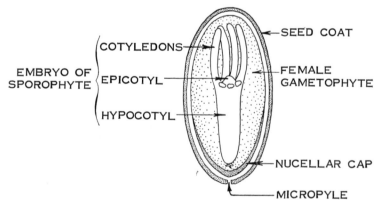

Fig. 3.75. Mature seeds of pine with attached wings.

In most pines, some of the surface tissue of the ovule-bearing scale remains attached to the seed as a wing (Fig. 3.75). When the scales separate and the seeds fall out of the cone the wings slow down the rate of fall so the wind movements can spread the seeds away from the base of the parent tree.

THE LIFE CYCLE OF FLOWERING PLANTS

The preceding brief discussions of the life cycles of lower plants serve as a background for the consideration of the life cycle of flowering plants, and, as soon will be evident, most of the terms which must be used in this discussion have been introduced already.

One reasonably good definition of a flower is that it is a modified branch bearing modified leaves. The leaves at the base of the flower are sterile while the ones near the tip are fertile. The fertile leaves, or sporophylls, are two types which are known as *stamens* and *pistils*. The sterile leaves in primitive flowers may have been all alike but, in many modern flowers, the lowermost ones are differentiated as *sepals* and those above, as *petals*.

Receptacle and Perianth

The *receptacle* is the part of the flower (Figs. 3.76, 3.77) to which the other parts are attached. Probably it represents the axis of the conelike primitive flower which no longer becomes elongated. If there is but one flower arising in the axil of a leaf, then the stalk of this flower may be called a *peduncle*. If the flowers occur in definite clusters, or *inflorescences*, then the stalk of each individual flower is called a *pedicel*, while the stalk of the whole inflorescence is the peduncle.

Sepals are the leaflike parts which are attached below (outside of) all of the others on the receptacle. Often they are smaller than the petals and are usually green. Normally, they enclose the rest of the flower parts during the bud stage. It should be noted that, in some plants such as lilies and tulips, the sepals and petals are similar in size and color. In some other plants they may be lacking entirely.

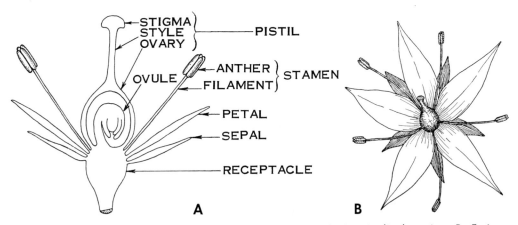

Fig. 3.76. Schematic representations of flower structure. A. Longitudinal section. B. Entire.

Fig. 3.77. Partial dissection of the flower of a member of the lily family.

Collectively the sepals of a flower are referred to as the *calyx*.

Petals are the leaflike parts which are attached immediately above (and thus appearing inside) the sepals. They are often brightly colored. In many plants they may be small and inconspicuous or even lacking. Flowers with showy petals often attract insects which come in search of nectar and pollen. In so doing they may do the plant a service by transferring pollen from one flower to another. When referred to collectively, the petals of one flower are termed the *corolla*.

The term *perianth* refers to all of the leaflike parts of the flower and thus includes both sepals and petals. Sometimes it is difficult to distinguish between sepals and petals. At other times one of these two parts is missing and it is difficult to decide which one is present. Under such circumstances it is helpful to refer to the structures as perianth parts.

Stamens

Stamens are commonly thought of as being the male parts of the flower. In terms used to discuss previous plants, however, stamens are microsporophylls. Their leaflike nature has become obscured by modification. All that is left, normally, is a slender stalk or *filament*, and the *anther*. The anther consists of four anther sacs with some connective tissue between them (Fig. 3.78).

Each anther sac contains a microsporangium which, when immature, is filled with a great many microspore mother cells (microsporocytes) (Fig. 3.79). Each one of the microspore mother cells undergoes meiosis to form microspores which are, of course, haploid (Fig. 3.80). The nucleus of each microspore then undergoes one mitotic division to form two haploid nuclei. At this stage, the microspore becomes a pollen grain. The wall of the pollen grain

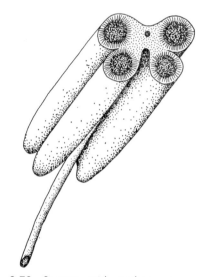

Fig. 3.78. Stamen with anther cut crosswise.

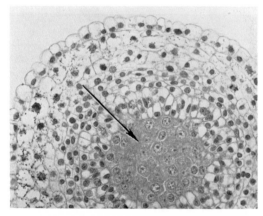

Fig. 3.79. Transverse section of one of the four lobes of an anther. The arrow points to the microspore mother cells in the microsporangium.

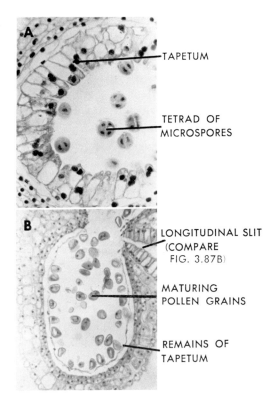

Fig. 3.80. Transverse sections of anther lobes:
A. With tetrads of microspores (after meiosis).
B. With maturing pollen grains.

becomes thick and cutinized and has characteristic markings (Figs. 3.80B, 3.81).

During this development the anther increases in size. The inner layer of wall cells of the anther sac, which is called the *tapetum,* breaks down to form a viscous fluid in which the microspore mother cells seem to float. This fluid may have an important effect on microspore development. When the pollen grains are mature, the wall between adjacent pairs of anther sacs breaks down so that two large chambers are formed, one on each side of the anther. Finally a lengthwise slit develops down each side of the anther and the mature pollen grains are exposed to the air (Fig. 3.87B).

Pistils

Pistils are commonly thought of as the female parts of the flower. Each one is composed of three major segments. The *stigma* is the terminal portion of a pistil adapted primarily to received pollen grains. The *style* is the portion which connects the stigma with the ovary. The *ovary* is the basal portion of a pistil and contains the ovules (Fig. 3.76).

Actually a simple pistil is a highly modified megasporophyll. In order to explain this concept it becomes necessary to discuss something of the theoretical origins of the pistil. According to a widely accepted theory the pistil evolved from a flattened megasporophyll with ovules on the upper surface. This structure became folded along the middle, or rather failed to unfold from the folded embryonic condition. The joined edges became sealed and thus the ovules were enclosed. As a result the ovules have an added degree of protection against desiccation and, to some

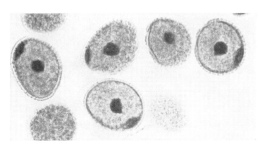

Fig. 3.81. Mature pollen grains as seen in transverse sections. Tube nuclei and generative cells are evident in some of them.

degree, against predation by other organisms. (See Figs. 3.82, 3.83 and further discussions of this topic in Chapter 4.)

Many plants have flowers with compound pistils which have resulted from the fusion of two or more simple pistils. The term *carpel* is used to designate each portion of a compound pistil which is recognizable as being one of the fused segments (Fig. 3.83C).

The Ovule

The ovule (Fig. 3.84) is the structure which eventually becomes the seed. Depending on the kind of plant there may be from one to several thousand ovules in each ovary.

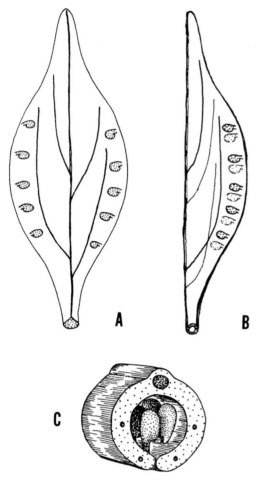

Fig. 3.82. Hypothetical origin of the simple pistil. A. Megasporophyll of a "pre-angiosperm" flower with ovules along the margin. B. Megasporophyll folded along the midrib, thus enclosing the ovules. C. Transverse section of the hypothetical simple pistil.

Each ovule begins as a small, dome-shaped swelling on the inner wall of the ovary. As it gets larger, two ringlike layers of tissue form around its base, one inside the other. These two layers are integuments. It will be recalled that the pine ovule has but one integument. The inner, dome-shaped mass is the nucellus or megasporangium. The integuments grow completely over the megasporangium except for a tiny hole in the center. This is the micropyle. (Note: In sections of the lily ovary which are widely used for teach-

ing purposes the ovules are not straight. Instead, they become curved during their growth in such a way that the micropyle end is next to the stalk — see Fig. 3.85).

One cell, deep within the megasporangium, enlarges enormously compared to its neighbors. The nucleus of this cell also

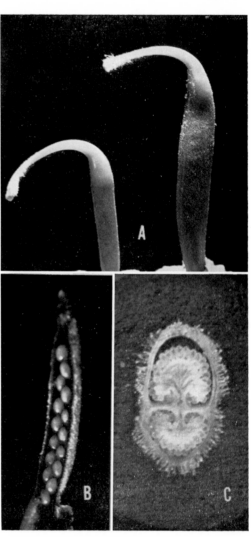

Fig. 3.83. Simple pistils and compound pistils. A. Simple pistils dissected from flowers of the perennial sweet pea. B. Longitudinal section of one of the simple pistils in A showing the double row of ovules. (Compare with the transverse section in Fig. 3.82C). C. Transverse section of the compound ovary of a snapdragon flower showing two fused carpels with numerous ovules in each.

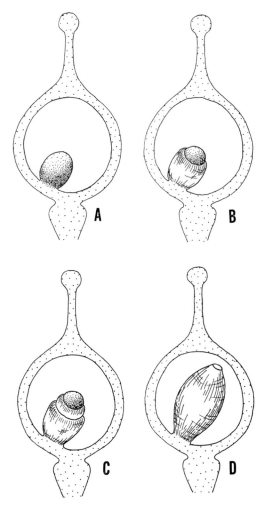

Fig. 3.84. Schematic longitudinal sections of a pistil illustrating stages in the development of an ovule. A. Origin of the megasporangium (nucellus) as a swelling on the inner ovary wall. B. Origin of the inner integument. C. Origin of the outer integument. D. Integuments completely enclosing the megasporangium except for the micropyle.

increases greatly in size. This cell is a megaspore mother cell (megasporocyte) and, like any other spore mother cell, its nucleus undergoes meiosis to form four haploid nuclei. The cytoplasm of the megaspore mother cell may become subdivided into four megaspores but, in some plants, the megaspore nuclei do not become parts of cellular units (Fig. 3.85).

The Female Gametophyte (Embryo Sac)

In many plants only one of the four megaspores formed after meiosis survives while the other three disintegrate and eventually disappear. The surviving megaspore grows rapidly and its nucleus divides by mitosis to form two haploid nuclei. These divide again to form four, and again to form a total of eight haploid nuclei which lie free in the cytoplasm of the megaspore. This structure was termed the *embryo sac* long before its nature as a *female gametophyte* was recognized. Both names are now in common usage. Since all eight nuclei were formed by mitosis from the megaspore nuclei, they are identical with respect to their numbers and kinds of chromosomes.

Commonly, the nuclei are in two groups of four, one group at each pole of the embryo sac. One nucleus from each group migrates to the center and this pair of nuclei is referred to as the *polar nuclei*. The remaining six nuclei and the cytoplasm around them become organized into six cellular units, three at one pole and three at the other. The three cells farthest away from the micropyle are called *antipodal cells*. Of the cells at the micropylar end of the embryo sac, one becomes the *egg*. The other two are called *synergids* (Fig. 3.85J).

Thus, the mature embryo sac has seven cells, three at one end and three at the other, with a large binucleate cell in the middle. Logically, it conforms to the definition of a gametophyte since it develops from a spore and produces a gamete. The three antipodal cells may be interpreted as the vestigial remains of the plant body of the female gametophyte. Whether or not the synergids are remnants of an archegonium is a question which cannot be answered with any of the facts at our disposal.

Students who have previously studied gamete formation in animals should again make a careful comparison with gamete formation in plants at this time. The interpolated gamete-producing gen-

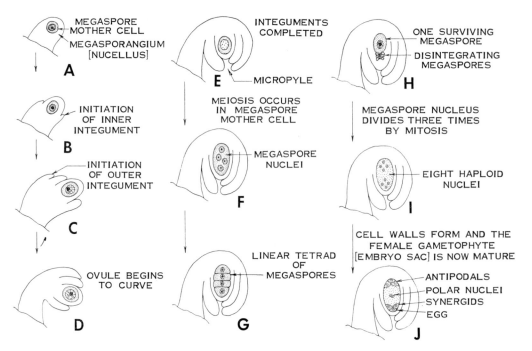

Fig. 3.85. Longitudinal, schematic sections of pistils illustrating ovule formation, differentiation of the megaspore mother cell, meiosis and embryo sac formation. Based in part on sections of lily ovules up to the point of megaspore formation.

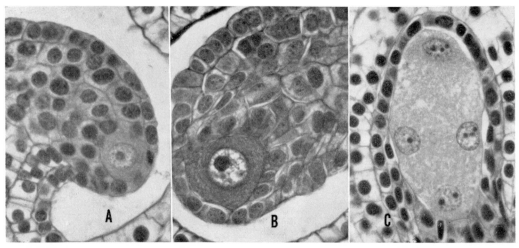

Fig. 3.86. Photomicrographs of sections of lily ovules for comparison with the early stages shown in Fig. 3.85. A. Compare with Fig. 3.85A. B. Compare with Fig. 3.85B. C. Compare with Fig. 3.85F.

eration is lacking in almost all animals and gamete formation follows immediately after meiosis. The cells which become microspores in plants are, in a sense, analogous to the cells which become sperms in animals while the cells which become megaspores in plants are analogous to those which become eggs in animals. An awareness of this difference will aid considerably in the understanding of problems in inheritance since genetics courses are often taught with examples from both the plant and animal worlds.

Pollination

At about the time when the embryo sac is mature, the pollen grains in the anther are also mature. The anthers open and the pollen is dispersed. The transfer of pollen from anther to stigma is properly called pollination, i.e., it is incorrect to refer to pollen transfer as fertilization (Fig. 3.87).

The two chief agencies of pollination are wind and insects. Wind pollinated flowers tend to have elaborate, sometimes feathery, stigmas which trap pollen from the air. Insect pollinated flowers tend to have sticky stigmas as well as devices which attract insects and cause them to be dusted with pollen. As the insects crawl around in the flower, or visit other flowers of the same kind, the pollen on their bodies becomes transferred to the stigma. Among the attractive devices are a general showiness of the flower and the secretion of nectar. Many flowers also have devices which tend to discourage the visitations of smaller insects which could rob the nectar without affecting pollination.

The Pollen Tube (Male Gametophyte)

Many pollen grains have three thin places, or pores, in their outer cell walls. When an individual pollen grain lands on a stigma one of these three pores comes into contact with the surface of the stigma. Through this pore a tubelike outgrowth (the pollen tube) emerges and penetrates the surface of the stigma. As was pointed out previously, the pollen grain has two haploid nuclei. One of these, the *tube nucleus*, stays near the tip of the pollen tube and apparently controls the growth of the tube (Fig. 3.88).

The other nucleus often has a layer of cytoplasm around it which forms a rather vaguely organized cell, the *generative cell*. During its journey down the pollen tube the generative cell divides once, by mitosis, to form two male gametes. Thus the mature pollen tube contains a total of three haploid nuclei. Since all three nuclei have important functions it is evident that the male gametophyte has been reduced to an absolute minimum.

Many pollen grains are transferred to a stigma at the time of pollination. Most

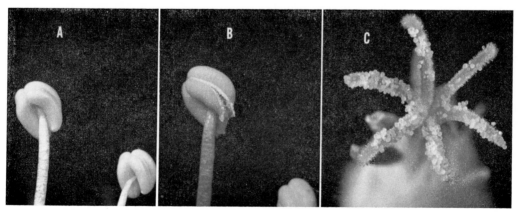

Fig. 3.87. Dispersal of pollen: A. Mature anther before pollen discharge. B. Mature anther with lengthwise split exposing the pollen for dispersal. C. Stigmas covered with pollen after pollination.

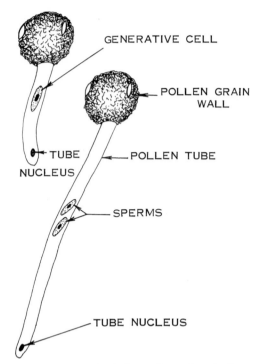

Fig. 3.88. Growth of the pollen tube: A. Emergence of tube from the pollen grain. B. Mature pollen tube.

of them begin growth and many more pollen tubes enter the cavity of the ovary than there are ovules present. There seems to be a chemical secretion from the ovules which directs the growth of the pollen grains toward the micropyles, but it is unusual for more than one pollen tube to enter a single micropyle (Fig. 3.89).

Fertilization

The pollen tube, after entering the micropyle, grows through the nucellus and bursts into the embryo sac where most of its contents are discharged. The tube nucleus has no further function and begins to disintegrate. One of the male gametes unites with the egg cell to form the zygote. The other one units with the two polar nuclei. This process, which involves two separate nuclear fusions, is called double fertilization (Fig. 3.90).

Growth of the Endosperm

The mass of cytoplasm enclosing the triple fusion nucleus is now referred to as the *primary endosperm cell*. The triploid nucleus with its three sets of chromosomes begins to divide rapidly by mitosis to form a large number of $3n$ nuclei. At first they lie free in the enlarging cytoplasmic mass of the endosperm cell but, eventually, the cytoplasm becomes divided into cellular units, each containing one nucleus. Large masses of reserve food are accumulated in the *endosperm* which is a unique tissue occurring only in the seeds

Fig. 3.89. Longitudinal section of a pistil with pollen tubes growing down style into cavity of the ovary. One tube is entering the micropyle of an ovule.

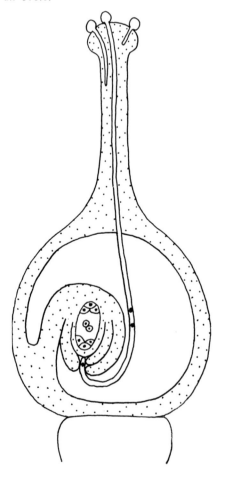

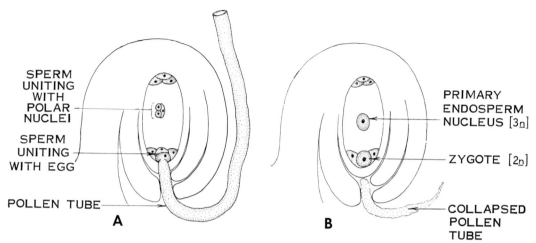

Fig. 3.90 Double fertilization: A. The sperms have been discharged from the pollen tube into the embryo sac. B. Union of one sperm with the egg forms the zygote, and union of the other sperm with the two polar nuclei forms the nucleus of the primary endosperm cell.

of flowering plants (Fig. 3.91). This food is eventually used by the plant as nourishment for the embryo but many other organisms, including man, have come to rely on endosperm as a source of food. Many cultivated crop plants are important because of the food stored in the endosperm and much of the history of civilization is involved with the need for controlling land where such plants can be grown successfully.

Divisions in the endosperm occur rapidly but soon the zygote begins to divide by mitosis also. A mass of diploid cells is formed which is the embryo of the sporophyte. As noted above the embryo obtains its nutrition from the food reserves in the endosperm. In some plants, corn being a common example, the seed becomes mature and enters a resting stage while the embryo is still small in comparison to the endosperm. In other plants, such as beans, the endosperm is completely used up before the seeds are mature. In such cases the reserve foods are transferred to the cotyledons of the embryo. Re-

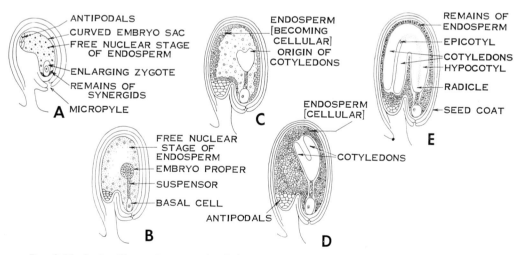

Fig. 3.91. Series illustrating growth of the endosperm and embryo based on **Capsella**.

serve foods, whether stored in the endosperm or in the cotyledons, are used during the germination period to provide young seedlings with metabolic materials until they are able to manufacture their own.

The Development of a Dicot Embryo

In many plants, following the first division of the zygote, the *basal cell* of the resulting cell pair enlarges considerably and does not divide further. The other member of this first cell pair divides several times in parallel planes to form a filament of cells which is called the *suspensor*. Eventually, the terminal cell of the suspensor begins to divide in several planes to form a small, spherical mass of cells which is the *embryo proper*. The function of the suspensor seems to be that of pushing the embryo proper into the endosperm tissue. It does not become a part of the mature embryo (Fig. 3.91).

The embryo proper soon loses its spherical shape and becomes somewhat elongated. One end remains rounded but the other end becomes "flat-topped" so that the whole structure is crudely triangular. Later the corners of the flattened side begin to grow rapidly, forming two lateral, earlike appendages which are essentially parallel to each other. These appendages are the *cotyledons*. It should be remembered that they are parts of the embryo. In bean seeds they become so much larger than the other parts of the embryo that it is easy to lose track of this point (Fig. 3.92).

The small mass of meristematic cells which arises between and at the base of the two cotyledons is the growing point or apical meristem of the shoot system. Very commonly this growing point becomes active for a time before the seed matures. As a result, several stem segments and young leaves may exist in miniature form between the cotyledons. The terms *plumule* and *epicotyl* are used interchangeably to describe this future shoot system in the embryo.

The major portion of the embryo axis below the cotyledons is called the *hypo-cotyl*. The root growing point at the basal end of the hypocotyl is the *radicle*. In the early phases of seed germination the radicle becomes active and gives rise to the primary root.

The Monocot Embryo

The flowering plants are divided into two large groups, *monocotyledons* and *dicotyledons*. One basic point of separation is an embryo difference: dicot embryos have two cotyledons while monocot embryos have but one. By and large the development of the monocot embryo (Fig. 3.93) is similar to that of the dicot embryo which has already been described.

The mature grain of corn is actually a one-seeded fruit in which the seed coat and the ovary wall have become completely fused. The major portion of the corn grain is filled with endosperm tissue which may be white and flourlike, or yellow and flinty. The outermost layer of cells in the endosperm contains considerable amounts of stored protein. It is referred to as the *aleurone layer*.

The embryo has a single cotyledon which is much larger than the embryo axis and attached laterally to it. Because the cotyledon is shaped somewhat like a shield it has long been called a *scutellum* (from a Latin word meaning shield). All

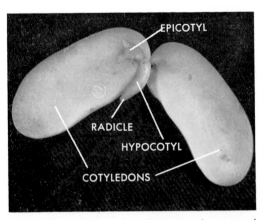

Fig. 3.92. Embryo of a bean seed removed from seed coat and spread apart to show the two massive cotyledons, the epicotyl, and the hypocotyl axis.

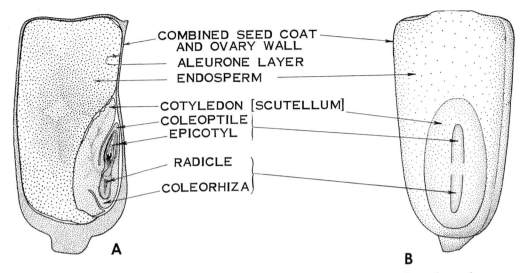

Fig. 3.93. Mature grain of corn: A. As seen in a section. B. As seen from the surface.

of the embryo axis below the attachment point of the cotyledon is the radicle. Technically it might be considered as being a hypocotyl but the organization of its tissues is so entirely rootlike that the term radicle is more appropriate. The radicle is covered by a special tissue known as the *coleorhiza*.

Above the attachment point of the cotyledon there is a leaflike membrane which is wrapped around the epicotyl as a protective sheath. This is the *coleoptile*. When the seed is mature, the *epicotyl* consists of several segments of the future stem plus a corresponding number of undeveloped leaves and the apical meristem.

THE FRUIT

As discussed above, ovules are developed inside the ovary of the pistil and, when mature, they become seeds. Meanwhile the pistil enlarges, particularly in the region of the ovary. The mature fruit may consist entirely of ovary tissue, or of ovary plus accessory tissues.

A *simple fruit* matures from an individual pistil which may be simple or compound.

An *aggregate fruit* is formed when several pistils in the same flower mature as a part of one compound structure.

A *multiple fruit* involves parts of several flowers which mature as one compound structure.

Each of the above can be classified further as a *true fruit* in which only the pistil is involved, or as an *accessory fruit* in which other parts of the flower, in addition to the pistil, are involved.

At maturity a given fruit may be dry or fleshy. Furthermore, dry fruits may be dehiscent meaning that they open at maturity, or they may be indehiscent.

These terms are useful in describing specific examples of fruits. In addition, many types of fruits have been given special names. A few examples of special fruit types are discussed below.

An *achene* is a dry, indehiscent fruit which contains a single seed and this seed is united with the ovary wall only by its stalk. Sunflower "seeds" are actually achenes (Fig. 3.94).

A grain or *caryopsis* is also a dry, indehiscent fruit containing a single seed. It differs from an achene in that the seed coat is completely and permanently united with the ovary wall (Fig. 3.93).

A *nut* is another example of a dry, indehiscent fruit which, in many cases, contains only a single seed. Nuts are usually larger than achenes and some portions of their ovary walls become very hard and

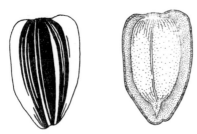

Fig. 3.94. Achene of sunflower entire and dissected.

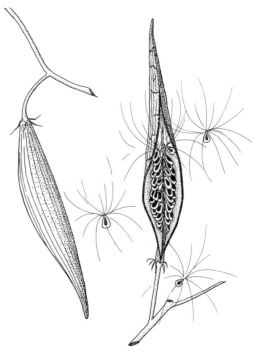

thick. Hazelnuts and hickory nuts (Fig. 3.95) are good examples of the fruit condition while Brazil nuts are seeds rather than true nuts.

A *follicle* is a dry, dehiscent fruit which splits open along one edge at maturity. The fruit of a milkweed plant is a familiar example of a follicle (Fig. 3.96A).

A *legume* is the characteristic fruit of many members of the legume family which includes peas, beans, alfalfa, clover, etc. It is a dry, dehiscent fruit which splits open along both edges at maturity (Fig. 3.96B).

A *capsule* is a dry, dehiscent fruit formed from a compound pistil. Capsules vary considerably in the exact manner in

Fig. 3.96A. Closed and open follicle of a milkweed.

Fig. 3.95. Hickory nut with the enclosing husk split apart.

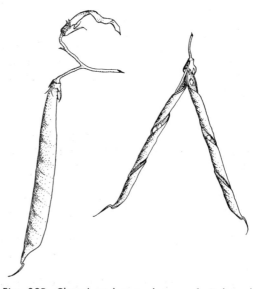

Fig. 39B. Closed and open legume fruit based on the pod of the perennial sweet pea.

which the individual carpels open at maturity to release the seeds. Irises, poppies, and lilies are examples of common plants which form capsules (Figs. 3.97, 3.103).

A *drupe* is a fleshy fruit in which the outer zones of the ovary wall become

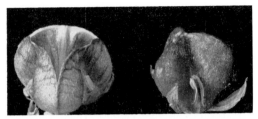

Fig. 3.97. Open and closed capsules of a member of the lily family (**Ornithogallum**).

fleshy while the inner zone becomes hard and stony. Cherries, plums, and peaches are classified as drupes (Fig. 3.98).

In true *berries* the entire ovary wall becomes fleshy. Tomatoes (Fig. 3.99) and grapes are good examples of berries. Citrus fruits such as oranges and lemons are usually classified as berries but are sometimes given a special name due to the presence of the characteristic rind.

Bananas, squashes, melons, blueberries, gooseberries, and many other fleshy fruits similar to these are generally classified as berries due to the fleshiness of the ovary wall. However, in each of these, other flower parts in addition to the pistil are involved in the fruit.

The fruits of apples and similar plants are called *pomes*. The inner, cartilaginous core of the pome is formed from the inner zone of the ovary wall while the outer

Fig. 3.99. Branch of a tomato plant with fruits (berries) in various stages of development.

zones are fleshy and united, almost indistinguishably, with accessory structures which have become fleshy also (Fig. 3.100).

The raspberry is an aggregate fruit composed of miniature drupes each of which matures from one of the many pistils in the flower.

The strawberry is an aggregate fruit in which the receptacle enlarges and becomes fleshy. The numerous pistils in the flower mature into tiny achenes which are imbedded in the fleshy receptacle (Fig. 3.101).

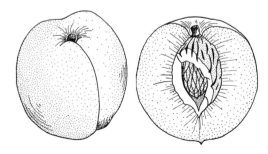

Fig. 3.98. Entire and dissected drupe of peach.

Fig. 3.100. Apple fruit (pome) entire and dissected.

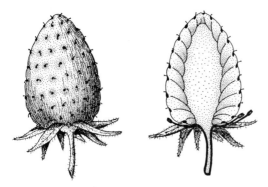

Fig. 3.101. Strawberry (an aggregate fruit with numerous small achenes embedded in the fleshy receptacle.)

The pineapple is a multiple fruit in which the receptacles, pistils, and sepal bases of several flowers are united to form the fleshy tissues of the fruit (Fig. 3.102).

SEED DISPERSAL

It may be assumed that the evolutionary development of fruits has been influenced by natural selection, i.e., the nature of the fruiting structure bears some positive relationship to survival of the species. Many factors might be considered in a full discussion of this topic but two of them are of major significance:

1. Protection of the immature seeds.
2. Dispersal of the mature seeds.

The fleshy portions of mature fruits are usually edible and form a part of the diet of numerous animal species. Before maturity such fruits are frequently inedible for reasons of taste or texture. This tends to prevent the destruction of the fruit before the seeds are mature.

When the seeds are fully mature it is advantageous for the species if they are transported away from the immediate vicinity of the parent plant. Animals may provide transportation by eating the flesh and throwing away the seeds. If one calls to mind the picture of a small boy trudging along a country road, munching an apple and finally tossing away the core with its enclosed seeds, he will realize how effective the apple fruit is as a device for seed dispersal.

In many cases the fruits are swallowed whole and the flesh is digested while the seeds pass through the digestive tract unharmed. Birds are particularly effective in spreading seeds this way. Such circumstances provide an explanation for the common occurrence of red cedars along fence rows.

Among the fruits which are classified as being dry and dehiscent there are many

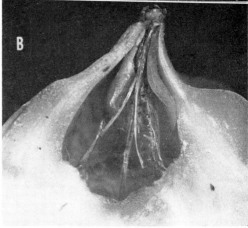

Fig. 3.102. Pineapple (a multiple fruit). A. Entire fruit. B. One of the segments, dissected and enlarged, showing the floral cavity with shriveled floral parts.

types in which tensions develop as the mature fruit dries out. When the fruit opens these tensions are released violently. The fruit seems to shatter and the seeds are hurled away from the parent plant. The fruit of a common barnyard weed known as touch-me-not, or jewel weed (*Impatiens biflora*) provides a classical example of such a mechanism. The illustrations in Figure 3.103 are of the fruits of a cultivated species of *Impatiens*.

Many fruits develop hooks or spines of various kinds which become caught in animal fur and are carried away as the animal moves about. Some of these (beggar's ticks, cockle-burs, stickseeds, etc.) are familiar to anyone who has tramped through a weed patch in the fall of the year (Fig. 3.104).

The fruits of dandelions, and many similar plants, are small and light in weight. As they mature, each of the many fruits in the characteristic compact heads develops a whorl of hairlike appendages. These serve as parachutes which allow the fruits to float for long distances in air currents (Fig. 3.105).

In each of these cases, and the many more which could be cited, a majority of the seeds are destroyed in various ways or transferred to places where successful growth of the next generation is impossible. However, seeds are produced in prodigious numbers and enough of them germinate in suitable environments to insure survival of the species.

SEED GERMINATION AND ESTABLISHMENT OF THE NEW SPOROPHYTE

The germination period may be defined to include the time between planting of the seed and development of the seedling to a point when it is self-supporting. Many seeds begin to germinate shortly after being placed in a suitable environment while others are truly dormant and do not germinate for long periods unless specially treated in one of several ways. Some of the important environmental conditions which may influence the germination of seeds are temperature, soil moisture, oxygen supply, and light.

Temperature affects the rates of physical and chemical reactions necessary to the germination process. Absorption of water and digestion of reserve foods are examples of important reactions influenced by temperature. Seeds of different kinds of plants vary in their optimum temperature requirements for germination. Soil temperature has another vital influence on successful germination in that it affects the growth rates of disease producing soil organisms which might destroy the germinating seeds.

The water content of mature seeds is usually low and the protoplasm of seeds has a low rate of metabolic activity. This dehydrated condition is important to the survival of seeds through periods of unfavorable environmental conditions. When water becomes available the cell walls and the protoplasm imbibe water

Fig. 3.103. Seed dispersal by shattering capsules. Capsule of a cultivated species of **Impatiens** before and after the violent dehiscence.

and swell (Fig. 3.106). As more and more water enters the seed, the speed of chemical reactions increases, particularly digestive and respiratory processes. The forma-

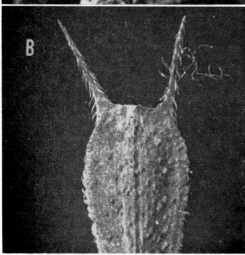

Fig. 3.104. Seed dispersal by hooks and spines. A. Cocklebur. B. One segment of the fruit of beggar's ticks.

tion of sugar from reserve foods lowers the relative concentration of water in the cell sap resulting in a further absorption of water by osmosis.

Oxygen is essential to the respiratory processes which release the energy essential to growth and which also form many intermediate products of metabolism. Some seeds can germinate in low percentages of oxygen but most seeds need

Fig. 3.105. Seed dispersal by "parachutes." Compact head of dandelion fruits, each of which is an achene with a whorl of radiating appendages.

the normal concentration of this gas found in the atmosphere.

The light requirements of seeds vary. Some germinate only in the dark, some germinate in the light, others require alternating periods of light and dark. Many are not sensitive to light conditions and germinate in either light or dark.

Soil fertility does not have an appreciable effect on seed germination since most seeds contain enough inorganic nutrients, as well as organic nutrients, to insure good germination.

Seed Dormancy

Dormant seeds frequently fail to germinate for considerable periods of time after being planted. Since many crop plants (clover, for instance) exhibit seed

Fig. 3.106. A comparison of dried peas (inner circle) with peas fully imbibed with water (outer circle).

dormancy, this is an important matter and considerable research has been done with factors controlling dormancy.

In many legumes the seed coat remains impermeable to water for long periods of time. In some species of plants the seed coat may be permeable to water but resists swelling because of its mechanical strength. In nature, various physical, chemical, and biological processes in the soil act on such seed coats, eventually softening them to the point where germination can occur. This process may take months or even years. However, germination can be hastened by a mechanical cracking of the seed coats or by one of several means of wearing them down (*scarification*).

In many plants, a mature, ripened seed may contain a very small or otherwise immature embryo. For considerable periods of time after planting such embryos develop slowly within the seed. Eventually, perhaps months later, they reach a size which permits them to emerge from the seed coat. Not much can be done in a practical way to hasten this slow process of embryo maturation.

Seeds of many plants have fully developed embryos as well as permeable seed coats, yet still fail to germinate for long periods of time. During this period of after-ripening important biochemical changes occur in the seeds. One such change commonly cited is a gradual increase in acidity of the cell sap due to accumulation of carbon dioxide from respiration. Many other changes of similar nature have been investigated in various research laboratories. One practical method of decreasing the length of the after-ripening period is storage under moist conditions at low temperatures.

THE GERMINATION PROCESS

The first important phase in germination is the absorption of water by imbibition (Fig. 3.106). Dried seeds commonly have less than 20 per cent water by weight. By way of contrast, young, actively growing plants may consist of 95 per cent or more water. The initial water which enters the seed becomes bound to the submicroscopic bundles of cellulose molecules in the cell walls and to the colloidal particles of protoplasm itself. These bound water molecules adhere tenaciously to the surfaces of such particles, increasing their volume and forcing them apart. Such imbibitional swellings, as noted previously, create tremendous pressures capable of moving or even cracking large stones.

A common laboratory demonstration of imbibition pressure involves placing a mixture of sand and dried peas in a jar. Enough water is added to thoroughly moisten the sand. Within a few hours the swelling peas exert enough outward pressure to break the jar. By filling the spaces between the peas, the sand prevents the peas from swelling into these spaces.

Once the forces resulting in the imbibitional swelling are satisfied free water accumulates in the cell wall and the protoplasm. This is free in the sense that molecules may escape from the wall into the cytoplasm and from the cytoplasm into the vacuole or in the opposite direction. This condition contrasts to that of the bound water molecules which are not mobile. Under these circumstances it is possible for water to enter the cell and increase the volume of the cell sap. The soil solution usually has a higher concentration of water than does the cell sap and thus water tends to diffuse inward.

The hydration of the protoplasm also results in an increased enzymatic activity. Stored food in the endosperm or in the cotyledons is acted upon by digestive enzymes. The resulting simple, soluble foods go into solution and this lowers the relative concentration of water in the cell. As a result, more water enters the cells from the soil. The soluble foods are also available for normal metabolic processes including respiration.

As a result of the changes above, the assimilation rate increases and more protoplasm is formed. This, in turn, makes it possible for nuclear and cell divisions to begin again and the number of cells in the embryo is thus increased.

The embryo increases in size to a point where it literally bursts out of the seed coat. The first part to emerge is the radicle, or primary root, which develops from the growing point at the basal end of the hypocotyl. The primary root grows downward and becomes anchored in the soil (Fig. 3.107).

The root tip is continuously forced through the soil due to enlargement of cells in the region immediately back of the tip. This enlargement is due mainly to water absorption but a significant amount of new protoplasm is manufactured also.

In some plants, beans for example, the hypocotyl also begins to elongate. Since one end of the hypocotyl is attached to the massive cotyledons and the other end is connected to the primary root, the stretching hypocotyl is forced to bend upwards, forming an arch (Fig. 3.108). This arch

HYPOCOTYL ARCH

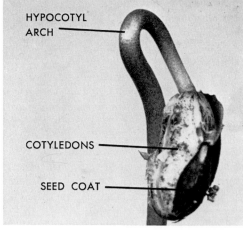

HYPOCOTYL ARCH

COTYLEDONS

SEED COAT

Fig. 3.108. Stages in the germination of bean seeds. A. Hypocotyl has elongated and bent upward to form the hypocotyl arch. B. Growth of the hypocotyl has pulled the cotyledons, epicotyl, and remains of seed coat above ground.

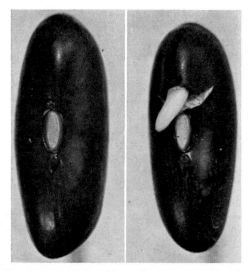

Fig. 3.107. Seeds of bean before and after the start of germination. Note the emergence of the radicle.

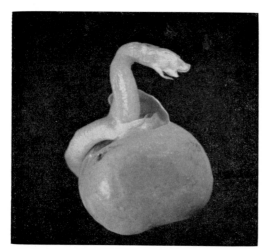

Fig. 3.109. Germination of a seed of the garden pea. Note that the epicotyl rather than the hypocotyl is emergent.

upward and out of the soil. In such plants, the cotyledons and the unelongated hypocotyl remain underground (Fig. 3.109).

The coleoptile of the corn embryo has a special function in germination. It has a pointed tip which penetrates upward as it grows. When the coleoptile emerges from the soil it stops growing and has no further function, other than providing a convenient tube through which the epicotyl can emerge from the soil without being mechanically injured (Fig. 3.110).

Perhaps the most important function of cotyledons is the absorption of food from the endosperm, either before the seed is mature or during the germination process. Sometimes the cotyledons shrivel up and drop off as soon as the young seedling has developed enough leaves to manufacture its own food (Fig. 3.111). However, in many plants the cotyledons may become green and function as leaves for long periods of time. The embryo and seedling development of castor beans provides a remarkable example. In the seed of this plant the cotyledons are thin, papery, and colorless, but in the seedling they become large and green.

pushes upward through the soil. When it emerges into the light it is stimulated to straighten up and, in this way, it pulls the cotyledons and the epicotyl out of the soil.

In other plants, peas for example, the hypocotyl does not elongate, instead, the epicotyl begins to grow, forcing its way

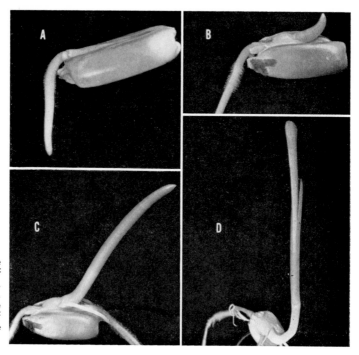

Fig. 3.110. Stages in the germination of a grain of corn. A. Emergence of radicle. B. Emergence of coleoptile. C. Upward growth of the coleoptile. D. Emergence of the epicotyl through the tube of the coleoptile.

Fig. 3.111. Bean seedling with primary leaves fully expanded. Note the shriveled cotyledons which will fall off shortly.

As the epicotyl begins to grow, its component stem segments and leaves enlarge. Soon the leaves are able to manufacture food for the entire plant which then becomes independent of food supplies stored in the seed. With the establishment of the independent sporophyte one complete cycle of gametic reproduction is accomplished.

<table>
<tr><td>CHAPTER 4</td><td># Meiosis, Inheritance, and Evolution</td></tr>
</table>

In any discussion of plant life cycles such as the one undertaken in Chapter 3 it is difficult to avoid creating an impression that the diploid chromosome number determines that a plant will be a sporophyte while plants with the haploid chromosome number are automatically gametophytes. Furthermore, meiosis and fertilization are depicted as being critical points in an endless alternation between sporophyte and gametophyte generations. In a great many cases these impressions are not contrary to fact but enough exceptions exist to warrant considerable caution in interpreting the significance of chromosome numbers as such.

For example, sporophyte tissues of certain mosses which are normally diploid have been stimulated to give rise to protonemal stages which are diploid rather than haploid. From these, diploid leafy gametophytes were formed which in turn gave rise to diploid gametes. The resultant zygotes were tetraploid ($4n$) and gave rise to tetraploid sporophytes.

Another well known situation exists in certain ferns in which diploid gametophytes develop directly from unreduced cells in the sporophyte leaves or from diploid spores. In some such cases cells of the gametophyte develop without fertilization into sporophytes.

It is also a well documented fact that in a number of species of flowering plants unfertilized eggs may develop into mature sporophytes which have the haploid chromosome number. Even more common is the formation of embryos directly from diploid cells of tissues surrounding the embryo sac, in this way bypassing the entire gametic cycle.

Despite such exceptions, however, the doubling of the chromosome number at fertilization and the halving of the chromosome number during meiosis are significant events in the normal gametic cycle. Furthermore, they play significant roles in the mechanisms of inheritance and evolution.

SYNOPSIS OF NUCLEAR EVENTS IN PLANT LIFE CYCLES

Because an understanding of meiosis is often attained without a corresponding awareness of where and when it occurs the following summary of nuclear events in the life cycles of plants has been included to place both meiosis and mitosis in proper perspective.

Mitosis in haploid cells occurs during growth of gametophytes from spore germination to maturity, including the divisions which lead to gamete formation.

Mitosis in diploid cells occurs during growth of sporophytes from zygote germination to maturity, including the divisions which lead to the formation of the spore mother cells.

Mitosis in triploid cells occurs during the formation of the endosperm from the primary endosperm cell in the ovules of flowering plants.

Meiosis in the zygote occurs in the life cycles of many algae, but not in all algae.

Meiosis in spore mother cells occurs in all groups having an alternation of diploid, spore-producing plants, with haploid, gamete-producing plants.

Meiosis prior to gamete formation occurs in certain algae and in most animals. In such cases the cells formed as a result

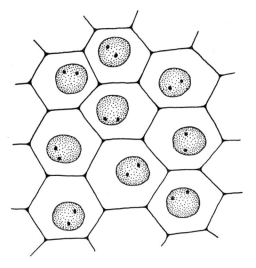

Fig. 4.1. Mass of spore mother cells prior to meiosis (compare Figures 3.27A and 3.79).

of meiosis become modified into gametes instead of spores.

The discussion of the details of mitosis was illustrated with diploid cells from the meristematic region of an onion root tip. However, the basic pattern of mitosis is the same in haploid cells and triploid cells. Similarly, the basic features of meiosis are the same whether the process is studied in zygotes or in spore mother cells (Figs. 4.1, 4.2). Also, despite the fact that the two divisions of meiosis have features which distinguish this process from mitosis, it is apparent that the basic mechanism is the same in both processes.

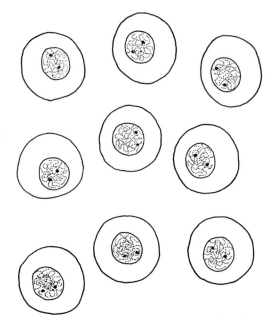

Fig. 4.2. Separation of spore mother cells which frequently occurs as meiosis begins. Each one tends to assume a spherical shape.

MEIOSIS

Meiosis can occur only in cells having two sets of like or homologous chromosomes, the two sets having been brought together previously at the time of fertilization. As a result of the two divisions of meiosis, the haploid chromosome number is restored and each of the four nuclei has one set of chromosomes.

In the following description of the process of meiosis an attempt has been made to eliminate many terms which have meaning to the specialist but which are distractions in an introductory discussion.

Prophase of the First Division of Meiosis (Prophase I)

In very early prophase of this division the chromosomes appear as long, slender, twisted threads much as in a prophase of mitosis. It is evident that the normal duplication of chromatids has not been completed since each chromosome appears to have only one chromatid instead of two (Fig. 4.3).

As prophase continues, the chromo-

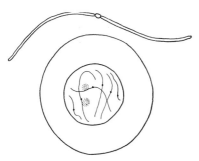

Fig. 4.3. Prophase of Meiosis I. Early stage when each chromosome consists of but a single chromatid. The chromosome number here, and subsequently, is 2 **n** = 6.

each other as they shorten and there may be frequent breaks in the chromatids. The fragments are quickly rejoined but, as the result of slight shearing movements, it often happens that the rejoining occurs between fragments of nonsister chromatids (Fig. 4.6). These *chiasmata*, as they are called, have a significant influence on the final distribution of genes. Also, when the paired chromosomes begin to repel

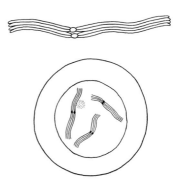

Fig. 4.5. Prophase of Meiosis I. Each of the paired, homologous chromosomes has completed a chromatid duplication. Each chromosome now has two chromatids and, thus, there are four chromatids in each chromosome pair.

somes no longer behave independently as they do in mitosis. Instead, the homologous chromosomes pair with each other intimately and, as a result, the apparent number of chromosomes is reduced to one half the normal diploid number (Fig. 4.4).

Shortly thereafter, the appearance of a lengthwise split in each of the paired chromosomes indicates the belated completion of the process of chromatid duplication. Since each of the chromosomes now has two evident chromatids, there are four chromatids in each of the joined chromosome pairs (Fig. 4.5). It takes both the first and the second division of meiosis to separate these four chromatids and each one of them ends up in a different nucleus.

As prophase I continues, the homologous chromosomes begin to twist around

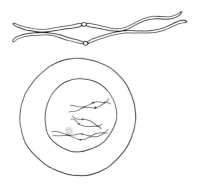

Fig. 4.4. Prophase of Meiosis I. The pairing of homologous chromosomes has occurred.

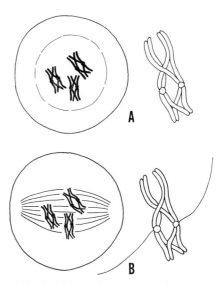

Fig. 4.6. Prophase of Meiosis I. A. The paired chromosomes have begun to repel each other. B. The nuclear membrane and the nucleoli have disappeared, spindle fibers have become attached at the kinetochores, and chiasmata are evident.

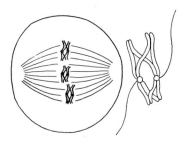

Fig. 4.7. Metaphase of Meiosis I. The chromosome pairs are distributed across the equatorial plate.

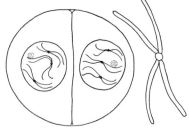

Fig. 4.11. Prophase of Meiosis II. Each nucleus has the **n** number of chromosomes (in this case **n = 3**), and each chromosome has the same two chromatids it had at the end of Meiosis I.

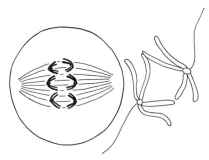

Fig. 4.8. Anaphase of Meiosis I. A separation of whole chromosomes, rather than chromatids, has occurred.

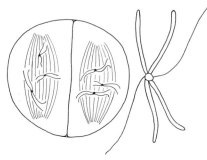

Fig. 4.12. Prophase of Meiosis II. The nuclear membranes and the nucleoli have disappeared and spindle fibers have become attached at the kinetochores.

Fig. 4.9. Telophase of Meiosis I. The chromosomes are arranged in dense clumps, one at each pole of the cell. Cytokinesis is in progress.

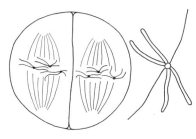

Fig. 4.13. Metaphase of Meiosis II. The chromosomes have become distributed across the equatorial plate.

Fig. 4.10. Interphase between Meiosis I and Meiosis II.

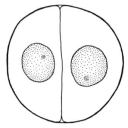

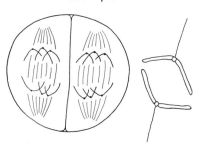

Fig. 4.14. Anaphase of Meiosis II. The chromatids of each chromosome have separated and become daughter chromosomes. Each of the four groups of chromosomes has the **n** number.

each other in late prophase the chiasmata serve to keep them from becoming completely separated.

Metaphase of the First Division of Meiosis (Metaphase I)

During late prophase the nuclear membrane disappears and spindle fibers are formed. Fibers from opposite poles become attached to the chromosomes at the kinetochores. Throughout the rest of the first division the two chromatids of each chromosome remain united at the kinetochore. The kinetochores of each member of a chromosome pair, however, are not united. Then the rearrangement occurs which distributes the paired chromosomes across the equatorial plate (Fig. 4.7). This is metaphase I and because of the denseness of the chromosomes, the apparent reduction in numbers, and their even distribution across the equatorial plate, it is an advantageous stage for the determination of chromosome numbers.

Anaphase of the First Division of Meiosis (Anaphase I)

During this phase the whole chromosomes, which had been united in pairs and held together by the chiasmata, separate and move to opposite poles (Fig. 4.8). The mechanics of this process are not much different from the same phase of mitosis. Each chromosome consists of two chromatids which are still united at the kinetochore and the chromosome number in each of the two separating groups is haploid.

Telophase of the First Division of Meiosis (Telophase I)

Except for the fact that each chromosome obviously has two chromatids there is no difference between the telophase of meiosis and the normal mitotic telophase. The chromosomes become clumped densely at the poles (Fig. 4.9) and after the nuclear membrane is re-formed they begin to swell and become diffuse. Depending on the plant being studied, cell division may or may not occur after the first division of meiosis is complete (Fig. 4.10).

Prophase of the Second Division of Meiosis (Prophase II)

This prophase follows rapidly after the telophase of the first division. The chromosomes each have two chromatids but aside from any crossovers which may have occurred these are the same two that were present in the first division, i.e., no chromatid reduplication has occurred during the brief interphase (Fig. 4.11). The number of chromosomes is, of course, haploid. As the nuclear membrane disappears, spindle fibers are formed and become attached to the chromatids at the kinetochores (Fig. 4.12).

Metaphase of the Second Division of Meiosis (Metaphase II)

This phase is no different from that of normal mitosis. The two nuclei formed in the preceding division usually divide in unison but frequently the plane of division of one member of the pair is oriented at right angles to the plane of division of its twin (Fig. 4.13).

Anaphase of the Second Division of Meiosis (Anaphase II)

In this phase, the kinetochores divide and, thus, the two chromatids of each chromosome which had remained together through the whole of meiosis I finally are able to separate and become daughter chromosomes. The groups of daughter chromosomes approaching opposite poles have the haploid number. In the two simultaneous divisions there are four such groups and in each of them there is one chromatid from each of the pairs of homologous chromosomes in prophase I (Fig. 4.14).

Telophase of the Second Division of Meiosis (Telophase II)

The chromosomes in each of the four groups clump together (Fig. 4.15) and then begin to re-form nuclei. The four daughter nuclei are usually contained within the original cell wall. Then cell walls form between them so that a tetrad of spores is formed (Fig. 4.16). Each spore has a haploid nucleus and can give rise to a gametophyte.

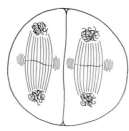

Fig. 4.15. Telophase of Meiosis II. The daughter chromosomes are now densely clumped at the poles and cytokinesis is in progress.

In summary, once again, meiosis is a process involving two successive and somewhat specialized nuclear divisions during which the chromosomes divide but once. As a result, four nuclei are formed, each of them having one-half the chromosome number of the parent cell nucleus.

BASIC MECHANISM OF INHERITANCE

Much of the success of modern agriculture depends on the efforts of plant breeders who constantly search for varieties of plants having desirable characteristics and then painstakingly breed them

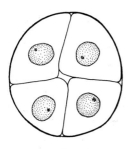

Fig. 4.16. Tetrad of Spores. With the completion of the second division of meiosis, and the associated cytokinesis, four spores are formed, each one of them having a haploid nucleus.

so that new varieties are formed having combinations of such characteristics. Although this is a complex procedure, there is a simplicity to the underlying mechanism of inheritance by which it is accomplished. It is the purpose here to relate the role of meiosis in the life cycle to the mechanism of inheritance.

This relation is most readily explained in plants which are genetically *homozygous*. Homozygosity is the condition in which both members of a given homologous pair of chromosomes of the diploid set contain identical genes for the char-

acteristics being studied. In such a plant, when pairing occurs during meiosis, there is a perfect matching of these genes. When tetrads of spores are produced after meiosis, each one contains one of the identical genes for each characteristic. Consequently, the resulting male and female gametophytes and the male and female gametes contain identical genes in their nuclei. When the gametes fuse at fertilization, the diploid zygote receives two sets of chromosomes and thus has two identical genes for each of the characters concerned. In this way the genetic constitution of a homozygous line is maintained.

If, however, the members of a gene pair are dissimilar the genetic constitution of the zygote would be *heterozygous* for the characteristic concerned and so would all the cells of the diploid plant which developed from the zygote.

A relatively simple example of how such a situation affects the gametophyte generation is offered by *Marchantia*. In this plant sperms are produced on one haploid thallus and eggs on another. The maleness or femaleness of a given thallus is controlled by genes. The zygote receives one set of chromosomes which contain a gene for maleness of the gametophyte and another set containing a gene for femaleness. The zygote and the resultant sporophyte are heterozygous with respect to sexuality of the gametophyte. Of course this has no significance in the development of the sporophyte but when meiosis occurs and spores are formed, one-half of the spores receive the gene for maleness and the other half the gene for femaleness. Consequently, half of the succeeding gametophytes are male and the other half female.

Since the nuclei of the cells of the gametophytes contain only one set of chromosomes apiece the question of homozygosity or heterozygosity does not arise. Nor does the matter of dominance versus recessiveness (discussed later) of the members of a gene pair have any significance in the gametophyte generation. These topics, however, are of great concern when a study of inheritance in flowering plants is undertaken.

In nature and in practice it often happens that pollen from one plant is transferred to the stigma of another plant whose genetical history is different. When such pollinations occur, many varied circumstances may determine the eventual success or failure of the hybrid. If it is successful, however, the genetic nature of the new plant will be mixed or heterozygous for many characteristics and it will show varying degrees of mixture of the characteristics of the parents.

The number of gene differences may be many or few depending on the degree of difference between the parents but, in an elementary consideration, it is usual to discuss first a situation in which only one gene difference exists. In a standard problem on which this discussion is based, a white-flowered plant is crossed with a red-flowered plant. The progeny from this cross all develop into red-flowered plants since red flower color is dominant over white.

Certain symbols are used to indicate characteristics being studied in such problems. The homozygous, red-flowered plant is indicated as RR, which means that its diploid cells contain two homologous chromosomes each one having a gene which determines red flower color. The homozygous white-flowered plant is indicated as rr. It is a current practice in introductory discussions that character symbols are derived from the first letter of the word describing the dominant character, in this case, red. Capital letters are used to indicate dominance. The same letter is used for the recessive character but recessiveness is indicated by use of the small letter. A scheme such as this is necessary in order to keep track of gene pairs in complex problems involving several characteristics.

There is an element of confusion in the usage of these symbols wihch the author has been unable to resolve. When mutations in the characteristics of a species are first observed the mutant types are given names which serve to identify the nature of the mutation. The symbols used in further discussions are then derived from these names, as might be expected. Since most mutations turn out to be recessive the derivation of symbols used by research workers is often directly opposite to that described above.

SIMPLE MONOHYBRID CROSS

The simple cross being discussed is summarized in the following diagram. The used of italicized symbols indicates that the chromosomes have two chromatids apiece while the roman symbols indicate the single chromatid condition which prevails briefly during anaphase II and telophase II. This is a temporary condition because normal chromatid duplication occurs before the nuclei concerned proceed with the next phase of the life cycle. Thus, the italicized form will be used in discussions.

Red-flowered Parent   X   *White-flowered Parent*

Microspore Mother Cells   Megaspore Mother Cells

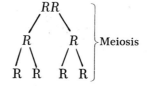

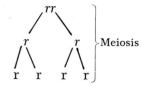

All four microspores can become pollen grains and eventually form pollen tubes with male gametes.

Three of the megaspores degenerate. One survives to produce the embryo sac with one egg.

In this example it does not matter which of the pollen grains produces the successful pollen tube which enters an embryo sac. The male gamete can contain only R and cannot contain r. Nor does it matter which of the four megaspores is the surviving one. The egg can contain only r and cannot contain R.

As a result of fertilization, the diploid nucleus of the zygote must contain both R and r. The new sporophyte generation is designated as the F_1 and all of its cells have this Rr constitution since they are derived from the zygote by mitosis.

It is now interesting to see what happens when the F_1 is self-pollinated. In such a case both the microspore mother cells and the megaspore mother cells are heterozygous and contain Rr. The eventual separation of this gene pair is indicated by the accompanying schematic diagram of meiosis in a spore mother cell which has the chromosome number $2n = 6$ (Figs. 4.17–4.20).

The significant feature here is that half of the nuclei formed by meiosis contain R and the other half r. This means that one-half of the pollen grains will carry R and the other half r. It also means that the surviving megaspore in any particular ovule will have an equal chance of containing R or r.

Since there is no change in the genetic make-up of nuclei between spore formation and gamete formation there is an equal chance that any particular gamete, egg or sperm, will contain R or r.

This situation may be presented in another way.

F_1 Plant (Self-pollinated)

Microspore Mother Cells   Megaspore Mother Cells

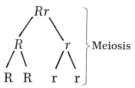

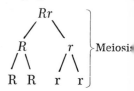

It is a matter of chance which of these forms the pollen tube which enters the embryo sac.

It is a matter of chance which one of these forms the embryo sac.

From the above it is evident that:
a. The female gamete can contain R or r.
b. The male gamete can contain R or r.

A simple checkerboard diagram shows the possible recombinations which might occur in the resulting zygotes which give rise to the F_2 generation. In plants which produce large numbers of seeds it is usual

Figures 4.17–4.20 are related to a simple demonstration of the mechanism of inheritance. Selected stages in the meiotic process are used to indiciate the distribution of genes for flower color during meiosis in spore mother cells of an F_1 plant which is heterozygous for flower color. The dominant gene R indicates red flower color while the recessive gene r indicates white flower color. The labeled dots in the chromosomes are schematic indications of the position of these genes.

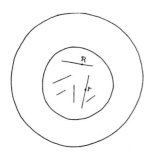

Fig. 4.17. Early prophase of Meiosis I. Before pairing of the homologous chromosomes and before the completion of chromatid duplication.

Fig. 4.18. Late prophase of Meiosis I. After pairing of the homologous chromosomes. The double dots indicate gene duplication which was accomplished as a part of chromatid duplication.

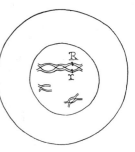

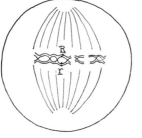

Fig. 4.19. Metaphase of Meiosis I.

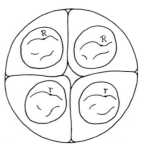

Fig. 4.20. Tetrad of spores. The daughter chromosomes in the respective nuclei show the final distribution of the genes R and r after the completion of Meiosis II.

to find all of these possible combinations in the predicted ratios.

Female Gametes

		R	r
Male	R	RR	Rr
Gametes	r	Rr	rr

a. The zygote RR would result in a mature plant which was homozygous for red flower color.

b. The zygote rr would result in a plant which was homozygous for white flower color.

c. The two zygotes Rr would result in heterozygous plants like the F_1 generation.

There are three *genotypes* (gentical types) above and they occur in a ratio of $1:2:1$.

Nothing has been said so far concerning the color of the flowers in this cross. The F_1 plants were all red-flowered because, as stipulated at the start, the red gene is dominant over the white although situations do exist where partial dominance might result in pink flowers. In the F_2 generation, the RR plant would be red-flowered and so would the two Rr plants and only the rr plant would be white-flowered. If a large number of plants were grown the observable results would be $3:1$ on the average in favor of red-flowered plants.

The observable ratios are spoken of as *phenotype* ratios. Often the true nature of the actual gene constitutions (genotypes) can be derived, mathematically, from the observed phenotype ratio.

In order to determine which of the red-flowered plants were homozygous or heterozygous for flower color it would be necessary to self-pollinate each one and grow the seeds to mature plants of the F_3 generation. The homozygous (RR) plants would give rise only to red-flowered progeny, while the heterozygous ones (Rr) would give rise to red-flowered plants and white-flowered plants in the ratio of about three to one.

SIMPLE DIHYBRID CROSS

In the following example plants are crossed which have two gene differences. In this example the following points are stipulated:

1. Flower color is influenced by a single gene. Red flower color (R) is dominant over white (r).
2. Height of the plant is influenced by a single gene. Tall (T) is dominant over dwarf (t).
3. The genes for height and color are located on different chromosomes.

Under such circumstances the number of possible recombinations in the F_2 generation is increased as will be seen below.

Tall, Red-flowered X *Dwarf, White-flowered*
Plant *Plant*

Microspore Mother Cells   Megaspore Mother Cells

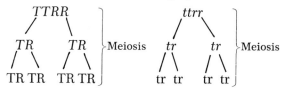

Megaspores, embryo sacs, and eggs can contain only tr in their nuclei.

Microspores, pollen grains, pollen tubes, and male gametes can contain only TR in their nuclei.

The zygote, therefore, will contain $TtRr$ and the resulting F_1 generation will be all tall and red-flowered. However, when the microspore mother cells and megaspore mother cells in the flowers of the F_1 generation undergo meiosis it normally happens that some of the resulting haploid nuclei contain gene combinations which had not existed together before in the haploid nuclei of gametes. The explanation for such recombinations of genes can best be undertaken with diagrams illustrating the orientation of paired chromosomes at metaphase I since it is there that the distribution of hereditary factors is governed by chance. The following diagrams (Fig. 4.21) show the possible orientations, at metaphase I, of the chromosomes containing genes for

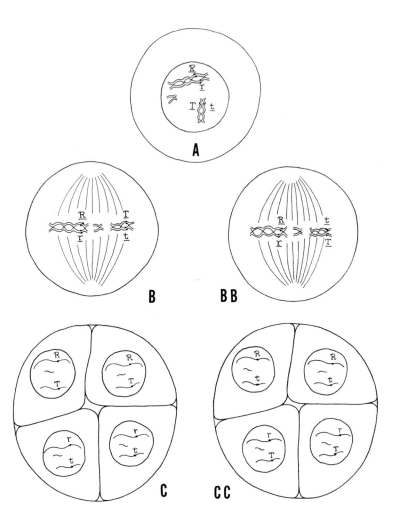

Fig. 4.21. Selected stages of meiosis in a spore mother cell from the F₁ generation of a plant heterozygous for flower color and height. The dominant gene R indicates red flower color while the recessive gene r indicates white flower color. The dominant gene T indicates tallness and the recessive gene t indicates dwarfness. Genes for flower color and height are on separate chromosomes. The labeled dots on the chromosomes are schematic indications of the positions of the genes in question.

A Prophase of Meiosis I. At a stage when paring of homologous chromosomes and chromatid duplication have been completed.

B and BB Metaphase of Meiosis I. Showing the two possible orientations (with respect to each other) of the paired chromosomes containing the gene pairs, **Rr** and **Tt**.

C and CC Tetrads of Spores. With daughter chromosomes shown in the respective nuclei. The distribution of the possible combinations, RT, Rt, rT, and rt, is indicated.

height and flower color. The vertical rows of diagrams show certain significant stages in the meiotic process which affect the segregation of the genes concerned.

It will be noted the series in one column produces two nuclei containing *TR* and two nuclei containing *tr*. In the other column two nuclei with *tR* and two nuclei with *Tr* are formed. The latter are the new gene combinations which, as indicated above, had not existed together previously in haploid nuclei.

To repeat, the orientation of the chromosomes at metaphase I is a matter of chance only and, thus, when large numbers of microspores are produced they will contain approximately equal numbers of *TR, Tr, tR,* or *tr*. The surviving megaspore in any particular ovule will contain one of these four possibilities, also, and when large numbers of ovules are considered there will be an approximately equal distribution of the four possible types among them.

Any particular spore, be it microspore or megaspore, has an equal chance of containing *TR, Tr, tR,* or *tr*. Thus, the gametes which are formed later, be they eggs or sperms, also have equal chances of containing one of the four. When the gametes fuse, the zygote could contain any of nine different gene combinations as indicated in the checkerboard below.

The information from the checkerboard can be summarized as follows:

Genotype	Number of Times Occurring	Phenotype
*TTRR	1 ⎫	Tall, Red-flowered
TTRr	2 ⎬ 9	Tall, Red-flowered
TtRR	2	Tall, Red-flowered
TtRr	4 ⎭	Tall, Red-flowered
*TTrr	1 ⎫ 3	Tall, White-flowered
Ttrr	2 ⎭	Tall, White-flowered
*ttRR	1 ⎫ 3	Dwarf, Red-flowered
ttRr	2 ⎭	Dwarf, Red-flowered
*ttrr	1 ⎭ 1	Dwarf, White-flowered

In the F_2 generation, on an average basis, 9 out of every 16 plants would be tall and red-flowered, 3 would be tall and white-flowered, 3 would be dwarf and red-flowered, and 1 would be dwarf and white-flowered. This phenotype ratio of $9:3:3:1$ is typical of simple dihybrid crosses.

The four combinations which have been asterisked (*) are homozygous. Two of them, *TTRR* and *ttrr*, are identical with the original parents. The other two, *TTrr* and *ttRR*, are new homozygous individuals which did not exist previously. Each of them would continue to breed true if self-pollinated. This is a most important point because such recombinations of characters into new homozygous lines play a part in the natural processes by which new organisms evolve. It is, also, a basic part of the technique used by plant breeders to fix desirable combinations of genetic characteristics in new varieties.

SIMPLE MENDELIAN GENETICS

The examples used in the preceding discussion are based on those discussed in a classical paper published in 1866 by Gregor Mendel who worked with varieties of the common garden pea. We now know

Female Gametes

	TR	Tr	tR	tr
TR	TTRR	TTRr	TtRR	TtRr
Tr	TTRr	TTrr	TtRr	Ttrr
tR	TtRR	TtRr	ttRR	ttRr
tr	TtRr	Ttrr	ttRr	ttrr

Male Gametes

that his choice of plant and the unit characters he studied were fortunate for several reasons, among them the following:

1. The genes for each of the characters studied were on different chromosomes.
2. The final expression of each of the chosen adult characteristics was greatly influenced by a single gene.
3. His first experiments involved characteristics showing definite dominance and recessiveness.

At the time that his work was published no scientists had any concept of chromosomes or genes. Mendel inferred that unit factors were involved but he could not have had any specific knowledge of what they were. His results were published at a time when the modern scientific caldron was just beginning to come to a boil and it was not until the early 1900's that the importance of Mendel's work was fully realized.

Modern genetical studies have shown that many problems of inheritance are much more complicated than indicated by simple Mendelian ratios. A few of the complicating factors are listed here.

1. Two or more of the characters to be studied might be controlled by genes located on the same chromosome.
2. Genes might exert only a partial dominance.
3. Many genes might influence the final expression of a single characteristic.
4. Chiasmata occurring in meiosis I might influence distribution of the genes being studied.
5. Recessive lethal genes could result in the death of homozygous individuals.
6. Gene mutations (changes) might occur during the course of an experiment.
7. The cytoplasm has been shown to have an influence on heredity.
8. The environment may influence the expression of a given gene.

MECHANISMS OF EVOLUTION

The word evolution implies change and change in any system can occur in many ways. Sometimes the original system undergoes so many changes that the modern version scarcely resembles it at all. For example, many people have witnessed the dramatic evolution of the modern automobile and know of the relationship between a Model T Ford and a modern Thunderbird. Yet it would be difficult for a child who had not been informed of the changes to pick these two automobiles from an assemblage of all models and makes of cars which exist, and identify them as belonging to the same family of cars. Changes such as these are built-in changes resembling hereditary changes in living organisms. They differ from environmentally induced changes, like dents in fenders, which affect only the present individual and are not inherited.

Living organisms tend to produce many more offspring than can survive to maturity. This is a fact of life which must be contemplated and accepted in man's attempt to understand the biological world. It leads to intense competition for space and food both between members of the same species and between different species.

If all of the elm seeds or maple seeds or poplar seeds which fall in a back yard each spring should grow to maturity, the homeowner would soon be faced with an impassable jungle. The few which do survive have overcome enormous odds. They have not been cut by a lawnmower. They have escaped the blade of a hoe. They have not been chewed off by a rabbit. They have not been killed by a plant disease. Their roots have managed to penetrate into soil already crowded with roots of other plants. Their leaves have managed to receive enough light for photosynthesis despite the shade of larger plants. And they have managed to crowd out their relatives which landed in the same fortunate spots.

Fitness for survival is certainly important but the matter of chance plays its part, too, in the survival of an individual. Many of the seedlings cut by a lawnmower may have been just as fit as the one which survived, unnoticed, in the lilac hedge, but they were not as fortunate. So it is not true that only the fittest survive. Instead it can be stated that the more fit survive in greater numbers than the less fit and over periods of time the progeny of the more fit gradually supplant the progeny of the less fit. This, in brief, is the basic theory of evolution which was synthesized by Charles Darwin (and independently by Alfred Wallace) and published in the year 1859.

Changes do occur in the inherited nature of living organisms and they may have one or more of the following effects on the progeny which inherit the changes:

1. Most frequently there is a weakening in the ability of the individual to survive under conditions of natural competition in the normal environment, in which case the individual or its progeny are selected against and eventually disappear.

2. There might be an increase in the ability of the individual to survive under conditions of natural competition in the normal environment. In this case the progeny of the individual would eventually replace their less well endowed relatives.

3. There might be an increase of the ability of the individual to compete in a different environment where the species had not been successful before. Providing a mechanism exists by which it can be transported, the species might successfully invade this new environment.

4. There might be no noticeable effect on the ability of the individual to survive in the normal environment. Such changes would tend to become randomly distributed in a population since they would not be affected by natural selection.

The above discussion emphasizes that the inherited changes must occur before the environment can act in the process of natural selection. When an individual organism is faced with the struggle for survival, it has certain inherited limits to its ability to be successful in the struggle. The environment cannot change these limits but, if certain individuals among the many have inherited changes which increase their ability to compete, it is natural that they will be more successful and produce more progeny than the rest of the population.

All such heritable changes are frequently called *mutations* although there is considerable latitude in the exact usage of this term. Sometimes, but not always, a simple doubling of the chromosome number by natural or artificial means will have the effect of noticeably changing the nature of the organism. Many cases are known wherein sterile hybrids have been made capable of producing fertile seeds in this way, thus making the organism capable of at least entering the struggle for survival.

More commonly the word mutation is used in connection with changes in single genes. These changes vary from complete obliteration of a gene, to rearrangement of a few of its many atoms, or even to a change in the position of a gene in a chromosome. Such mutations result frequently from natural radiation. Most of them probably occur in vegetative cells and are neither known nor significant. A few of them occur in cells which are, or become, part of reproductive tissues. Most of these result in death of the cell or its incapacity to take part in normal meiosis. Thus the mutation cannot proceed past this point. A smaller number pass through meiosis but the spores which contain them are unable to produce normal gametophytes. Of the few which are able to do so, most give rise to gametophytes which are unable to form fertile gametes. Occasionally a fertile zygote is formed and gives rise to an embryo but then the seed is unable to mature or to germinate. In the remote instances when the seed does germinate, the seedling is likely to be weak and unable to survive normal competition. Moreover, if it does grow to maturity it will very likely be sterile.

Finally, if all of the obstacles are overcome and a fertile individual with a mutated gene is produced, then begins the long process of natural selection which eventually determines whether or not the mutation has any positive survival value. Most mutated genes turn out to be recessive and it is only when the chance recombinations of genes bring together two of the recessive genes that the ultimate test can be undertaken.

It is small wonder that evolution is a process which requires long periods of time. But, then, time is of no importance except to man who is a most impatient creature.

CHAPTER 5

Life On Land

The changes that have occurred in plants which make it possible for green cells to exist out of the submerged environments in which they had their evolutionary origins were important in the development of present-day green plants. The leaf is a major achievement in this aspect of plant evolution since it provides an extensive internal environment suitable to the existence of green cells. Before undertaking a discussion of the possible evolutionary changes leading to the leaf, it seems advisable to review certain aspects of the relationship of green cells to the environment. In this connection, the exchanges of carbon dioxide and oxygen between green cells and the environment are especially important.

GAS EXCHANGES BETWEEN THE CELL AND ITS ENVIRONMENT

The gaseous carbon dioxide reservoir in the atmosphere amounts to approximately 0.03 — 0.04 per cent of the total volume of the atmosphere. A somewhat larger reservoir of this gas occurs in the oceans and other waters of the world. In solution it often exists as a mixture of carbonates, bicarbonates, and dissolved molecular carbon dioxide. Certain physical and chemical laws govern the balanced relationship between the carbon dioxide in solution and that in the gaseous form.

If the carbon dioxide in any given volume of water is used up by the photosynthetic activity of water plants, or by chemical reactions which form insoluble carbonates, it is replaced from the atmosphere. Conversely, when the percentage of carbon dioxide in the atmosphere is lowered, some of the dissolved gas goes back into the gaseous state.

The burning of organic matter, the respiration of living organisms, and the chemical "weathering" of insoluble carbonates in the earth's surface tend to increase the available supplies of carbon dioxide. On the other hand, photosynthesis and formation of insoluble carbonates tend to decrease the available supplies.

Another important factor in this complex matter of the carbon dioxide balance is the average temperature of the oceans. Cooler waters hold more carbon dioxide in solution than do warmer waters and, hence, a change in the average temperature of the oceans would, theoretically, result in a corresponding change in the total volume in solution. This would affect the amount of carbon dioxide in the atmosphere and, in the light of a demonstrable relationship between carbon dioxide concentration and the absorption of infrared radiation by the atmosphere, a change in the average temperature of the atmosphere might be induced.

It is unlikely that our present-day atmosphere contains the same concentration of carbon dioxide and other gases as did the atmosphere of the earth when living matter first appeared. Furthermore, many of the significant changes in the evolutionary development of plants and animals have been accompanied by major changes in the atmosphere itself.

It is probable, for instance, that the original atmosphere of the earth contained significant concentrations of hydrocarbon gases such as methane (CH_4). Electrical discharges and other forces accomplished chemical unions between these gases and other chemical substances, particularly ammonia, to form a wide variety of organic chemicals which accumulated in the oceans. The postulated series of events by which these compounds became organized into aggregates and eventually evolved into protoplasm will not be dwelt on here since we are concerned mainly with photosynthetic organisms. Most modern concepts concerning the origins of life include the idea that photosynthesis is a sophisticated process and should not be considered as an attribute of primitive life forms.

However, the evolutionary advent of photosynthetic organisms must have had a tremendous impact on the evolution of all existing life forms. The ability to tap the limitless supplies of energy available in sunlight meant an enormous increase in the rate of formation of basic food. Also, the increased availability of oxygen fostered the evolution of biochemical mechanisms which could more efficiently release the energy stored in these basic foods.

The oxygen formed during photosynthesis is in the dissolved form. It diffuses outward through the cell membranes into the external water. When the concentration of oxygen in the water reaches the saturation point it evolves into gaseous oxygen and passes off into the air.

The utilization of carbon dioxide in photosynthesis also depends on its solubility in water since it is only in the dissolved condition that carbon dioxide can diffuse through the cell membranes of plants and thus reach the site of the reduction reaction.

From this discussion it is evident that gaseous exchanges between any living organism and its environment require that the gases be in solution. How, then, do the green cells of the higher plants function when the plants exist in an atmosphere of relatively dry air? One answer to this question will become clear as the sporophyte structure of the higher plants is analyzed.

THE RELATION OF LEAF STRUCTURE AND FUNCTION

The outermost layer of cells in leaves and the younger parts of stems and roots is the *epidermis*. In leaves and stems the epidermal cells secrete a waxy substance, *cutin*, which forms a protective surface layer over these parts of the plant. To a greater or lesser degree this *cuticle* is impervious to the diffusion of water vapor and thus retards the drying out of the interior green cells.

A complete vapor seal would inhibit the very necessary exchanges of carbon dioxide and oxygen between the external atmosphere and the internal photosynthetic tissues. Thus we find that an evolutionary compromise exists in which the cutinized epidermis is perforated with minute openings called *stomates*. These openings are numerous and more or less evenly distributed (Fig. 5.1). Depending on the plant, they may be equally numerous in both the upper and lower epidermis or there may be decided differences in numbers between the two. Wheat, for instance, may have 2,000 stomates per square centimeter in the upper epidermis and 4,500 per square centimeter in the lower epidermis. Apple leaves have no stomates in the upper epidermis but often have 25,000 per square centimeter in the lower epidermis.

Each stomate is a lens-shaped opening surrounded by a pair of *guard cells* or, to put it another way, the stomate is an opening between a pair of guard cells (Fig. 5.1B). Usually the guard cells are shaped

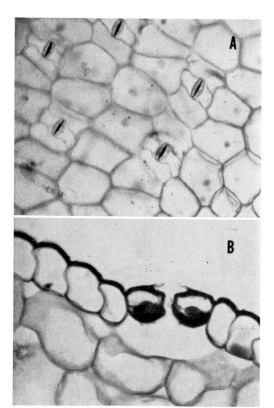

Fig. 5.1. Stomates. A. Epidermis of a **Zebrina** leaf showing distribution of stomates. B. Epidermis of a lily leaf in transverse section showing relation of guard cells to the stomate.

lower epidermis are more loosely packed. They have irregular shapes and larger spaces between them. This is the *spongy parenchyma*. Some leaves have a palisade layer next to the lower epidermis as well as the upper and the spongy parenchyma is between these two layers in the middle of the leaf. Others may lack palisade tissue entirely (Fig. 5.6).

If the leaf of a bean plant is held up to the light the vein system shows up clearly as a branching network (Fig. 5.4A). The veins branch repeatedly and exhibit considerable variation in size. The smallest ones are invisible without a microscope. In corn and many other monocots the veins are parallel but are cross connected by veinlets at intervals (Figs. 5.4B, 5.6B).

The smaller veins in both monocots and like beans (Fig. 5.2A), a major exception being the stomates of grasses which appear somewhat like "dog bones" (Fig. 5.2B).

The photosynthetic cells of a leaf are packed together in such a way that spaces occur between them permitting air to circulate in an internal atmosphere (Fig. 5.3). The compactness of the packing varies between plants and between leaves on the same plant but, with few exceptions, some part of each green cell is in contact with the internal atmosphere. The total volume of internal atmosphere is important in determining the rate of gas exchange with the external atmosphere.

In many leaves the green cells next to the upper epidermis are elongated and cylindrical with only small spaces between them (Fig. 5.3). This tissue is called *palisade parenchyma*. The cells next to the

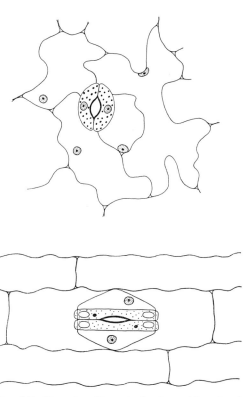

Fig. 5.2. Stomates. Stomate in the epidermis of a snapdragon leaf (upper). Stomate in the epidermis of a corn leaf (lower). The cells adjacent to the guard cells in this leaf are called accessory cells.

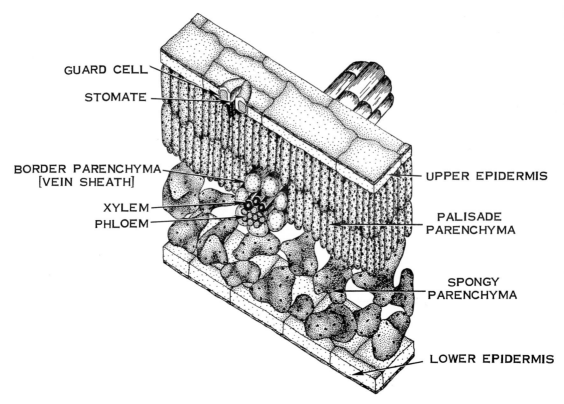

GUARD CELL

STOMATE

BORDER PARENCHYMA
[VEIN SHEATH]

XYLEM
PHLOEM

UPPER EPIDERMIS

PALISADE
PARENCHYMA

SPONGY
PARENCHYMA

LOWER EPIDERMIS

Fig. 5.3. Schematic, three-dimensional representation of leaf structure.

dicots are vitally important because they accomplish most of the exchanges of substances between the green cells and the conducting system.

The veins contain two separate conducting tissues lying one above the other in the middle of each vein (Fig. 5.5). The upper tissue, *xylem*, conducts water and inorganic chemicals towards the ends of the veins. The water-conducting elements have thickened walls and are empty of living contents. They are discussed in greater detail in a later chapter. The lower tissue, *phloem*, conducts organic foodstuffs in solution away from the green cells which manufacture them. The types of cells in phloem tissue also will be discussed later. The xylem and phloem of the leaf veins connect with similar tissues in the stem. These, in turn, connect with the xylem and phloem of the root system giving rise to a continuous, two-way conducting system from the top to the bottom of the plant.

The larger veins become surrounded by mechanical supporting tissue (Fig. 5.5) and thus form a framework for the leaf. However, it is the mutual pressures of turgid chlorenchyma cells which make leaves appear fresh and crisp.

The larger veins probably do not function at all in the actual exchanges between the vascular tissues and the green cells. This is accomplished only by the smaller veins which have, thus, a significance in leaf functions similar to that of capillaries in the blood system.

The smaller veins are usually surrounded by a layer of thin-walled living cells called *border parenchyma* (Fig. 5.3). This may be seen to good advantage in many leaf sections but it is particularly evident in cross sections of young corn leaves (Fig. 5.6).

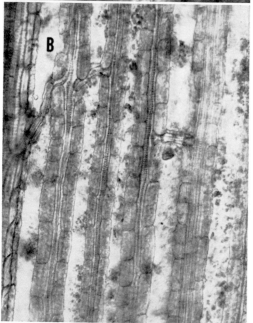

Fig. 5.4. The vein systems of leaves. A. Branching network of veins as seen in an immature bean leaf. B. Parallel veins of a corn leaf with cross-connecting veinlets.

The major significance of the open stomates is that they permit exchanges of carbon dioxide and oxygen between the external and the internal atmospheres. As has been noted carbon dioxide must be in solution in order to diffuse inward in the cells to the site of the photosynthetic reactions. The walls of the green cells which are exposed to the internal atmosphere contain a film of moisture. When carbon dioxide molecules in gaseous form come into contact with this water film some of them go into solution and then diffuse into the protoplasm.

The same sequence applies in reverse to the disposal of the oxygen formed during photosynthesis. The oxygen molecules in solution diffuse outward, ending up in the water film in the cell wall. From there they evolve into the gaseous state in the internal atmosphere, and proceed to diffuse into the external atmosphere through the open stomates.

It should be noted here that once the rate of photosynthesis falls below the

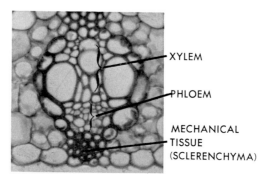

Fig. 5.5. Cross section of a major vein of a corn leaf illustrating xylem, phloem, and mechanical supporting tissue (sclerenchyma).

rate of respiration the direction of diffusion for both carbon dioxide and oxygen is reversed.

The significant point of transfer is the water film in the cell wall since it is here that the change from the gaseous form to the soluble form (or the reverse) must take place. When a film of water is in contact with atmosphere it is unavoidable

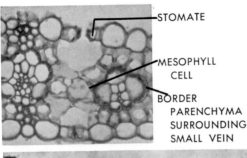

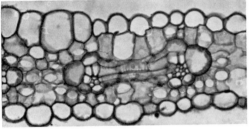

Fig. 5.6. Transverse sections of corn leaves showing organization of photosynthetic tissues and details of the smaller veins. The section in **B** is similar to that in **A** except that one of the cross-connecting veinlets is included. (Compare Fig. 5.4B.)

that water molecules escape from the film into the air. This evaporation process is an inescapable result of leaf structure. The rate of evaporation depends on factors such as temperature, relative humidity of the internal atmosphere, osmotic concentration of the cell sap, and the colloidal organization of the cell itself.

If the stomates are open, it follows that water vapor molecules will diffuse into the external atmosphere. This loss of water in the vapor form from the aerial parts of the plant is known as *transpiration*. As noted above it is an unavoidable result of leaf structure.

TRANSPIRATION

Transpiration involves two processes: (1) evaporation of water from the moist cell walls into the intercellular spaces, and (2) diffusion of the water vapor molecules through the stomates. The rate of outward diffusion depends largely on the difference between the concentrations of water vapor molecules inside and outside the stomates, i.e., the diffusion gradient of water vapor.

When the stomates are closed, the internal atmosphere soon becomes saturated with water vapor. This means that just as many water molecules return to the water films in the cell wall as escape from them, and there is no net loss or gain of water in the cells.

Water Movements Due to Transpiration

When the stomates are open and outward diffusion occurs, then there is a net loss of water from the walls of the internal cells. This is replaced by water from the cell sap resulting in a lower relative concentration of water in the cell sap. The water deficit in any given cell is made up by diffusion of water from adjacent cells and finally from the border parenchyma cells. The deficit in the border parenchyma is made up by diffusion from the xylem. The xylem solution normally has a negative pressure due to the downward pull of gravity and, to some extent, the frictional resistance to water movement in the xylem. However, the energy of water molecules in diffusion is greater than these opposing forces and the water diffuses out of the xylem into the border parenchyma cells.

Water molecules are mutually attracted by intermolecular (cohesive) forces and, when a molecule escapes from the xylem, there tends to be a shrinkage of the water column. Due to the adherence of water to the cell wall such a shrinkage would tend to cause a collapse of the xylem but, as is discussed in detail elsewhere, the cells of the xylem are internally reinforced to prevent such a collapse. Instead, the cohesive forces are satisfied by pulling up another water molecule from below. This transfers the deficiency downard through a vast number of almost simultaneous steps until it is finally satisfied by entrance of another molecule of water from the soil into the root.

The water in the xylem is in a sealed system and contains no gas bubbles. Hence, it is extremely difficult to stretch or break the water column which, in a very crude sense, can be compared to a wire being pulled upward. The energy creating this so-called *transpiration pull* is the kinetic energy of water molecules in the exposed cell walls of the leaf which enables them to escape into the internal atmosphere.

The magnitude of the pressures involved in transpiration pull can be roughly estimated in the following example. A redwood tree may extend 300 or more feet into the air and have roots extending downward 30 or more feet into the soil. The total height of the continuous water column would thus be over 330 feet. By way of comparison, a vacuum pump, under ideal conditions, can lift water only 33 feet, i.e., the pressure of the atmosphere (approximately 15 pounds per square inch) can support a column of water 33 feet high. The upward movement of water in a 330 foot column would require at least 10 times this pressure or 150 pounds per square inch to overcome the force of gravity alone, to say nothing of the frictional resistance to water movement in the small pores of the conducting tissue.

Relation of Stomates to Transpiration

In the previous discussion of stomates, it was noted that each stomate is surrounded by a pair of guard cells. The stomate is a lens-shaped opening which is longer than wide (Fig. 5.2). The degree of opening of the stomates is determined directly by the turgidity of the guard cells. When they are fully turgid the stomates are wide open but, as the turgidity of the guard cells decreases, the walls of the guard cells come together and the stomates close.

Experiments with diffusion of gases through small pores have shown that the diffusion rate depends more on the circumference of the opening than on its area. Due to the shape of the stomates the circumference of the opening is not much altered by partial closing and, apparently, no significant reduction of transpiration occurs until the stomates are practically closed.

Another significant point is that the rate of diffusion through a large number of minute openings such as stomates is much greater than the diffusion rate through one large opening having the same total area as all of the minute openings together.

The control of transpiration by plants is difficult to analyze. Although the cutinized epidermis reduces direct water loss to a minimum, direct cuticular transpiration might account for as much as 10 per cent of the total transpiration rate. As has been established, the stomates permit diffusion of carbon dioxide and oxygen as a primary function and the escape of water vapor is unavoidable when the stomates are open. If the stomates should close whenever the transpiration rate became high, the vital exchanges of carbon dioxide and oxygen with the atmosphere would be interrupted and the plant would suffer. In many plants stomates do not close until definite wilting has occurred, so the closing is something of an emergency measure. The availability of soil water, the extent of the root system, and the relative efficiency of the water transport system all have a bearing on stomate closing in such cases.

Some plants never close their stomates but these are usually restricted to wet environments. Other plants have definite cycles of stomatal behavior: opening in the morning, remaining open during most of the day, and closing in late afternoon. The stomates of some plants may close in the afternoon and then open again at night.

The effect of increasing light intensity on the opening of stomates in the morning has been much discussed. An increased turgidity of the guard cells results in the opening of the stomates but the cause for the increase is not clear. The increased sugar content of the guard cells due to photosynthesis alone would not, apparently, be enough to account for the change. One ingenious theory suggests that the removal of carbon dioxide from solution by photosynthesis in the guard cells changes the acidity of the cell sap.

This change affects the rate of enzymatic digestion of stored starch to sugar in the guard cells and, thus, a much greater amount of sugar is put into solution than could be produced by photosynthesis alone in a short time. This might well account for the rapid osmotic uptake of water which makes the guard cells turgid enough to open the stomates.

Factors Affecting Transpiration

The rate of vaporization inside the leaf is affected by the radiant energy to which the leaf is exposed and some cooling may result from this evaporation. Most of the heat which is absorbed is promptly reradiated and, in thin leaves, the whole leaf tends to maintain a temperature close to that of the surrounding atmosphere. In thick leaves, on the other hand, the cooling effect may be significant if more energy is absorbed than can be effectively reradiated.

Air temperature is important in another way since air can hold more water at higher temperatures than at lower ones. The term *relative humidity* which expresses this ability may be defined as the percentage of water vapor in the air at a given temperature compared to the maximum amount that it could hold at the same temperature. If the temperature rises and the actual amount of water vapor in the air remains unchanged then the relative humidity is lowered. This increases the steepness of the water vapor gradient between external and internal atmospheres of the leaf and the transpiration rate increases accordingly. Conversely, when the temperature falls and the actual water vapor content remains unchanged, the relative humidity increases and the transpiration rate is lowered.

The internal structure of leaves also has an effect on transpiration rates. Leaves with loosely packed cells and large, internal air spaces tend to lose water through open stomates at more rapid rates than leaves with more compactly arranged tissues and smaller air spaces.

Wind movements serve to carry water vapor away from the layers of atmosphere near the ground, thus affecting the relative humidity. Wind action also hastens the drying of the soil, and in this way, affects the rate of water absorption by roots. Another action of wind is the dispersal of minute clouds of water vapor which form over the open stomates. When present, these clouds decrease the steepness of the diffusion gradient. Their removal by wind action removes this deterrent to transpiration and the rate increases.

The possible beneficial or harmful effects of transpiration on the life of plants have been topics of dissension for many years. Since transpiration is an unavoidable result of leaf structure and life on land, it follows that any beneficial effects would have had a secondary origin. Also, under certain conditions excessive transpiration does occur and plants suffer thereby.

One possible advantage is the cooling effect of evaporation in thick leaves. Another is the much disputed role of the transpiration stream in the upward movement of inorganic chemicals absorbed from the soil. There is scarcely any question that these chemicals do move in the xylem solution but the main point at issue seems to be whether or not the aerial parts of plants would receive enough of such chemicals if the transpiration stream were greatly reduced. This question has not been settled to the complete satisfaction of all interested authorities.

THE ESCAPE FROM THE SEA

It is evident that the leaf is a highly modified structure and to understand its possible evolutionary origin it is necessary to consider some of the factors affecting the origins of land plants in general.

The molecular oxygen in the upper layers of the present atmosphere of the earth exists in the form of ozone which provides a protective shield for land-dwelling organisms against excessive concentrations of ultraviolet radiation from the sun. It is generally considered, though, that the earth's atmosphere was originally free of any significant amounts of molecular oxygen and thus the intensity of ultraviolet radiation reaching the earth's surface would have been a serious hazard for any organisms which crawled out of the sea.

It follows that living organisms must have had a long evolutionary history in aquatic environments before the oxygen released by photosynthesis could accumulate in the atmosphere to a concentration capable of providing an effective ultraviolet screen.

The emergence of both animals and plants from aquatic to aerial environments was a colossal struggle which captivates the imagination. Unfortunately our direct knowledge concerning the emergence of plants is meagre and much of what can be said of the process is admittedly speculative.

As indicated previously, heritable changes occur constantly in living organisms. Environmental influences then affect a natural selection among the progeny and, eventually, new types of organisms develop which possess characteristics enabling them to exist in environments which were untenable by their ancestors.

This argument is often reversed in what has been termed teleological thinking. One might state or imply, for instance, that primitive plants developed a cuticle in order to withstand desiccation in an aerial environment. This statement is teleological and if it were rephrased to avoid the teleological implications, one could state more correctly that the development of the cuticle enabled plants to withstand the desiccating effects of an aerial environment. In any discussion of cumulative evolutionary changes the danger of teleological expression is ever present and must be guarded against.

When living forms of green algae are considered as a whole it may be seen that they have many of the attributes of the higher green plants. Among these are similarities in pigmentation, an ability to form starch, oogamous reproduction, and alternation of generations. In addition, many of them are able to produce resist-

ant cells which enable the species to survive desiccation. In considering the possible plant body types among the green algae which may have been ancestral to the higher green plants the most logical choice is that of the branching filament.

The fossil record has given us evidence of the general nature of primitive land plants but, unfortunately, not much evidence of the transitional stages. Thus, we can deal only with speculations concerning the events which led to the conquest of the land. One popular theory is based on an interpretation of plants shaped like certain of our common seaweeds which have dichotomously branching (Y-shaped) plant bodies. In a simple expression of this theory one of the branches remained in the mud and evolved into the root system while the other turned upward and evolved into the shoot system.

One criticism of this theory is that the living seaweeds of this general nature are more apt to be among the brown or red algae while most authorities agree that the land plants evolved from the green algae. However, some species of green algae have plant bodies which are made of densely intertwined branching filaments held together in a tough mucilage. These structures often show irregular branching which approaches dichotomy at times and might serve as examples of green algae to fit the above theory (Fig. 5.7).

The Hypothetical Emergent Sporophyte

The author has taken considerable license with the thoughts of others in suggesting that there may have been an invasion of the atmosphere before there was an invasion of the land and that this was accomplished first by branches of the sporophyte generation. The hypothetical plant to be considered had a complex, erectly growing axis of some sort (Fig. 5.8) in which the component cells were firmly bound together by a cementing substance derived from pectic compounds.

Cell division became more or less limit-

Fig. 5.7. A green alga with a complex, branching thallus composed of intertwined branching filaments embedded in firm mucilage. Schematic but based on specimens of **Chaetophora incrassata.**

ed to the terminal portion of the axis, a feature not unknown in the algae where many branching forms undergo cell division only in the younger cells near the tips of the branches. Spore formation became limited also to the terminal portion of the axis where the branching was profuse and compacted. The external layers of cells in this region remained sterile and eventually gave rise to the wall of a spore case or *sporangium*. The spore mother cells inside the sporangium probably occurred in lengthwise rows, each row representing the terminal portion of a filament in the plant body. Each spore mother cell underwent meiosis to produce four haploid spores.

A plant body of this type would have had a certain rigidity due partly to the firmness of the gelatinous substances and partly to mutual pressures of the cells. It might have grown upward out of the water or have been exposed periodically by the lowering of the water level in shallow ponds or tidal seas. In whatever manner the actual emergence was caused, the out-of-water branch tips would have been exposed to the drying action of the air. The external gelatinous covering would have dried and hardened but, in so doing, would have protected the living cells somewhat from direct water loss. In this way the stage may have been set for the evolution of the cuticle. However, a complete seal over the surface would have interfered with the gas exchanges necessary to both photosynthesis and respiration. Thus it is probable that the cuticle did not become a completely successful innovation until stomates evolved.

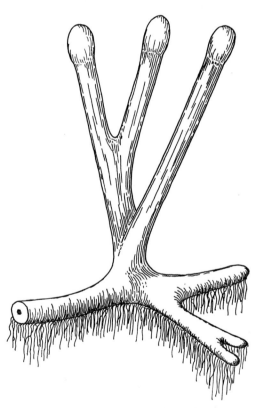

Fig. 5.8. Appearance of hypothetical emergent sporophyte branches in the evolutionary transition stages between the green algae and the land plants.

The Wind-Disseminated Spore

Stresses and strains due to drying eventually caused the sporangium wall to tear open exposing the mature spores inside to the atmosphere. The gelatinous walls of the spores hardened and the protoplasm became partially dehydrated. The ability to exist in such a condition was not entirely new to the green algae since many of them had evolved spores resistant to desiccation previously. The spores in this dehydrated condition became subject to wind dispersal as soon as the walls hardened enough so that one cell did not stick to the next.

The evolution of the wind-disseminated spore may or may not have occurred in this way but the fact that it did occur meant a tremendous advantage to the species concerned in the struggle for survival. Wind-spread spores are disseminated over far greater distances than zoospores and the dissemination of progeny is one of the more important selective factors in evolution.

*   *   *

To recapitulate briefly, an invasion of the atmosphere may have occurred when portions of an alga with a rather firm body emerged from the water. Subsequent developments were the evolution of cuticle, stomates, and wind-spread spores. The spores were produced in terminal sporangia which had an outer jacket of sterile wall cells.

It follows that the higher the sporangia were pushed above the water level, the farther the spores were spread and the height of the axis above water thus became an important selective factor in evolution. However, mechanical factors in the support of the aerial tissue may have limited this growth and, additionally, there are physical limits to the rate at which simple cell to cell diffusion of water can replace that unavoidably lost by transpiration. Both of these factors placed restrictions on the attainable height of the aerial branches.

PRIMITIVE VASCULAR PLANTS

The development of a central core of elongated, thick-walled cells effectively increased the mechanical strength of the aerial branches. Certain similarities between these supporting cells and the water-conducting cells of xylem suggest an evolutionary relationship. It is equally possible that the conducting cells of the xylem had an independent origin. Nonetheless, once a water conducting tissue did become functional the aerial branches were able to attain greater heights without being dessicated.

The hypothetical vascular invader of the atmosphere would thus have been a plant with a slender axis consisting of parallel rows of cells bound together by derivatives of pectin. It would have had a terminal sporangium and a central core of xylem. Portions of the plant were submerged and attached to the muddy bottom.

The question of whether plants such as these ever existed was answered dramatically by the discovery of fossilized plants which had been living in a Devonian swamp (approximately 350 million years old). The plants of this Devonian swamp are known to us as *psilophytes* (Fig. 5.9). Their stems were slender and several centimeters in height. They did not have true leaves. The terminal sporangia consisted of layers of sterile wall cells enclosing masses of spores. The fact that these spores occurred in tetrads (groups of four) is considered satisfactory evidence of the occurrence of meiosis. This means that the known plants were the diploid sporophyte generation. The epidermis had a rather thick cuticle and possessed stomates. There was a central core of xylem and around it was a layer of phloem. The tissue inside the epidermis consisted of chlorenchyma which was the functional photosynthetic tissue. These plants did not have roots but some of the branches were prostrate and anchored to the mud with rhizoids.

One of the prominent features of the

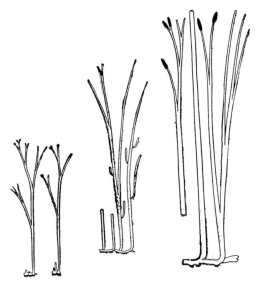

Fig. 5.9. Appearance of a group of psilophytes as reconstructed from fossil remains in a Devonian swamp. (Courtesy of Chicago Natural History Museum. After Kidston and Lang.)

aerial system was that the stem branched dichotomously. This feature has significance in the origin of the fern-type leaf, as will be seen.

The discovery of the psilophytes led to the solution of a puzzle concerning the classification of two living plants which seemed to have no real niche in the then-existing classification schemes. One of these plants, *Psilotum*, grows in the tropics and subtropics the world around, while the other, *Tmesipteris*, is restricted to Australasia.

A Comparison of *Psilotum* With the Fossil Psilophytes

Psilotum bears a striking resemblance to the fossil psilophytes. Its stem is dichotomously branched (Fig. 5.10) and lacks true leaves. It has a central core of xylem surrounded by phloem and a cutinized epidermis with stomates (Fig. 5.12). Its outer cortex is green and photosynthetic. It has a subterranean branching rhizome but does not have true roots. The only significant point of difference is that the sporangium of *Psilotum* is three-parted

and attached laterally (Fig. 5.11). Even this feature can be interpreted as an extreme reduction of a short branch system bearing three terminal sporangia. Quite possibly *Psilotum* is a living representative of the group of plants which were the first true vascular plants.

It can be said that the vascularized stem was a major breakthrough in the evolution of plants. Most of what has happened to the higher plants since then may be interpreted as an elaboration of the basic pattern set at least four hundred million years ago.

So far the fossil record has not shown us any evidence of the gametophyte generation of the ancient psilophytes. However, the gametophyte generation of *Psilotum* is well known. It consists of an axis much like a short segment of a sporophyte rhizome and grows buried in the soil. It is associated with a fungus which invades its outer tissue. The fungus obtains its basic organic foods from the humus in the soil and, presumably, makes

Fig. 5.10. Aerial branches of **Psilotum.** Note dichotomous branching and position of sporangia.

Fig. 5.11. Portion of a stem of **Psilotum** showing details of the three-parted sporangium.

them available to its host. It is possible, but not known, that the *Psilotum* gametophyte "pays for its keep" by creating certain essential organic chemical substances for which the fungus lacks the necessary enzyme systems.

It seems apparent that such a condition has resulted from a degeneration of a gametophyte plant body which was once much larger and self-supporting. The gametophyte generation of the ancient psilophytes may have been like the sporophyte generation in general appearance or may have been entirely different.

The gametophyte of *Psilotum* produces antheridia and archegonia which are similar in some respects to those of the mosses and ferns. The egg is fertilized in the archegonium and the zygote gives rise to a mass of diploid cells which is the embryo of the sporophyte generation.

* * *

During the millions of years that the primitive vascular plants existed many different types were developed. Some of them are known to us rather completely as fossils but others left no more than a fragmentary record and can never be known completely.

From the ancient stock of primitive vascular plants many divergent lines emerged, prospered, and vanished. Of

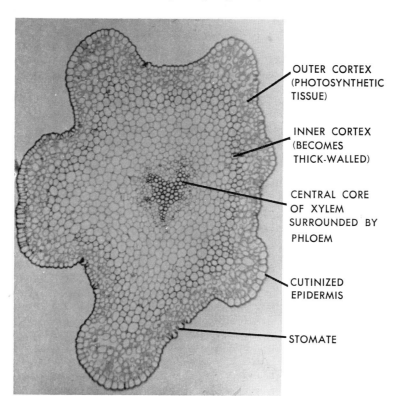

Fig. 5.12. Transverse section of a stem of **Psilotum**.

OUTER CORTEX (PHOTOSYNTHETIC TISSUE)

INNER CORTEX (BECOMES THICK-WALLED)

CENTRAL CORE OF XYLEM SURROUNDED BY PHLOEM

CUTINIZED EPIDERMIS

STOMATE

these, the following four major groups still occur in our time:

1. Remnants of the ancient psilophyte stock
2. The club mosses
3. The horsetails
4. The ferns, gymnosperms, and flowering plants

THE CLUB MOSSES

The major features of the life cycle of one of the club mosses have been discussed previously in the chapter on reproduction where *Selaginella* was used to introduce the concept of heterospory. Here the significance of leaf structure in this group will be considered. Microscopic examination of a leaf of *Selaginella* shows that it has a cutinized epidermis with stomates (Fig. 5.13), chlorenchyma tissue, and an internal atmosphere. In these ways it is like the leaf of a flowering plant. A peculiar fea-

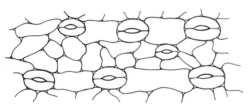

Fig. 5.13. Stomates in the epidermis of a leaf of **Selaginella.**

ture is the presence of a minute, tongue-shaped flap, the *ligule,* at the base of the leaf.

The leaf of *Selaginella* possesses only one vein and this is unbranched. If this single vein is traced to its connection with the vascular tissue of the stem (Fig. 5.14) it can be seen that there is no *leaf gap* or break in the stele at the point of union. These two characteristics mark this type of leaf as being fundamentally different from the fern type leaf which will be discussed later.

The club moss leaf is said to be a *microphyll* (a term which should not be confused with microsporophyll). Two

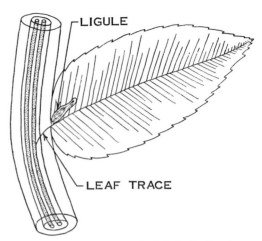

Fig. 5.14. Vegetative leaf of **Selaginella** drawn to show the nature of a microphyll. Note the single vein, the single leaf trace, and the absence of a leaf gap in the vascular tissues of the stem.

theories exist as to the possible origins of the microphyll.

1. It could have resulted from the enlargement, flattening, and vascularization of spinelike outgrowths (*enations*) which occurred on the stems of many psilophytes. *Psilotum* (Fig. 5.10) still has such outgrowths.
2. It could have resulted from a flattening process affecting one member of a dichotomous branch pair. The other member of the pair would have continued as a stem segment.

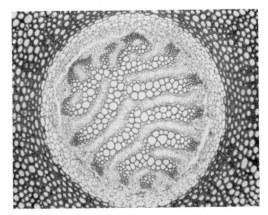

Fig. 5.15. Cross section of the stem of a species of **Lycopodium.**

Whether or not either theory is correct, the microphyllous nature of the club mosses distinguishes them as a group. The functional value of such leaves lies in the fact that they increase the total surface area of photosynthetic tissue exposed to light and carbon dioxide absorption.

It should be noted that fossil records uncovered in recent years indicate that the ancestors of the club mosses coexisted with the psilophytes and, thus, the possi-bility exists that they may have had sep-arate origins.

It will be recalled that *Selaginella* pro-duces microspores and megaspores. Each microspore produces a complete but high-ly reduced male gametophyte within itself. The nourishment for this development comes from food stored in the microspore and not from photosynthetic activity of the gametophyte. The female gametophyte develops partially within the megaspore and is dependent, in large part, on food

Fig. 5.16. Reconstruction of **Lepidodendron** from fossil remains in a Coal Age swamp forest. (Courtesy of Chicago Natural History Museum.)

stored in the spore. This illustrates a trend among vascular plants towards the reduction of the gametophyte generation to the minimum responsibility of producing gametes.

Lycopodium (Fig. 3.53) is a homosporous club moss. The strobili are basically similar to those of *Selaginella* but contain only one kind of sporophyll and produce only one kind of spore.

The gametophyte generation of *Lycopodium* shows a wide range of expression from being green and independent to being nongreen and associated with fungi which invade its tissues. These gametophytes are subterranean and so hard to find that it has only been in relatively modern times that they have been known at all.

Many club mosses have central cores of xylem surrounded by phloem. In others the xylem becomes deeply lobed and in some there are broad bands of parenchyma tissue extending across the xylem (Fig. 5.15). One eminent authority has advanced the hypothesis that the proper functioning of xylem elements is conditioned by their proximity to living tissue. The leaf of *Lycopodium* differs from the leaf of *Selaginella* primarily in the absence of the ligule.

Many of the fossil club mosses such as *Lepidodendron* and *Sigillaria* were giant treelike forms existing in swamp forests which would be strange sights to our modern eyes (Figs. 5.16, 5.17). In some of them the base of the tree was branched several times, dichotomously, to form a broad supporting base for the aerial stem. These bases are called *stigmarian appendages* and from them the much smaller roots emerged. Some species of *Selaginella* have leafless branches called *rhizophores* from which the roots emerge when the tip touches the ground.

The evolutionary origins of roots are still somewhat of a mystery. All roots, even those of flowering plants, have the primitive arrangement of vascular tissues and this suggests that they evolved as modifications of the mud-inhabiting portions of the psilophyte branch system. However, the positive geotropism (see Chapter 6) of roots, their lack of chloro-

Fig. 5.17. Reconstruction of **Sigillaria** from fossil remains in a Coal Age swamp forest. (Courtesy of Chicago Natural History Museum.)

phyll, the presence of the characteristic root cap, and the mode of origin of lateral roots all point to their being special organs. The evolutionary development of phloem tissue to the point where it could transport large quantities of food rapidly was a likely prelude to the evolution of roots.

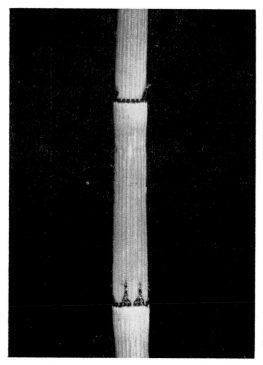

HORSETAILS

The genus *Equisetum* consists of a number of species characterized by jointed, hollow stems, bearing scale leaves at the nodes (Figs. 5.18, 5.19). The leaves are nonfunctional and occur in definite whorls. Photosynthesis is carried on in the green stems. The stems are lined with vertical ridges which are harsh to the touch because they are covered with small tubercules of a siliceous substance. *Equisetum* is often called scouring rush because pioneers used these stems for scouring pots and pans.

Some species branch freely (Fig. 5.19) while others do not branch at all. Many of them have underground rhizomes which spread the plant very effectively by vegetative means. True roots are attached to the rhizomes.

Fig. 5.18. Portion of a stem of an unbranched species of **Equisetum** showing gross details of stem structure.

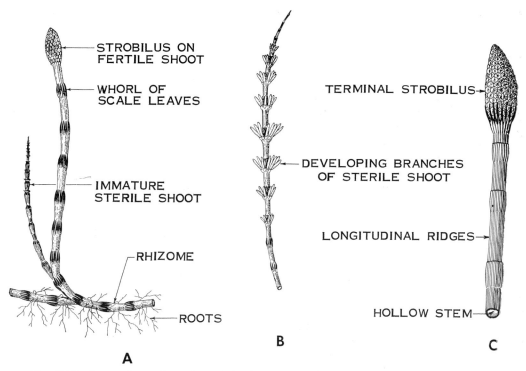

Fig. 5.19. Comparison of sterile and fertile shoots of **Equisetum**. A. Plant of **E. arvense** showing rhizome with roots, mature fertile shoot, and immature sterile shoot. B. Sterile vegetative shoot of the same species at a later stage of development, showing the whorls of branches arising from the nodes. C. Terminal portion of the stem of **E. hyemale**, a tall unbranched species, with mature strobilus.

Fig. 5.20. **Equisetum arvense.** The photographs A, B, and C, show changes in the mature strobilus as the sporangiophores separate allowing spore dispersal, while D is the terminal portion of a sterile shoot for comparison with Fig. 5.19B.

Spore production occurs in terminal strobili (Figs. 5.19, 5.20) each of which consists of a central axis to which are attached numerous *sporangiophores*. Each of these bears several sporangia. The sporangiophore is not called a sporophyll because it is interpreted as a reduced branch system which never went through the leaf stage. The sporangia are terminal on portions of this branch system which have become fused into the form of peltate, hexagonal plates with the sporangia pointing inwards (Fig. 5.21).

The spores have two ribbonlike, hygroscopic appendages called *elaters* (Fig. 5.22). The elaters straighten out as they dry, loosening the spore mass and helping the spores to float more readily in the air while being dispersed.

The gametophytes are small, but independent, and green. They are lobed, or even shrubby in appearance when viewed under the microscope. The gametangia are partially imbedded in the gametophyte. It is known that many species produce antheridia and archegonia on the same gametophyte while others seem to have separate male and female gametophytes.

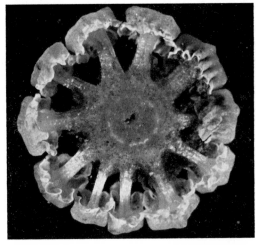

Fig. 5.21. A single whorl of sporangiophores dissected from a strobilus of **Equisetum.** The several sporangia on each sporangiophore are evident.

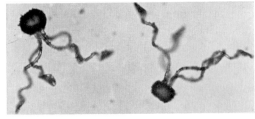

Fig. 5.22. Spores of **Equisetum** with extended elators.

Fig. 5.23. Reconstruction of a Coal Age swamp forest. The large tree in the right foreground is **Calamites**. (Courtesy of Chicago Natural History Museum.)

Equisetum is the only living genus in this group but it had many relatives in the Coal Age swamp forests. Some of them, like the giant *Calamites* (Fig. 5.23), were treelike and had secondary growth. *Sphenophyllum* was smaller and vinelike with wedge-shaped functional leaves (Fig. 5.24).

FERNS

The living ferns of today comprise a group of several thousand species growing in many diverse habitats. Some float in water and a few have become adapted to very dry habitats but most of them grow in shady places where abundant moisture is available in the soil.

It will be remembered from the discussion of the life cycle of ferns that the spore gives rise to a small, independent green gametophyte, the prothallus. This delicate, membranous plant begins as a short, algalike filament which later broadens out due to the meristematic activity of an apical cell. It is seldom more than a few cells in thickness and is anchored to the soil by rhizoids. Its close association with the soil indicates that water lost from the noncutinized surface is replaced by direct absorption from capillary water films. The gametangia are usually born on the lower surface. Sperms are released into the capillary water films and then swim to the archegonia.

The young sporophyte begins as an embryo with four lobes. Two of these become the primary leaf and the primary root, one is the foot which serves as an

Fig. 5.24. Reconstruction of **Sphenophyllum** from fossil remains of a Coal Age swamp forest. (Courtesy of Chicago Natural History Museum.)

absorbing organ imbedded in the gametophyte, and the fourth lobe gives rise to the rhizome growing point. As soon as the primary leaf and primary root are well established the sporophyte becomes completely independent of the gametophyte.

It is not known whether the fern gametophyte has been reduced from a more complex structure or has merely failed to develop beyond the present level in which its algal ancestry is apparent. Note, however, that the sporophyte generation can begin only where the gametophyte generation is able to grow. Presumably, fern spores are scattered into all sorts of environments but they develop into mature gametophytes only where supplies of water near the surface of the soil are reasonably constant.

Leaves of the sporophyte generation of ferns are much like those of higher plants in that they have a branching system of veins, a cutinized epidermis with stomates, and internal atmosphere associated with the chlorenchyma tissue. One au-

thority terms this tissue a "ventilated mesophyll."

The primary leaf of a young sporophyte is of particular interest in an analysis of the fern type leaf. The veins of the primary leaf are branched from one to several times in a distinctly dichotomous fashion (Fig. 5.25). When this vein system is compared with the dichotomously branching stem system of a plant like *Psilotum* or one of the fossil psilophytes one is led to a basic hypothesis that the fern leaf evolved through a flattening of a branch system and the development of tissue between the branches. This type of leaf is called a *macrophyll* in contrast to the microphyll of a club moss. The dichotomy of the veins in the mature secondary leaves of many ferns is not always as obvious as it is in the primary leaf but it is illustrated in classical fashion by the leaflets of the common maidenhair fern.

Most fern leaves are called *fronds*. They may be very large and are often several times compounded. The stems of many of the so-called modern ferns are *rhizomes* from which many short roots originate. The rhizome also gives rise to new leaves near its tip. In the bud stage each leaf is curled up like a fiddle-head. As the leaf matures it seems to unroll towards the tip (Fig. 5.26).

The vascular connections between the main vascular tissue of a fern rhizome and the base of the petiole are called *leaf traces*. Just above the point where the leaf traces join with the main vascular supply of the stem there is an apparent

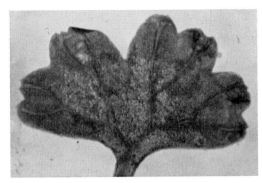

Fig. 5.25. Primary leaf of a young fern sporophyte showing dichotomous venation.

Fig. 5.26. "Fiddle heads" (young fern leaves).

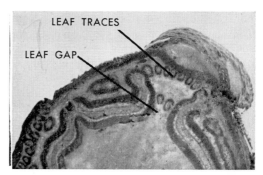

Fig. 5.27. Appearance of leaf traces and leaf gaps as seen in a transverse section through the nodal region of the stem of a tree fern.

break in the vascular continuity of the stem. This is called a *leaf gap* (Fig. 5.27). Such gaps are common in the stems of plants which bear macrophylls but, as was noted in the discussion of the club mosses, they do not occur in stems bearing microphylls. The vascular tissue at the level of a leaf gap is not actually interrupted, however. Instead it is deflected slightly to both sides of a small mass of parenchyma tissue, much as the current of a river is deflected by an island (Fig. 5.28).

There are a few living ferns which have erect stems and these may grow to several feet in height. The trunks of these tree ferns are somewhat barrel shaped and are clothed with the stubby remains of dead leaf bases and roots. Usually the fronds are very large and compound.

The occurrence of sporangia in clusters (*sori*) on the lower surface of many fern leaves may seem difficult to reconcile with the terminal position of the sporangia of the psilophytes. But there are numerous ferns, both living and fossil, in which the sporangia are born along the margins of a leaf in close association with the ends of the branching vein system.

Most of the common ferns are homosporous and the gametophytes are usually homothallic, producing both antheridia and archegonia on the same plant body. However, the so-called water ferns including *Salvinia*, *Azolla*, and *Marsilea* (Fig. 5.29) have highly advanced heterospory. Details of the life cycles of these plants will not be discussed.

Not so many years ago the classification of plants which was used in most standard textbooks divided the plant kingdom into the following four divisions: The *Thallophytes* included all of the algae and the fungi; the *Bryophytes* included the mosses, liverworts, and hornworts; the *Pteridophytes* included the ferns and their

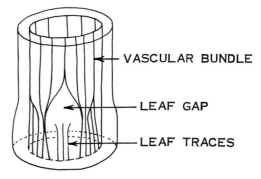

Fig. 5.28. Appearance of a leaf gap as seen in longitudinal perspective following removal of leaf base and axillary bud. Based on a dissection of the nodal region of a stem of nasturtium.

"allies," the club mosses and horsetails; and the *Spermatophytes* (seed plants) included the gymnosperms and the flowering plants. A comparison of this classification system with those in current use is given in Chapter 8.

During this century there has been a growing realization that the ferns are more closely related to the modern seed plants than they are to the club mosses or the horsetails. Moreover, the ability to produce seeds is no longer the primary criterion by which a major group of plants

Fig. 5.29. "Water ferns." **Azolla** (A) and **Salvinia** (B) have a floating habit. The leaves of **Marsilea** (C) are aerial but are attached to a rhizome which is mud-inhabiting.

is separated from all others. As has been indicated elsewhere, this change in point of view was bolstered by the discovery and appreciation of fossilized primitive vascular plants.

ORIGIN AND SIGNIFICANCE OF THE SEED HABIT AS IT AFFECTS BOTH ANGIOSPERMS AND GYMNOSPERMS

In mature seeds, the embryo is packaged in a protective tissue, the seed coat, and is provided with an adequate supply of food for the resumption of growth during germination. In the dormant state the embryo can withstand severe environmental conditions and yet is stimulated to rapid growth when conditions become suitable. Seeds cast on periodically dry surface soil germinate during periods of favorable surface moisture. The roots then penetrate deeply into the soil where they come in contact with more constant sources of water. When the surface soil dries out again the new plant is able to survive because it is able to transport water from the underground source to all of its parts which are exposed to the atmosphere.

In the following paragraphs certain concepts and speculations concerning the origin of the seed habit are discussed at some length. In particular, the significance of heterospory and the related assumption of parasitic growth habits by gametophyte generations are considered.

The female gametophyte of heterosporous plants has a somewhat more extensive growth than does the male gametophyte. The food stored in the megaspore (as in *Selaginella*) or immediately available from the sporophyte (as in the modern seed plants) has made possible the essentially parasitic growth of the female gametophyte. One advantage of such an arangement lies in the fact that when the female gametophyte is parasitic on the preceding sporophyte generation it is able to supply the embryo with far greater supplies of food than it could produce itself as a small, independent entity.

The retention of the megaspore in the megasporangium was an important step in this direction. But this development posed a serious problem for it tended to interfere with the normal mechanism by which the sperm reached the egg. In the primitive condition the enlarging female gametophyte may have exerted so much pressure on the megasporangium that it was cracked open enough to expose the archegonia allowing fertilization of the egg by swimming sperms. It is very likely that the evolution of the pollen tube was an essential corollary to the complete retention of the female gametophyte within sporophyte tissue.

The pollen tube may not have been an entirely new device since it bears considerable resemblance to a rhizoid. If the male gametophyte, as it developed within the microspore, produced a rhizoid capable of penetrating the megasporangium, that rhizoid would have served as a very convenient passageway for the movement of the male gametes inward to the female gametophyte.

This is, of course, a highly speculative interpretation. Most authorities feel that the pollen tube had its origin as a type of haustorium, i.e., a device for penetrating and obtaining food from the nucellus tissue of the ovule.

No matter what its origin, the pollen tube has eliminated the dependence of the plants which possess it on the presence of surface films of moisture in which sperms must swim to reach the egg.

In this connection, the cycads illustrate an interesting transitional stage. In the ovules of these plants there is a small space between the enclosed female gametophyte and the megasporangium wall. When the pollen tube penetrates this cavity it discharges two sperms in a drop of fluid near the archegonia. These sperms do not swim to the egg but it has been observed that they are motile in the pollen tube just before the discharge.

The megasporangium alone is not truly an ovule. In the seeds of modern plants it is equivalent to the tissue which is commonly called the nucellus. Each ovule has one or more additional layers (integuments) which overgrow the megasporangium leaving a small hole (the *micropyle*) at the tip. The concentration of stored food and other organic matter in primitive seeds would have been attractive to other organisms such as insects, birds, primitive rodents, fungi, and the like. Thus the development of the integument as an additional protective layer over the megasporangium would have had a survival value.

The integument presented an additional barrier to the eventual union of gametes. In gymnosperms this barrier is passed by the device of secreting a droplet of sticky fluid through the micropyle. Pollen grains become adherent to this fluid and are drawn through the micropyle when the fluid is reabsorbed.

In flowering plants the pollen tube passes the integument barrier by growing through the micropyle. A secretion of chemical substances from the micropyle guides the direction of growth of the pollen tube.

The female gametophyte of pines was discussed in some detail as part of the gymnosperm life cycle. This gametophyte exhibits considerable growth and produces recognizable archegonia. It nourishes the embryo even though it must obtain the necessary food from the sporophyte. At maturity it is the largest structure in the pine seed.

In the flowering plants the embryo sac is interpreted as a much reduced female gametophyte. The primary function of the embryo sac is the production of the egg. The nourishment of the embryo is accomplished by a special new tissue, the *endosperm*, which develops from the triple fusion nucleus formed as a result of the fertilization of two polar nuclei by the second sperm from the pollen tube. The endosperm has a tremendous capacity for rapid growth at first and later it accumulates large quantities of reserve food which are utilized by the embryo in its development.

It is possible to interpret the antipodal cells in the embryo sac as vestigial body cells of the female gametophyte and (by stretching the imagination considerably) to interpret the two synergids as vestigial neck cells of an archegonium.

Vascular plants had a long evolutionary history before the advent of the seed habit and it is possible that they were able to grow in more diverse habitats than they actually occupied. The ability of the root system to penetrate deeply into the soil and thus tap water supplies not available at the soil surface undoubtedly made growth possible in other than swampy habitats.

The independent gametophytes of the pre-seed plants may have been unable to survive in areas other than those with moist surface soils. Moreover, there was an added requirement that free surface water be available in order that fertilization by swimming sperms could occur. Since the sporophyte has to begin its existence as an embryo in the gametophyte, the distribution of the more vigorous sporophyte generation was limited to the habitats where the gametophyte could exist.

The retention of the female gametophyte in the megasporangium eliminated the first of these limitations and the concurrent evolution of the pollen tube eliminated the second. Thus, the seed habit meant a profound increase in the ability of plants to continue the conquest of the land. When they left the swamps the plants left behind the conditions which favored fossilization of plant remains and we have very scanty and fragmentary fossil records of the early dwellers of the uplands.

Perhaps the seeds of these plants were rather heavy and not well equipped for dispersal. They fell near the parent plant and the spread of species was very slow at first. Later, devices evolved which served to increase the dispersal rate. One simple and very effective device is that of the pine where a layer of epidermis from the seed-bearing scale remains attached to the seed. This wing causes the pine seed to whirl like a single helicopter blade as it falls from the tree. The rate of fall is slowed and wind movements carry pine seeds as much as a quarter of a mile away from the parent tree. And everyone is familiar with the parachutes of dandelion achenes and the efficiency of this particular device in spreading the dandelion across the face of the earth.

EVOLUTION OF SPOROPHYLLS

Primitive vascular plants bore their sporangia at the tips of dichotomous branch systems. In plants with fern type leaves (macrophylls) the sporangia are born on the leaf and the spore-bearing leaf is called a sporophyll. At various times and in various ways a division of labor has occurred between vegetative and fertile parts of plants. Even in some of the psilophytes portions of a branch system are known to have been smaller and more branched than others. In such cases the sporangia were restricted to the tips of the smaller branches while the larger ones were, presumably, vegetative.

The nutrition of the developing sporogenous tissue in such situations must have depended in part on the ability of the rest of the plant to produce and transport food to the sporangia.

In many ferns, portions of a single frond are fertile and nonphotosynthetic, while other parts of the same frond are sterile and vegetative. In the interrupted fern the middle pinnae of a frond are fertile, while in the royal fern it is the upper pinnae which bear the sporangia. In some other ferns whole leaves are fertile and entirely different in appearance from the much larger vegetative leaves. This is true of the cinnamon fern, the sensitive fern, and the ostrich fern.

In the cycads which are the oldest living group of seed plants, the vegetative leaves are large and much like the fronds of the ancient ferns (Fig. 5.30). The sporophylls, however, are much reduced in size. The megasporophylls in many species are scalelike and bear two seeds apiece. But, in at least one species, *Cycas revoluta,* the

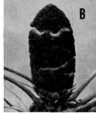

Fig. 5.30. Cycads: A. A species of **Cycas.** Note the large, fernlike leaves. B. Female cone (megasporangiate strobilus) of a species of **Zamia.**

tem without passing through a leaf stage. However, most interpreters of the evidence consider the stamen as being a true microsporophyll in which the leaf tissue has been reduced.

The evolution of the simple pistil was a basic step in the evolution of the flowering plants. This structure is considered to be a modification of the megasporophyll. Possibly the first step was a failure of the megasporophyll to flatten out from the folded condition which it normally has as an immature leaf in the stem tip. This folded condition resulted in the enclosure of the ovules in such a way that they were provided with added protection against predators and desiccation.

Because of the added protection, this device had considerable survival value

sporophyll (Fig. 5.31) has a vestigial resemblance to a vegetative leaf and bears several seeds.

The microsporophylls of the cycads are scalelike and bear a great many microsporangia which are scattered over the leaf surface (Fig. 5.32). This is in contrast to the microsporophylls of pine which bear only two microsporangia apiece.

There seems little question that the sporophylls of the cycads are modified leaves. Nor is there much question as to the basically leaflike nature of the microsporophylls of pine.

The nature of the ovule-bearing scale of pines and related types is another matter. The presence of the subtending bract is scarcely evident in pines but, in larches and some other conifers, it is a highly developed structure which is larger than the ovule-bearing scale. Since the scale is formed in the axil of the bract, a well-substantiated hypothesis has been advanced that the scale is a reduced branch system.

In recent years there has been some discussion of the possibility that the stamen of the flowering plants might have been derived directly from a branch sys-

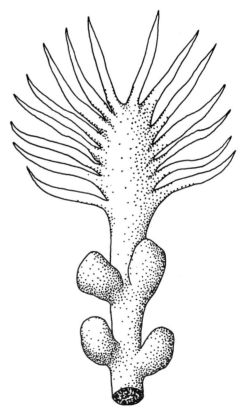

Fig. 5.31. Megasporophyll (with ovules) of **Cycas revoluta** in which the resemblance to a vegetative leaf is evident.

Fig. 5.32. Microsporangiate strobilus (male cone) of a cycad cut crosswise to show the numerous microsporangia on each of the microsporophylls.

and was, thus, favored in the process of natural selection. There followed a gradual sealing of the suture and a progressive migration of the area receptive to pollen to the position which we now recognize as the stigma.

The postulated series of changes which led to the modern pistil must have been accompanied by evolutionary changes in the abilities of the pollen tube since it must often grow for long distances through the stigma, style, and ovary cavity before reaching the ovules.

EVOLUTIONARY TRENDS IN FLOWERING PLANTS

Although we have no fossil evidence of the exact nature of the first flowering plants nor of the intermediate forms between them and the fernlike plants from which they arose, it is possible to arrive at a concept of the probable nature of the primitive flower on the basis of comparative studies of living plants.

The primitive flower (Fig. 5.33) was probably a bisporangiate strobilus having both stamens (microsporophylls) and simple pistils (megasporophylls) on the same axis. In addition, the primitive flower had modified sterile leaves attached to the basal portions of the axis. These have become further modified into the petals and sepals of the modern flower. The receptacle of the flower is interpreted as having been modified from the axis of a strobilus.

Some of the characteristics of primitive flowers were these:

1. The axis was more elongated than the present day receptacle.
2. The different parts of the flower were all numerous.

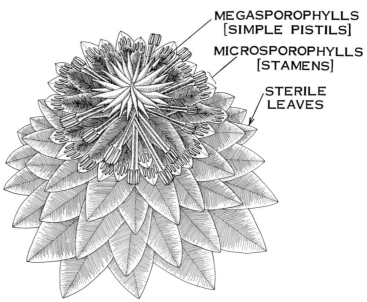

MEGASPOROPHYLLS
[SIMPLE PISTILS]

MICROSPOROPHYLLS
[STAMENS]

STERILE
LEAVES

Fig. 5.33. Appearance of a hypothetical primitive flower with numerous parts, spirally arranged, and separately attached.

3. They were spirally arranged on the axis.
4. They were separately attached.
5. The megasporophylls were clustered near the tip of the axis.
6. The megasporophylls resembled the present-day simple pistils.
7. The microsporophylls were below the megasporophylls.
8. The microsporophylls were more leaf like than present-day stamens but possibly had only four microsporangia.
9. The basal leaves were sterile but not differentiated into sepals and petals.

It is also probable that the plants which produced the first flowers were treelike and had woody stems with secondary growth. Among living flowering plants, the magnolia is an example of a plant which has retained many primitive features. The buttercups also have flowers with primitive features but most of the species are herbaceous rather than woody. Members of the rose family have also retained many of the characteristics of primitive flowers.

The evolution of the vast array of modern flowering plants can be appreciated best as being a matter of progressive change along any or all of the following lines:

1. Reduction in the numbers of parts.
2. Change from the spiral arrangement to a whorled or cyclic arrangement.
3. Fusion of the parts in a whorl.
4. Fusion of one whorl to another.
5. Change from radial symmetry to bilateral symmetry.
6. Change from hypogyny, a condition in which the flower parts seem to arise below the ovary, to epigyny, a condition in which the flower parts seem to arise above the ovary.
7. Elimination of one or more whorls.
8. Reduction in the number of ovules in each carpel.

The legume family, which includes the familiar beans and peas, provides an example of the reduction of the numbers of

simple pistils. The flowers of members of this family have but one simple pistil and this bears many resemblances to the hypothetical primitive pistil (Fig. 5.34).

The change from the spiral arrangement to the whorled arrangement is related to the apparent shortening of the receptacle which is not so much a shortening as a failure to elongate. The unexpanded spiral pattern of flower parts has

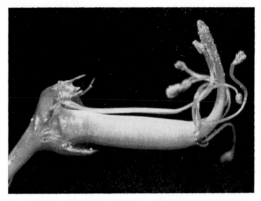

Fig. 5.34. Flower of the perennial sweet pea (legume family) with sepals and petals removed to show the single, simple pistil and fusion of the filaments of 9 of the 10 stamens.

become broken up into separate whorls of sepals, petals, stamens, and pistils. Sometimes there are two or more whorls of the same kind of part.

The true geraniums, for instance, have five whorls of five members each: 5 sepals, 5 petals, two whorls of 5 stamens each, and 5 carpels (Fig. 5.35).

Flowers of the mustard family have one whorl of 4 sepals, one whorl of 4 petals, one whorl of 2 short stamens, a second whorl of 4 longer stamens, and a single compound pistil in the center (Fig. 5.36).

Lily flowers have 3 sepals, 3 petals, two whorls of 3 stamens each, and a compound pistil in the middle (Fig. 5.37).

Tomato flowers have only four whorls: 5 sepals, 5 petals, 5 stamens, and a pistil in the center (Fig. 5.38).

There is an interesting comparison between the number of parts per whorl in monocot flowers and in dicot flowers. The

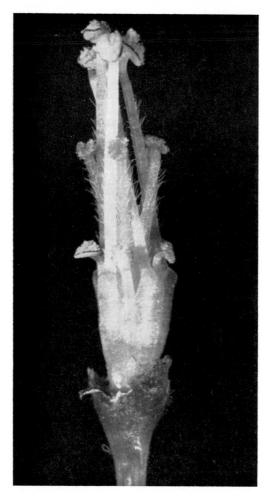

Fig. 5.35. Flower of **Oxalis** (geranium family) with sepals and petals removed. In order from top to bottom note 5 long stamens, 5 stigmas, and 5 short stamens.

basic number of parts per whorl in monocots is three, while dicots have four or five parts per whorl. (This comparison holds best for those members of both groups which do not exhibit extreme reduction.)

The fusion of parts in a whorl has occurred to varying degrees in many plant families. The flowers of the common garden plant, petunia, serve to illustrate the fusion of petals (Fig. 5.39).

In the flowers of the sweet pea and many other legumes 9 of the 10 stamens have their filaments fused to form a tube around the ovary (Fig. 5.34).

In dandelions, daisies, and other members of the composite family the anthers of the five stamens are fused to form a cylinder through which the stigma of the pistil emerges like a piston when the style elongates (Fig. 5.40).

One of the most interesting of all evolutionary studies concerns the relation of insects to flowering plants. As is well known, insects are the natural pollinating agents for many kinds of flowers. In numerous cases, there is abundant evidence that evolutionary modifications in flower structure have been matched by evolutionary modifications of the insects which pollinate them.

One especially remarkable example is that of a species of moth which accomplishes pollination in a species of *Yucca* by carefully packing pollen into the stigma. Having insured the normal development of the *Yucca* fruit in this way she proceeds to lay a few of her own eggs in the ovary where the larval stages develop.

EVOLUTION IN THE NONVASCULAR LAND PLANTS

Although we do not know the nature of the gametophyte generation of the plants which produced the first aerial sporophyte

Fig. 5.36. Flower of the sweet alyssum (mustard family) with sepals and petals removed. Note the one whorl of 4 long stamens and the second whorl of 2 short stamens.

Fig. 5.37. Flower of a member of the lily family (**Ornithogallum**) with 5 whorls of 3 members each.

Fig. 5.39. Flower of **Petunia** illustrating fusion of petals.

Fig. 5.40. Dissected flower from the compact flower head of a marigold (composite family). The portion illustrated shows the characteristic fusion of the anthers.

Fig. 5.38. Flower of the tomato plant with 5 sepals, 5 petals, 5 stamens, and a compound pistil in the center.

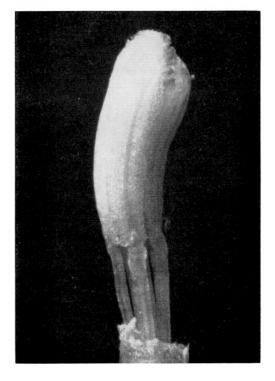

branches, we can proceed with a reasonable assumption that the selective factors in the evolution of the gametophyte differed from those affecting the sporophyte in at least one major requirement: namely, that sperms were dispersed in water while the spores were dispersed in air. Thus, the dissemination of reproductive cells would not have been a primary selective factor in the evolution of aerial branches of the gametophyte.

On the other hand, the atmosphere does represent an enormous reservoir of carbon dioxide for photosynthesis, and the surface of the land contains many of the essential inorganic chemicals for plant growth. The available concentrations of carbon dioxide and inorganic chemicals are often limiting factors in the growth of algae. Also, the absorption of light by dense growths of algae near the surface often means that light becomes a limiting factor in deeper waters. Thus, emergence of the gametophyte from the water would have certain beneficial aspects.

Another important factor influencing the gametophytic invasion of the land was the fact that wind-blown spores would be just as likely to come to rest on the land as in the water. If the land were moist enough to support growth of the germinating spores then there would be nothing to prevent the beginnings of such growth on land. The formation of the algalike protonemal stage in the life cycle of mosses may be cited as an illustration of such an event.

Adaptations of Mosses to a Terrestrial Existence

The gametophyte generation has never achieved the ultimate size of the sporophyte generation but has shown much diversification in its adaptation to life on land. Mosses seem to be able to endure desiccation. It is a common observation that moss gametophytes which are so dry and shrivelled up that they appear dead will become bright green and look fresh within minutes after being wetted. Moss leaves, in many species, are completely free of a cutinized surface. Thus mosses

are wettable and water moves on their surfaces by capillary action. Also, when moss leaves are wet they are totally exposed for absorption of carbon dioxide from the air.

Resistance to water loss is not entirely lacking in the mosses. Some species have erect sheets of green cells on the upper surface of the leaves. These are spread apart and exposed to the air when the plant is moist. But under dry conditions the rest of the leaf curls up over these photosynthetic layers in a protective fashion. Most moss leaves are one cell in thickness except in the central portion. The thickened midrib is called a *costa* and is not a true vein since it lacks vascular tissue (Fig. 5.41).

The moss sporophyte is nonvascular. It has a single axis of growth with the capsule at the upper end and the foot at the lower. The foot is an absorbing organ imbedded in the gametophyte. The stalk is tough and wiry. Most immature moss capsules contain chlorenchyma and

Fig. 5.41. Leaf of a moss.

manufacture their own organic food. Thus the sporophyte is only partially dependent on the gametophyte.

Moss capsules have a cutinized epidermis and the basal portions of the capsules of many mosses have stomates surrounded by pairs of functional guard cells (Fig. 5.42). The cutinized epidermis enables the sporophyte to reduce the transpiration rate and it rarely exhibits evidences of wilting as does the gametophyte.

As noted above, the main survival mechanism of the moss gametophyte is an ability to remain alive in the desiccated condition and to recover quickly when water becomes available. The major water movements are capillary in nature and occur in the surface films which cover the plant body. There is, thus, a striking contrast between the two generations of mosses with respect to the mechanisms by which they exist in the aerial environment.

The gametophyte of the peat mosses (*Sphagnum*) is one of the few moss types which has economic significance. In either the living or the dead condition these plants have a tremendous capacity for absorbing and holding water and this makes them valuable as mulches in garden soil, in the packing of live plants for shipment, and in other ways.

Sphagnum grows in many parts of the world but achieves its greatest develop-

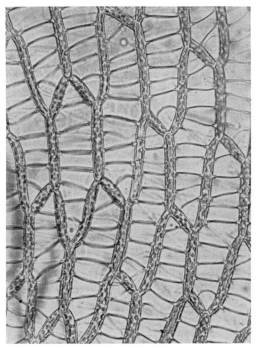

Fig. 5.43. **Sphagnum** leaf showing arrangement of chlorenchyma cells and water storage cells.

ment in the cooler regions, particularly in the areas where retreating glaciers have created numerous small lakes and ponds which have no drainage outlets. In such conditions the waters become acid and this favors the growth of *Sphagnum*.

The stems of this plant are densely covered with overlapping leaves. Some of the branches hang downward and twine about the central axis thus serving as effective wicks in moving water upwards. The leaves are only one cell in thickness and have two kinds of cells: narrow, green photosynthetic cells, and large, dead water storage cells which are spaced between the green cells (Fig. 5.43). The space occupied by the water storage cells is much greater than that of the green cells so the color of the leaf is pale green.

Under the conditions of growth in highly acid waters the older parts of the plants do not decay after death. They sink to the bottom and gradually accumulate to form deposits of *peat* which, in time, fill up the lake completely.

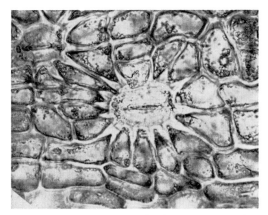

Fig. 5.42. Stomate from the basal region of a moss capsule.

The sporophyte of *Sphagnum* consists of a foot and a capsule connected by a short stalk which never elongates. When the spores are mature, the tip of the gametophyte branch in which the foot of the sporophyte is imbedded begins to grow upwards and carries the whole sporophyte up into the air (Fig. 5.44).

Fig. 5.44. **Sphagnum** gametophytes with attached sporophytes. The capsules shown are actually somewhat smaller than BB shot.

The capsule is dark in color and heavily cutinized. It is possible to recognize pairs of cells arranged like guard cells in the capsule wall but the stomates do not develop between them. The heat of the sun causes gases within the sealed capsule to expand and, eventually, it explodes and discharges the spores into the air violently.

The Plant Body of Marchantia

One of the common representatives of the *liverworts* is *Marchantia*, a plant with many remarkable features including the development in the gametophyte generation of a cutinized epidermis with perforations like stomates. The gametophyte of *Marchantia* (Fig. 5.45) is a flat, ribbon-like thallus which is held close to the soil by numerous rhizoids. The upper epidermis appears to be divided into rhomboidal areas which are actually the outlines of

air chambers below. Each air chamber is separated from the next one by a wall of cells and the walls of all of the chambers support the epidermis as walls of the rooms in a house support the roof (Fig. 5.46).

The epidermis is cutinized and in the center of the portion of the epidermis over each air chamber there is a round air pore surrounded by a "chimney" consisting of four tiers of four cells each. This opening functions as a stomate and it is possible that the lowermost tier of cells in the chimney may be able to regulate the size of the opening. This arrangement of cells around an opening, when compared to the stomates and guard cells of the sporophytes of many plants, is certainly an outstanding example of parallel evolution.

From the floor of each air chamber in the thallus there arise numerous algalike filaments of densely green cells which comprise the main photosynthetic tissue of *Marchantia*.

Leafy Liverworts

The gametophytes of the leafy liverworts are small and delicate plants much like mosses. Their leaves are one cell thick and lack the midribs (costae) which are characteristic of many moss leaves. Most of the common leafy liverworts are prostrate and appear to have only two rows of leaves (Fig. 5.47). A third row of leaves may be reduced in size or missing

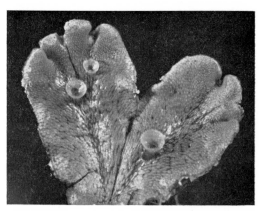

Fig. 5.45. **Marchantia** thallus.

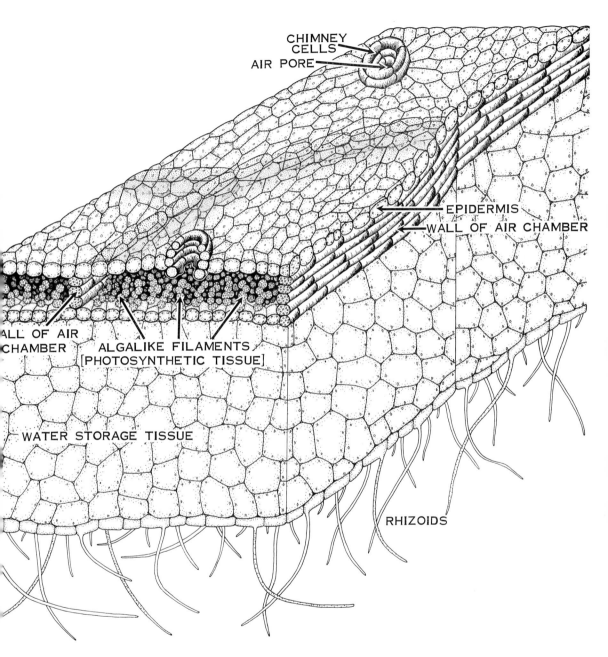

CHIMNEY CELLS

AIR PORE

EPIDERMIS

WALL OF AIR CHAMBER

ALL OF AIR CHAMBER

ALGALIKE FILAMENTS [PHOTOSYNTHETIC TISSUE]

WATER STORAGE TISSUE

RHIZOIDS

Fig. 5.46. Three-dimensional, schematic representation of the structure of the **Marchantia** thallus.

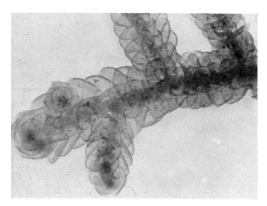

Fig. 5.47. Photomicrograph of a species of the leafy liverwort, **Porella.**

entirely but there is little doubt that the primitive members of this group had three rows of leaves and grew erect. In some species the leaves are finely dissected, appearing like branched filaments of algae. Frequently, the leaves overlap and this increases the efficiency of capillary water movements. Members of this group are like mosses in that they are able to endure dessication. They are not, apparently, as aggressive in temperate regions as mosses and do not occur in as many diverse habitats. Certainly they are unknown to the vast majority of people while mosses are familiar to almost everyone.

The gametangia of leafy liverworts are borne at the tops of the main stem or on short side branches. They differ from the gametangia of mosses in minor respects. The sporophytes are like those of the mosses in that they have a single axis of growth with a foot, a stalk, and a capsule in which the spores are formed. They are, however, much simpler structures and are more completely dependent on the gametophyte generation than are moss sporophytes. The stalk does not elongate until the spores are mature. When it does grow, it elongates rapidly. This thrusts the capsule up into the air and the drying action of the air causes it to rupture immediately. Prior to this stage the capsule is immersed in protective leaves and membranes at the tip of the gametophyte. The capsule does not open by a lid as does

the moss capsule. Instead it splits open lengthwise into four valves (Fig. 5.48).

Hornworts

The most common plant of this group is *Anthoceros* and it holds a special place in the thinking of many authorities in the study of plant evolution because of its unique sporophyte.

The gametophyte of *Anthoceros* is a small, thin, dark green thallus which lacks the internal differentiation found in *Marchantia*. The gametangia are borne on the upper surface and are imbedded in the thallus.

The sporophyte becomes a slender, erect, green spire, possibly an inch or more in height (Fig. 5.49). The epidermis is cutinized and has stomates surrounded by

Fig. 5.48. Leafy liverwort with attached mature sporophytes.

Fig. 5.49. Gametophytes of **Anthoceros** with attached sporophytes.

pairs of functional guard cells. The central core of tissue, which is called the *columella*, becomes sclerenchymalike. This is surrounded by a cylinder of spore-bearing tissue (Fig. 5.50). Outside this is the green photosynthetic tissue. At the base of the sporophyte is a foot which is imbedded in the gametophyte tissue (Fig. 5.51). Between the foot and the capsule is a zone of meristematic cells which adds new tissues to the base of the capsule. The youngest spore mother cells are at the base of the capsule adjacent to the meristematic region. Above them the spore mother cells are in the early stages of meiosis. By following the sporogenous tissue upwards in the capsule, one can often observe all stages in meiosis from spore mother cells at the base to mature spores at the tip (Fig. 5.52). The tip of the capsule splits into two valves and permits the mature spores to be blown away.

The reason why evolutionists take such appraising looks at the sporophyte of *Anthoceros* is that it is so close to being an independent plant like a simple psilophyte. If the columella were to evolve a little bit further towards being xylem, and if the foot could be stimulated to grow rhizoids into the soil instead of parasitizing the gametophyte, then the resulting plant would indeed be a psilophyte. However, this should be recognized as being

only an interesting speculation since there are several serious objections to using *Anthoceros* as an ancestor to the vascular plants.

THEORETICAL ORIGINS OF ALTERNATION OF GENERATIONS IN LAND PLANTS

There are two major hypotheses concerning the origins of alternation of generations in land plants. The proponents of one of these maintain that the primitive algal ancestors of land plants had an alternation of two independent generations which were alike or *homologous*. This means that the diploid generation was more or less similar to the haploid

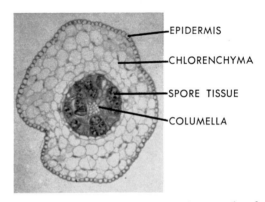

Fig. 5.50. Transverse section of the capsule of **Anthoceros.**

generation and that the existing differences between them were acquired gradually. The proponents of the other hypothesis do not deny that an alternation of homologous generations does occur in some algae. They maintain, however, that the sporophyte of land plants has always been basically different from or *antithetic* to the gametophyte generation, i.e., that it is a new structure interpolated between two successive haploid generations.

The mosses, liverworts, and hornworts are usually grouped together in a division of the plant kingdom called the *Bryophyta*. The major features of this group are the nonvascular sporophytes, the development of an embryo stage of the sporophyte, and the presence of sterile wall cells in the gametangia. Also, in

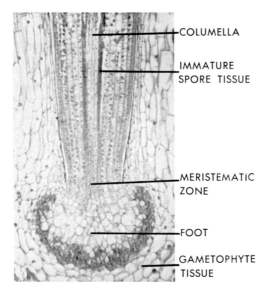

COLUMELLA

IMMATURE
SPORE TISSUE

MERISTEMATIC
ZONE

FOOT

GAMETOPHYTE
TISSUE

Fig. 5.51. Longitudinal section of the basal portion of an **Anthoceros** sporophyte showing the foot and the intercalary meristem.

this group, the gametophyte is the dominant and completely independent generation.

In the past it has been considered possible that the vascular plants may have evolved from the bryophytes by a progressive increase in the complexity of the sporophyte and a corresponding decrease in the complexity of the gametophyte. This hypothesis was generally abandoned, however, when investigations of the fossil psilophytes indicated a very distinct possibility that the vascular plants and the bryophytes arose independently from the green algae.

In many green algae, the zygote is formed by fusion of two gametes outside the parent body. In others, fertilization occurs inside the oogonium but the oogonium wall eventually breaks open allowing the zygote to separate from the parent plant. In either circumstance, the germination of the zygote occurs outside the parent gametophyte tissue, often long after the gametophyte has disappeared.

In the bryophytes as well as in all of the lower vascular plants the archegonium not only retains the egg so that fertilization occurs within its tissues, but also re-

tains the zygote. Thus, when the zygote germinates, the embryo of the sporophyte develops within the archegonium. This means that the early stages in the development of the sporophyte have been adopted by the gametophyte.

It has been suggested herein that the conquest of the land began with the invasion of the atmosphere by an erect branch of an algal system and, furthermore, that this erect axis developed a terminal sporangium as well as a cutinized epidermis with stomates before it developed vascular tissue.

If such structures ever existed, they may have been modified on the one hand into the primitive stems of vascular plants while, on the other hand, they may have been modified, without vascularization, into the sporophytes of the bryophytes.

In many bryophyte groups the prototype of the gametophyte seems to have been an erect, aerial stem with numerous leaflike parts attached. The archegonia were formed at the tips of this axis. The embryos of the adopted sporophytes would have had to begin development in the same place and were probably unable to sever the relationship and become independent plants. In this way the sporophytes of bryophytes may have lost the evolutionary initiative and become subordinate to the gametophytes as they are today.

If such an interpretation is correct then

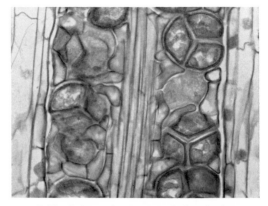

Fig. 5.52. Enlarged portion of the **Anthoceros** sporophyte showing tetrads of spores.

sporophytes such as those of mosses would be close to the ancestral type, while the simpler sporophytes of liverworts could well have resulted from degenerative evolution.

In the case of the primitive vascular plants the lack of fossil evidence concerning their gametophytes is disappointing and we may never know what they were like. The fact that in most living groups of vascular plants the sporophytes become independent from the gametophytes at an early stage makes reasonable a hypothesis that the primitive vascular plants behaved in a similar manner. The structure of these unknown gametophytes must have permitted the separation readily.

As a conclusion to this discussion the hypothesis is presented that the divergence between the bryophytes and the vascular plants began before the aerial sporophyte axis became vascularized and that the divergence was influenced by basic but unknown differences between the gametophytes of these two evolutionary lines of development.

CHAPTER 6

Growth and Differentiation of the Plant Body

The growth of many-celled plant parts is the composite result of the growth of their individual cells. These cells are formed as a result of nuclear and cell divisions. They grow larger because of water absorption and an increase in the volume of protoplasm. Finally they become modified in various ways during the complex process of differentiation.

In the simplest plants, cells separate shortly after division and the whole plant consists of a single cell which carries on all of the essential functions. As many-celled plants evolved and became more complex, a division of labor occurred with different organs taking on specific functions. The leaf of the higher plants, for instance, has become the major photosynthetic organ, the root has become an organ for absorption and anchorage, and the flower has become specialized to facilitate the gametic reproductive cycle.

One of the more significant changes was the segregation of cells responsible for new cell formation into special areas called *meristems*. Some of the more complex algae and all of the higher plants have a meristem at the tip of each growing axis.

In some cases, especially among the lower forms of land plants, the meristem consists of a single apical cell (Fig. 6.1). The cells derived from the apical cell are capable of further division but the numbers of such divisions are limited. The apical cell, however, is capable of dividing indefinitely as long as the plant remains in a strictly vegetative condition.

On the other hand, the apical meristems of the higher land plants consist of groups of apical initials rather than single apical cells. Also, in many of the higher plants the girth of the plant is increased as the result of cell divisions in lateral meristems (see the discussions of cambium).

ORIGINS OF PRIMARY TISSUES IN STEMS AND LEAVES

In order to understand the growth of a stem and the formation of the attached leaves it is necessary to investigate the tip region of a stem where new leaves are developed. Young corn plants are very useful in such an exercise. With a little care and patience the leaves can be removed one by one from the base upward. Each leaf is smaller and more delicate than the one below. The successive internodes are seen to be shorter and smaller in diameter as each leaf is unwrapped (Fig. 6.2). Also the stems' growth in length by elongation of the internodes becomes readily apparent. Soon the leaves get so small that the aid of a hand lens or a dissecting microscope is needed to make the final

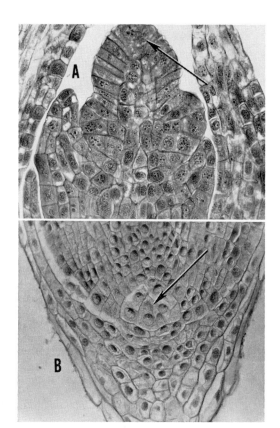

Fig. 6.1. Longitudinal sections of meristems with the conspicuous apical cells indicated by arrows. A. Stem tip of **Equisetum**. B. Fern root tip.

manipulations. When the smallest leaf has been removed, a minute, dome-shaped structure is exposed at the tip of the stem. If the corn plant happened to be approaching the "knee-high" stage, it would be usual to find a miniature tassel already formed at the tip of the stem. Corn stops producing new leaves prior to this stage and begins to form the flowers of the tassel (Fig. 6.3).

The dome-shaped structure at the tip of the stem is the *apical meristem* (Figs. 6.4, 6.5). A small mass of cells in this tissue has the essential nature of remaining undifferentiated and capable of indefinite cell division at least during the phase of vegetative growth. These cells are sometimes called the apical initials and constitute the *promeristem* (Figs. 6.6, 6.7). They divide in several planes but their rate of

division is not especially rapid. Actually, those cells which are formed in the promeristem but forced out of it may divide much more rapidly. The latter cells are often called tissue forming initials and the term, *histogen*, may be used to describe groups of such cells which give rise to specific tissues. They divide rapidly for some time but are not capable of indefinite division. The planes of cell division are most frequently at right angles to the long axis of the stem and, thus, the developing stem consists mainly of lengthwise rows of cells.

There are three basic tissue systems in the primary body of plants. They are the *epidermis*, the *vascular system*, and the *fundamental* or *ground tissues* (Figs. 6.6, 6.7). Each of them develops from a specific histogen. The epidermis consists of a single layer of cells which completely covers the primary plant body and the histogen from which it develops is called the *protoderm*. The primary vascular system includes the veins of the leaf, the central cylinder of the root, and the vascular bundles of the stem. Each of these is derived

Fig. 6.2. Young corn stem with leaves removed to show nodes and internodes. The minute tassel at the tip is enlarged in Fig. 6.3.

Fig. 6.3. Photomicrograph of the newly-formed tassel shown in position in Fig. 6.2.

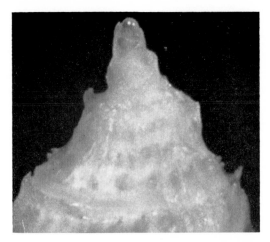

Fig. 6.4. Dissected stem tip of a young corn plant showing a dome-shaped apical meristem producing vegetative leaves.

from a histogen called *procambium*. The remaining tissues are the fundamental, or ground tissues, and the histogens which give rise to them are called *ground meristems*. Some of the fundamental tissues which will be discussed in more detail when particular plant parts are considered are the pith and cortex tissues of stems and roots, and the photosynthetic tissues of leaves.

The first indication of a new leaf is a localized swelling on the sloping surface of the apical meristem (Figs. 6.6, 6.7, 6.8). This seems to be due to an increase in the division rate of cells under the surface at that point. The swelling is called a *leaf primordium*. The rate of formation of new leaf primordia and their "positioning" on the meristem follow definite patterns which are characteristic of the particular plant. Sometimes they are placed oppositely while, in other plants, they are arranged in spiral patterns exhibiting definite mathematical regularity.

Shortly after the initiation of leaf primordia it is possible to demonstrate that each of the three histogens in the leaf is

Fig. 6.5. Photomicrograph of a dissected stem tip of **Elodea** with both a vegetative apical meristem and a lateral floral primordium.

continuous with a corresponding histogen in the stem.

In sectional view the very young leaves appear to be long and narrow but actually they soon take on in miniature scale the

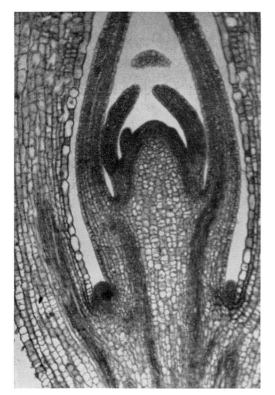

Fig. 6.6. Longitudinal section of the stem tip of flax. Compare with Fig. 6.7 for appropriate labels.

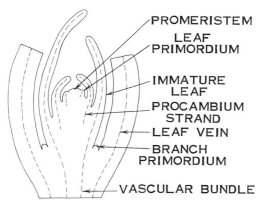

PROMERISTEM
LEAF PRIMORDIUM
IMMATURE LEAF
PROCAMBIUM STRAND
LEAF VEIN
BRANCH PRIMORDIUM
VASCULAR BUNDLE

Fig. 6.7. Schematic diagram of a longitudinal section of a stem tip based on Fig. 6.6.

characteristic outlines of mature leaves. Commonly they curve up and over the meristem, with the older and larger ones protecting the smaller ones inside.

The tissue of the stem at the level where a leaf is attached is the *node* and the stem segments between nodes are *internodes* (Fig. 6.2). Nodes and internodes do not become distinguishable until the internodal cells begin to elongate. Internodes many inches below the tip often continue to grow longer as may be observed by making periodic measurements of the internodes of immature stems.

When the young leaves reach a certain size, *branch primordia* appear in the leaf axils ("arm-pits") (Figs. 6.6, 6.7). At first these are merely dome-shaped masses of cells like the apical meristem itself. In fact, they become active apical meristems and

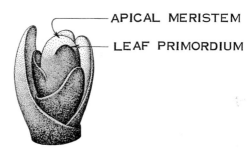

APICAL MERISTEM
LEAF PRIMORDIUM

Fig. 6.8. Three-dimensional drawing of a stem tip showing the positional relationships of the leaf primordia and the apical meristem.

form branches of the stem system. In many plants this development is continuous but the woody plants of the temperate region form *dormant buds* (Fig. 6.9) in which no detectable growth occurs during the winter season. Each dormant bud contains unelongated stem segments with attached leaves, or immature flowers, or both. The whole structure is enclosed with small, tough, modified leaves called *bud scales*. It is possible, in many cases, to remove these bud scales and observe the immature leaves (Fig. 6.10) or flowers with the aid of a hand lens or a dissecting microscope. Careful observations of opening buds in the spring is a valuable exercise (Fig. 6.9C).

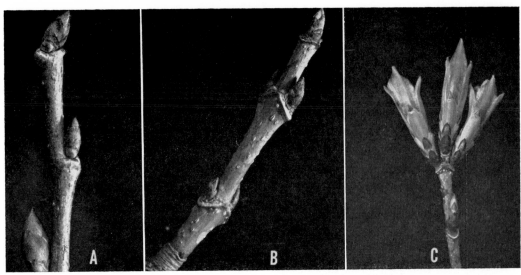

Fig. 6.9. Woody twigs with dormant buds. A. Elm. B. Maple. C. Maple buds as they begin to open in spring.

Fig. 6.10. Dormant buds of maple with bud scales removed to show next year's leaves.

CELL AND TISSUE TYPES

The various types of tissues occurring in plants contain a variety of cell types. Many of the cell types discussed below are found in several tissues while others may be limited to a particular one.

Parenchyma consists of cells which mature without major changes other than increase in volume (Fig. 6.11). They remain relatively thin-walled and have large,

central vacuoles. Commonly, they store reserve foods and may provide a type of "water reservoir" during periods of water shortage. They may contain chloroplasts. In fact, the term *chlorenchyma*, refers to green parenchyma whose major function is photosynthesis. The green cells of leaves and stems would be classified as chlorenchyma on this basis.

In young plant parts the parenchyma cells are highly turgid. Their mutual

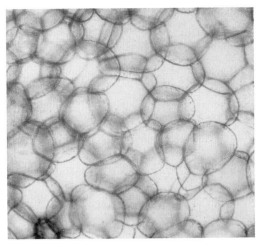

Fig. 6.11. Parenchyma cells (pith tissue of elderberry).

pressures give considerable mechanical support to such parts and in this way they aid in the maintenance of shape. The absorption of water into parenchyma cells is one of the main factors in the enlargement of the primary plant body. They may also become meristematic under certain conditions. There is some cell to cell conduction of substances in parenchyma tissue but this occurs at a relatively slow rate.

Sclerenchyma consists of cells whose walls are uniformly thickened (Fig. 6.12) and impregnated with the complex carbohydrate lignin. At maturity, the walls may

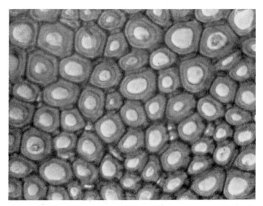

Fig. 6.12. Sclerenchyma cells (bundle sheath fibers from a corn stem).

be so thick that the hollow center or lumen appears as a pin-point in cross section. This type of cell is not specialized for conduction. Instead, it affords a semirigid mechanical support to the plant parts wherein it occurs. The places where sclerenchyma develops are usually located with engineering precision. In some plants the angles of the stem are filled with sclerenchyma. In a plant with a smoothly cylindrical stem the sclerenchyma may occur as a cylinder inside the epidermis, or as a strand (*bundle cap*) outside each of the vascular bundles. In leaves, the major veins which form the leaf framework are heavily invested with sclerenchyma.

This type of cell is frequently long and pointed and is the source of many com-

mercial fibers. In flax, for instance, each of the linen fibers is a bundle of sclerenchyma fibers which remain united as a unit.

The so-called *stone cells* of pears which give a gritty texture to the fruit are non-elongated sclerenchyma cells. They are often objects of intricate design since the wall thickenings occur in layers which are crossed by many minute canals radiating from the lumen (Fig. 6.13).

Collenchyma consists of cells which also function in mechanical support. However, they differ from sclerenchyma in several ways: they provide an elastic rather than a semirigid support, the thickenings of the wall are of cellulose and pectin rather than lignin, and they are thickened unevenly instead of uniformly as are sclerenchyma cells. Cross sections of beet petioles offer a remarkable example of collenchyma cells (Fig. 6.14).

It should be noted that a clear distinction between parenchyma, sclerenchyma, and collenchyma cannot always be made.

In many plant parts, groups of cells take on the specialized function of secretion. Many types of substances are secreted and some of them have important economic significances.

Resin is secreted in the resin ducts of many gymnosperms. These ducts are actually elongated spaces between the secretory cells. They may be observed to good advantage in cross sections of pine

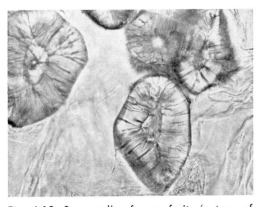

Fig. 6.13. Stone cells of pear fruits (a type of sclerenchyma).

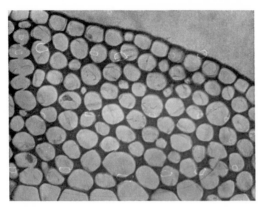

Fig. 6.14. Collenchyma cells from a beet petiole.

stems or needles (Fig. 6.15). The function of resin in the plant is not clear but it has become an item of commerce, being the source of turpentine and a number of other products.

Various kinds of *oil* are secreted in oil ducts which occur in various plants. Sections of sunflower stems show them to good advantage. Oils collected from members of the mint family are a valuable economic product.

Nectar is a sugary solution which is secreted or excreted by nectar glands in flowers. It attracts insects and thus aids in pollination. Bees are able to convert nectar into honey.

Latex is a milky appearing fluid secreted in the latex tubes of rubber plants

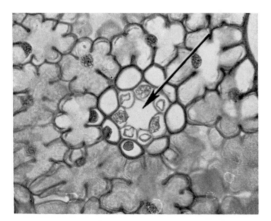

Fig. 6.15. Partial section of a pine needle with arrow pointing to a resin canal.

and many others. It is a source of natural rubber.

The aerial parts of plants are often partially covered by hairlike outgrowths from the epidermis. These *epidermal hairs* may be single-celled or many-celled and they may be branched or unbranched. Some of them, as in the common geranium (Fig. 6.16), have bulbous glands at the tips which contain a volatile oil. Interpreting the functions of such hairs is a dangerous pastime, scientifically. At first glance, one might assume that they cut down transpiration but this has been proved incorrect in several instances. Another likely

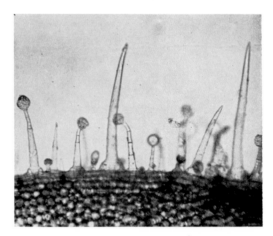

Fig. 6.16. Transverse section of a geranium stem showing epidermal hairs.

possibility is that they interfere with the movements of small insects which feed on plant substances.

Phloem

The tissue which is specialized for conduction of organic substances in solution is called *phloem*. In this tissue there may be four different kinds of cells which occur in various proportions in different kinds of plants. They are:

a. sieve tube elements
b. companion cells
c. parenchyma cells
d. fibers

The parenchyma cells of phloem are

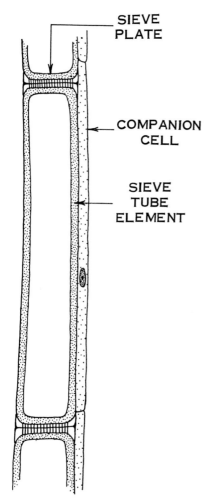

SIEVE
PLATE

COMPANION
CELL

SIEVE
TUBE
ELEMENT

Fig. 6.17. Drawing of a sieve tube and a companion cell as seen in a longitudinal section.

perforated walls have the appearance of sieves and this accounts for their name. Parts of the lateral walls between adjacent elements may be perforated also. When the phloem is functionally mature, i.e., when it is actually transporting foods, the cytoplasm of each sieve tube element is functional but the nucleus has disappeared.

Companion cells are intimately associated with the sieve tube elements (Figs. 6.17, 6.18) since they are sister cells derived by a longitudinal division of a preceding cell. The companion cells remain small in diameter and retain their nuclei which appear to be very active, metabolically. It is a somewhat obvious hypothesis that the companion cell has a great influence on the functioning of the sieve tube element. Such simple theories are often difficult to substantiate, however, espe-

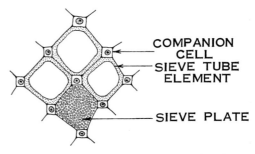

COMPANION
CELL
SIEVE TUBE
ELEMENT

SIEVE PLATE

Fig. 6.18. Drawing of a portion of the phloem tissue from a large vein of a corn leaf, showing sieve tubes and companion cells. One transverse wall of a sieve tube element is included to show the sieve plate.

essentially similar to the parenchyma of nonvascular tissue while the fibers are elongate sclerenchyma cells. The *sieve tube elements* are the particular cells which are specialized for conduction of organic foods in solution. In most angiosperms the individual sieve tube elements are connected together end to end to form long sieve tubes (Fig. 6.17). The end walls which separate each cell of the tube from the next one appear to be perforated with many fine pores and it is possible that minute protoplasmic strands pass through them. When seen in end view, as in cross sections of stems (Fig. 6.18), the

cially when one realizes that companion cells do not occur at all in the phloem of gymnosperms.

By means of several different techniques, including the use of radioactive tracers, it has been shown that the phloem solution moves at a rate of speed much greater than can be accounted for by any of the mechanisms proposed to explain it.

However, the fact that the majority of organic food transfer does occur in the phloem can be demonstrated by cutting a girdle around a stem in such a way that the phloem is completely severed. Plants girdled in this way eventually die because of starvation of the roots. However, there is usually an abundant supply of stored food in the roots and a girdled tree might not die for several years. Also, the roots might obtain food through natural grafts with the roots of nearby trees.

In the spring of the year, before the leaves mature, there may be an upward movement of a solution containing soluble foods derived from digestion of stored foods in stems and roots. This solution seems to move in the xylem and is associated with an active absorption of water by the roots. Transpiration pull is not involved in this movement in any way. If sugar maples are punctured with small holes into the wood at this time of year, the sap will flow outward. Dehydration changes this sap into the maple syrup and sugar of commerce.

Xylem

The major function of *xylem*, however, is the conduction of water and dissolved inorganic chemicals throughout the plant. The general direction is upwards from roots to stems to leaves. In xylem tissue there may be four different kinds of cells which occur in various proportions in different kinds of plants. These cells are:

    a. tracheids
    b. vessels
    c. fibers
    d. parenchyma cells

Tracheids and *vessels* are the important conducting elements of the xylem and will be discussed in some detail here. Parenchyma cells have been discussed elsewhere. Fibers in the xylem are long and slender and have very thick walls.

Tracheids are long, slender cells with tapering, chisel-shaped end walls (Fig. 6.19). In some plants they may be hundreds of times longer than wide. The walls are lignified and thickened, but not uniformly. Thin areas, or pits, occur in the secondary wall layers and they permit rapid diffusion of water from one tracheid

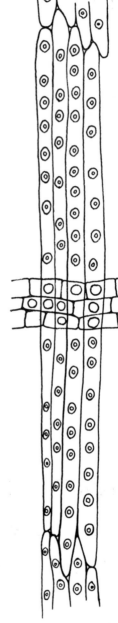

Fig. 6.19. Tracheids as seen in a longitudinal radial section. The transverse band of cells is a portion of a xylem ray.

to another. The pits are not actual holes in the walls between cells since the primary wall remains intact.

Tracheids do not function in conduction until they are dead and empty of protoplasmic contents. It follows that they play only a passive role in the movement that vessels are made up of longitudinal series of cells attached end to end. The cross walls between cells are eliminated by digestive processes (Fig. 6.20). In some plants, a single vessel is composed of hundreds of segments forming a microscopic water pipe and may extend from root to stem to leaf. The vessel is a much more efficient water conductor than the tracheid and makes it possible for plants with high transpiration rates to replace the lost water quickly. Since high transpiration rates are the price that plants pay for efficient absorption of carbon dioxide it follows that the vessel has played an important part in the evolution of many modern plants.

The vessels of corn, as seen in sections, are excellent examples since each vascular bundle of the stem contains two vessels which are exceptionally large and well developed (Fig. 6.26).

Many of the cell types which have been discussed can be seen in entirety in macerated tissues. Preparations of this sort are made by treating small segments of plant parts with strong acids which dissolve out the middle lamellae holding the cells together. The thickenings of wall layers and the open ends of vessel segments show up very clearly in such material.

The walls of vessels and tracheids become thick due to the increase of cellulose in the secondary walls and the impregnation of the entire wall with lignin. These thickenings absorb stains readily and cause the xylem cells to stand out prominently in stained sections. The thickenings are important factors in the mechanical strength of stems, particularly woody stems. A more basic function may be the resistance to collapse which is afforded by these thickenings under conditions of negative pressure in the water column due to high transpiration rates.

At least four patterns of secondary wall thickenings are recognizable although they frequently intergrade.

Annular thickenings consist of separate ringlike bands (Fig. 6.21).

Fig. 6.20. Drawing of a xylem vessel in which the vessel segments are evident. The disintegration of one of the cross walls is indicated.

of water. Tracheids may be observed to good advantage in cross and longitudinal sections of pine wood, which is composed largely of this type of cell (Figs. 6.19, 6.39).

Vessels are often larger in diameter than tracheids although it is difficult to tell them apart in cross sections. In lengthwise sections it may be observed

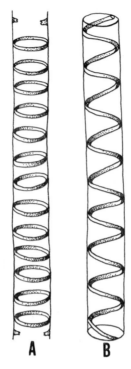

Fig. 6.21. Wall thickenings in protoxylem elements. A. Annular thickenings. B. Spiral thickenings.

uted thin spots which are called *pits* (Fig. 6.22).

Annular and spiral thickenings occur in elements of the earliest formed xylem (*protoxylem*). Their design permits the vessels and tracheids to elongate as the young plant parts grow in length. Scalariform and pitted thickenings occur in later formed xylem (*metaxylem*) cells which mature after the plant part has finished its lengthwise growth.

Simple pits, as noted above, are merely areas of the cell wall which do not develop secondary thickenings (Fig. 6.23). They are not holes in the wall since the primary wall is not perforated. *Bordered pits* are more complicated since the secondary wall partially overgrows the simple pit to form a dome-shaped structure with a tiny perforation in the middle (Fig. 6.23). The central portion of the primary wall between a pair of bordered pits develops a thickening, called a *torus,* which acts as a valve membrane. When the pressures in two adjacent xylem cells are not much different, the torus stays in the middle and water diffuses readily through the pit openings and the unthickened primary wall around the perimeter of the torus. But if there is a sudden change in the water pressure in one of the cells, the torus between each pit pair is pushed over in such

Spiral thickenings consist of spirally wound bands of secondary wall substance which resemble coiled springs (Fig. 6.21).

Scalariform thickenings consist of transversely disposed rings of secondary wall substance which are vertically connected by numerous short segments of the same material. The uniform distribution of both components creates a ladderlike effect (Fig. 6.22).

Pitted thickenings are, probably, the most advanced type, and the whole wall is thickened except for uniformly distrib-

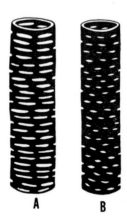

Fig. 6.22. Wall thickenings in metaxylem elements. A. Scalariform thickenings. B. Pitted thickenings.

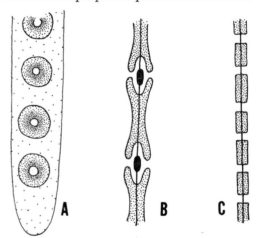

Fig. 6.23. Simple pits and bordered pits. A. Bordered pits as seen in the surface of a tracheid. B. Bordered pits as seen in a section of a tracheid wall. C. Pairs of simple pits in a cell wall section.

a way that it plugs the opening to the pit, thus slowing down water movement between the two cells. This neat and simple safety device may be observed clearly in sections of the tracheids of pine wood.

THE DIFFERENTIATION OF TISSUES IN PRIMITIVE VASCULAR PLANTS

It will be recalled from a previous discussion that the aerial portion of the plant body of a primitive vascular plant consisted of a branching, green stem system. The stem contained a central core of vascular tissue. The epidermis was cutinized and had stomates. Tissues underlying the epidermis were green and photosynthetic. Some further details of the differentiation of tissues in such a stem are included here as being significant in laying a ground-

work for a discussion of the tissues of higher plants (Fig. 6.24A and B).

The apical meristem of the primitive stem gave rise to a protoderm, a ground meristem, and a procambium strand. These, in turn, gave rise to the epidermis, the cortex, and the central core of vascular tissue.

In the cortex, three types of tissue are recognizable in sections of fossilized stems of such plants. The outer layer, next to the epidermis, was green and photosynthetic. Numerous air spaces existed between the green cells. Interior to the green cells were several layers of parenchyma which became thick-walled and lignified into sclerenchyma tissue. The innermost layer of the cortex was a highly specialized layer, one cell in thickness, which is known as

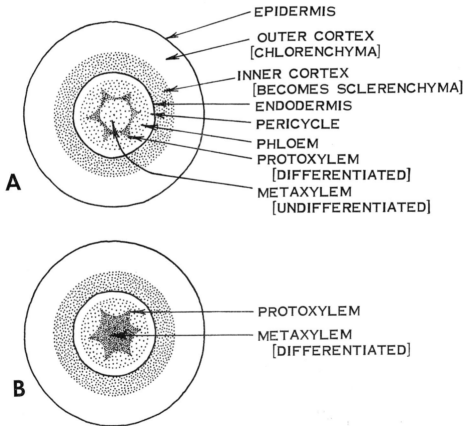

EPIDERMIS

OUTER CORTEX
[CHLORENCHYMA]

INNER CORTEX
[BECOMES SCLERENCHYMA]

ENDODERMIS

PERICYCLE

PHLOEM

PROTOXYLEM
[DIFFERENTIATED]

METAXYLEM
[UNDIFFERENTIATED]

A

PROTOXYLEM

METAXYLEM
[DIFFERENTIATED]

B

Fig. 6.24. Schematic representations of stem sections with exarch xylem, i.e., the protoxylem is outside the metaxylem indicating a centripetal direction of differentiation of the primary xylem. A. Early stage with only protoxylem differentiated. B. Later stage with both protoxylem and metaxylem differentiated. Compare Fig. 5.12.

the *endodermis*. The functional significance of this layer is discussed under the general heading of root structure.

All of the tissues inside the endodermis matured from the procambium which, in these plants, existed as a central strand of thin-walled, elongated cells. The innermost cells of this core matured as xylem while the cells immediately surrounding the xylem matured as phloem. The outermost cells of the procambium strand matured as parenchyma cells and comprise the *pericycle*. The functions of the pericycle in primitive stems remain obscure but, as will be seen, the pericycle in the roots of higher plants has at least three important functions.

The direction of differentiation of the xylem elements in the primitive stem is significant in discussions of the evolution of vascular plants. In these plants the outermost cells of the potential xylem tissue differentiated first to form a tissue known as the *protoxylem* (Fig. 6.24A).

Differentiation of the remaining central cells then proceeded inward (centripetally) with this later maturing tissue constituting the *metaxylem* (Fig. 6.24B). Commonly the metaxylem cells are larger in diameter than those of the protoxylem. It must be noted here that in some species not all of the central cells matured as conducting elements.

The stem which has been described is considered to have the most primitive type of arrangement of vascular tissues and this type is known as a *protostele*. In some living plants, including *Psilotum* and certain species of ferns and club mosses, the vascular tissue is arranged in this manner. In the flowering plants, however, the stem structure is of a more advanced type.

By way of comparison, the roots of all plants, including those of flowering plants, have vascular arrangements which are protostelic.

     *   *   *

In passing from a discussion of the vascular tissues of primitive vascular plants to those of the flowering plants it seems desirable to begin the discussion with the leaf. Presumably the vein system of the leaf has been modified from the stem system of primitive plants while the stem of the higher plants is a complex structure which lacks a counterpart among the stems of primitive plants.

DIFFERENTIATION OF VASCULAR TISSUES IN LEAVES

Sections of moderately large veins in corn leaves show xylem and phloem tissue which is almost diagrammatically clear and thus they make ideal subjects for microscopic study of these tissues. Furthermore, the veins are parallel and, in cross sections, they are oriented well for microscopic examination. In sections of young leaves in the epicotyl of a corn seedling a whole series of developmental stages in the differentiation and maturation of vascular tissue can be observed.

In the very young leaf the future vascular tissues exist as strands of cells which are all much alike. These are the procambium strands. The component cells are elongated, thin-walled, densely protoplasmic, and small in cross sectional area. The strands lie lengthwise in the leaf. Cells toward the lower epidermis eventually become phloem cells while those toward the upper epidermis become xylem.

The first cells in a procambium strand to differentiate are the ones along the lower and the upper surfaces of the strand (Fig. 6.25). The first formed phloem is called protophloem and consists of a few sieve tube elements. The first formed xylem is the protoxylem. It consists of a few very small vessels with annular and spiral thickenings. In the corn leaf, these first formed xylem vessels appear to be in a radial row as seen in cross section. The cells of the strand which lie between the protoxylem and the protophloem remain undifferentiated for some time although some of them increase in size and there may be a certain amount of cell division which increases the size of the strand.

Protoxylem and protophloem function

during the period when the leaf is enlarging even though they are stretched by this growth. Eventually they are destroyed or become functionless.

Once elongation of a part of the leaf is complete the metaphloem and metaxylem begin to differentiate. In the metaphloem there is one final division in each of the phloem mother cells. This is an unequal division which results in one member of a cell pair being larger than the other. The large one differentiates into a sieve tube element while the small one becomes a companion cell. Thus the metaphloem has the appearance of a mosaic in transverse sections (Figs. 6.18, 6.26).

In the major veins of corn, two of the metaxylem vessels become very large before they differentiate (Fig. 6.26). This growth is so pronounced that it results in the tearing apart of nearby tissue and a lengthwise space develops in the xylem. The two large metaxylem vessels and the smaller metaxylem vessels between them develop very thick, lignified walls with numerous pits as they differentiate.

The larger veins also become invested to varying degrees with a sheath of mechanical supporting tissue consisting of thick-walled, lignified *sclerenchyma fibers*. These larger veins are continuous with the vascular bundles of the stem which follow the same general pattern of maturation and differentiation (Fig. 6.27).

Many small veins lie parallel to and between the major veins. These smaller veins are surrounded by parenchyma instead of sclerenchyma. In addition, there are many short, cross-connecting veinlets occurring at right angles to the lengthwise veins (Figs. 5.4B, 5.6B).

TISSUE SYSTEMS OF THE CORN STEM

Corn leaves have a clasping leaf base which is wrapped around the stem and attached to the stem at a joint or node. At this point the major veins enter the stem, or to put it more precisely, the veins are connected to and continuous with the vascular bundles of the stem. In the nodal region, the vascular bundles are much twisted and form a complex network

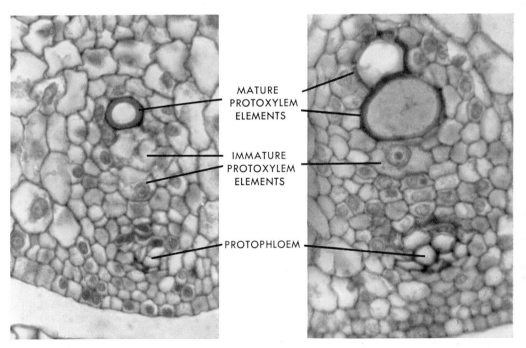

MATURE
PROTOXYLEM
ELEMENTS

IMMATURE
PROTOXYLEM
ELEMENTS

PROTOPHLOEM

Fig. 6.25. Differentiation of protoxylem and protophloem as seen in sections of immature veins in very young corn leaves.

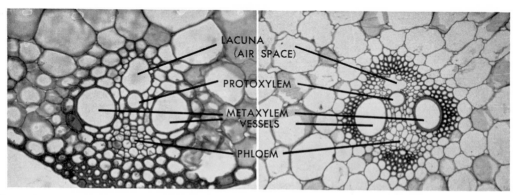

Fig. 6.26. Transverse section of a major vein in a nearly mature corn leaf. Note the two large metaxylem vessels and the lacuna (air space).

Fig. 6.27. Vascular bundle from a corn stem. Compare with Fig. 6.26.

which is difficult to trace. In the internodes of the stem, however, the vascular bundles extend lengthwise and are essentially parallel.

When cross sections of corn stems are cut in an internodal region it may be observed that the vascular bundles are scattered throughout a background tissue called *ground parenchyma* (Fig. 6.28). (Such an arrangement is characteristic of many monocot stems). It has been noted that the vascular bundles have much the same structure as the larger veins of the leaf. The phloem is oriented toward the outer surface while the xylem is oriented oppositely, toward the center of the stem. In mature stems especially, the bundles are heavily invested with sclerenchyma fibers (Figs. 6.27, 6.28).

THE TISSUES OF A HERBACEOUS DICOT STEM

A herbaceous stem is one which completes its growth during a single season and does not continue growth in the next season. In herbaceous dicot stems the vascular bundles are often arranged in a ring at some distance inward from the epidermis as opposed to the scattered arrangement of bundles in the corn stem (Figs. 6.29, 6.30, 6.31). The tissue between

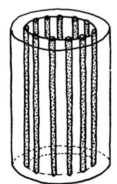

Fig. 6.29. Drawing showing the arrangement of vascular bundles in a ring as is characteristic of many herbaceous dicot stems.

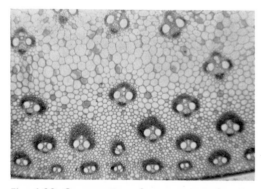

Fig. 6.28. Cross section of a corn stem showing the scattered distribution of vascular bundles in the ground parenchyma tissue.

the epidermis and the vascular bundles is the *cortex*. The tissue inside the vascular bundles is the *pith*. In cross sections of a young internode the recognizable tissues are epidermis, cortex, vascular bundles, and pith. The parenchyma tissue between two bundles is sometimes referred to as a *medullary ray*. In corn, by way of comparison, there is no obvious distinction between pith, cortex, and rays and the background tissue is referred to as ground parenchyma.

Not all herbaceous dicot stems have separate vascular bundles and the procambial tissue may be in the form of a hollow cylinder separating the cortex from the pith.

The first-formed xylem (protoxylem) differentiates from the innermost cells of the procambium strands and differentiation of the xylem proceeds outwards from these protoxylem points (rather than inwards as in the protostele). The first-formed phloem (protophloem) develops from the outer cells of the procambium strands and differentiation proceeds inwards. The xylem and phloem are thus opposite each other along a radial line through each bundle and differentiate towards each other (Fig. 6.30).

Differentiation of xylem and phloem elements proceeds until all, or most, of the procambium cells are converted. The

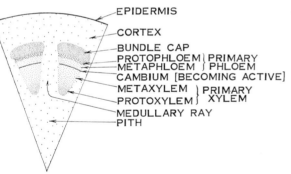

EPIDERMIS
CORTEX
BUNDLE CAP
PROTOPHLOEM ⎫ PRIMARY
METAPHLOEM ⎭ PHLOEM
CAMBIUM [BECOMING ACTIVE]
METAXYLEM ⎫ PRIMARY
PROTOXYLEM ⎭ XYLEM
MEDULLARY RAY
PITH

Fig. 6.30. Schematic drawing of a wedge-shaped section of a herbaceous dicot stem.

strand may then be called a *vascular bundle*. In some plants the procambium tissue becomes completely changed to xylem and phloem. In others the procambium cells lying between xylem and phloem may retain their meristematic abilities and give rise to a lateral meristem called the *vascular cambium*. This will be discussed later.

Most of the cells of the cortex are parenchyma. Frequently they contain chloroplasts and, in young stems especially, the cortex is a photosynthetic tissue. Many stems are angled in cross section. Supporting tissues, collenchyma or sclerenchyma or both, are found in the corners. Also the *bundle cap* outside each vascular bundle is made up of supporting tissue.

The pith tissue also consists mainly of parenchyma cells. In many mature stems the cells of the pith are dead or have been torn apart by stem enlargement. In young stems the turgidity of the pith cells (and the cortex cells) is largely responsible for mechanical support.

The *medullary rays* which connect the pith with the cortex consist of parenchyma cells. When the rays are broad as they are when the vascular bundles are spaced far apart, there is no sharp separation between cortex, rays, and pith. When the bundles are close together the rays appear as radially and longitudinally disposed sheets of cells. Very frequently, rays occur in the bundles as well as between them. These are referred to as *vascular rays* or as *xylem and phloem rays*. The ray cells possibly accomplish radial translocation between xylem and phloem and are also important in many plants as food storage tissues.

A careful distinction should be made between the epidermis of young stems and the cork tissue in the bark of older stems. The epidermis is a primary tissue which is developed from cells derived directly from the apical meristem. It consists of a single layer of cells which is cutinized and has stomates. Cork tissue is a secondary tissue formed by a cork-cambium, as will be discussed later. It displaces the epidermis when the stem enlarges beyond a certain size.

In summarizing the basic structure of the stem it should be noted that all the tissues which have been discussed in detail are *primary tissues*. This means that they have been formed from cells laid down in the stem tip. The primary tissues include epidermis, cortex, protophloem and metaphloem, protoxylem and metaxylem, pith, and rays.

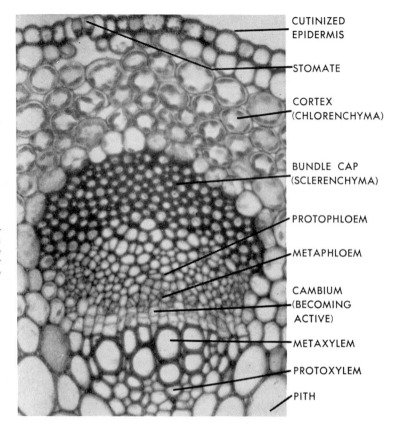

CUTINIZED
EPIDERMIS

STOMATE

CORTEX
(CHLORENCHYMA)

BUNDLE CAP
(SCLERENCHYMA)

PROTOPHLOEM

METAPHLOEM

CAMBIUM
(BECOMING
ACTIVE)

METAXYLEM

PROTOXYLEM

PITH

Fig. 6.31. Photomicrograph of a cross section of one vascular bundle from a herbaceous dicot stem, in this case, Alsike clover.

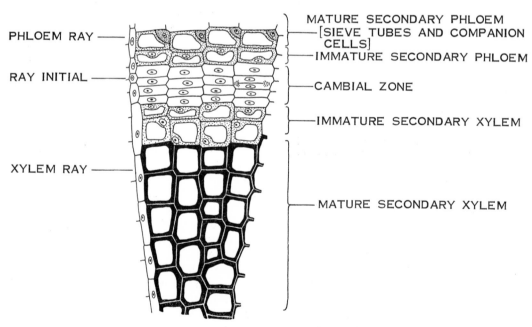

PHLOEM RAY

RAY INITIAL

XYLEM RAY

MATURE SECONDARY PHLOEM
[SIEVE TUBES AND COMPANION CELLS]
IMMATURE SECONDARY PHLOEM

CAMBIAL ZONE

IMMATURE SECONDARY XYLEM

MATURE SECONDARY XYLEM

Fig. 6.32. Schematic drawing of a portion of a section of a woody stem showing relation of cambium to secondary xylem and phloem.

CAMBIUM AND THE CONCEPT OF SECONDARY GROWTH

In the discussion of the maturation of tissues in the vascular bundle it was noted that, in many plants, a zone or layer of cells between the metaxylem and the metaphloem fails to differentiate and retains its meristematic nature. This layer is the *vascular cambium* and it is a lateral meristem. By division of its cells it gives rise to *secondary xylem* and *secondary phloem* (Figs. 6.32, 6.33). It should not be surprising that the cambium cells are able to grow and divide since they have immediate access to soluble organic foods in the phloem, and to water and inorganic chemicals in the xylem. Most of the divisions of the cambium are longitudinal and parallel to the outer surface of the plant. As a result, the daughter cells are produced in radial rows. When the division rate is high, the rows of undifferentiated daughter cells may be several cells in depth. Divisions may occur in more than one cell in each radial row but the greatest rate of division appears to occur in the middle of this cambial zone.

Differentiation of cells occurs at both the outer end and the inner end of each radial row in the cambial zone (Figs. 6.32, 6.33). The innermost cells become part of the xylem and the outermost cells become part of the phloem. The cambium may be a deep zone of tissue or may be reduced to a single layer when the differentiation rate catches up with the division rate.

In the above described manner the cambium is able to increase both the xylem and the phloem while remaining as a meristematic layer between them. The differentiating xylem cells increase in size considerably before maturing and this constantly forces both the cambium and the phloem outward. This process of expansion is resisted by the outer tissues of the stem and, as a result, cells in the cortex become greatly distorted. Also, the older, nonfunctional phloem cells become crushed. The cambium itself is under stress due to the increase in circumfer-

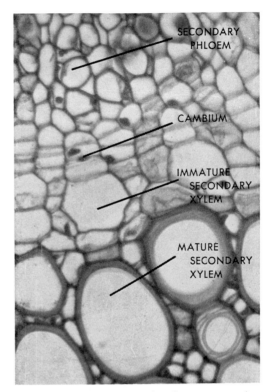

Fig. 6.33. Photomicrograph of a stem section showing cambium and immature xylem elements.

ence of the enlarging xylem mass inside it. This stretching is accommodated by periodic radial divisions of cambial initials which result in pairs of initials lying side by side where only single ones existed previously. Evidence of this can be seen in cross sections of stems by tracing a radial row of xylem cells outward to a point where it becomes two radial rows.

ORIGIN OF THE CORK CAMBIUM

With the increase in mass of secondary tissues, the epidermis is subjected to such pressures that it is eventually broken. Before this happens, another lateral meristem is formed which is capable of producing cork tissue. This is the *cork cambium* and it may form in the epidermis, in the cortex, or even in the parenchyma cells of the phloem (Fig. 6.34).

The divisions of the cork cambium are parallel to the surface of the stem. Radial

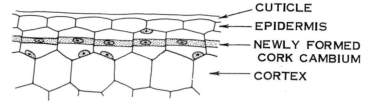

Fig. 6.34. Origin of the cork cambium in outer cells of the cortex.

CUTICLE
EPIDERMIS
NEWLY FORMED CORK CAMBIUM
CORTEX

rows of cells are formed in this way and most of them differentiate into *cork cells*. However, a limited number of cells within the cork cambium layer become *cork parenchyma*. The cork cells eventually die but before they do their walls become heavily impregnated with a fatty substance called *suberin* which gives cork its characteristic nature (Fig. 6.35). Such cells are the major component of the bark of woody stems.

SECONDARY GROWTH IN HERBACEOUS STEMS

In some herbaceous dicot stems, as in almost all monocot stems, there is little or no cambial activity and consequently no secondary growth. In others there is a limited amount of secondary growth due to a cambium within each bundle. In a third category, ray parenchyma cells between bundles revert to a meristematic condition and form an *interfascicular cambium* which is continuous with the cambium in the bundle. In this way a complete cylinder of cambium is formed. In those stems where the procambium tissue is a cylinder rather than a series of separate provascular strands, the cambium develops from the beginning as a continuous cylinder.

Differentiation of xylem cells results in the formation of vessels, tracheids, fibers, and parenchyma. In the newly formed phloem tissue, sieve tubes, companion cells, fibers, and parenchyma may be differentiated. As noted previously, each sieve tube-companion cell pair results from a final division of one of the cells in the immature phloem tissue.

The vascular rays are continuous from xylem to phloem across the cambium. They are extended in both directions by cells of the cambium called *ray initials* (Fig. 6.33). Periodically, the number of rays is increased by conversion of cambial cells which had been producing vascular elements into ray initials. Observation of cross sections of stems shows many rays of various lengths with the shortest rays being the newest.

SECONDARY GROWTH IN WOODY STEMS

The evolutionary history of seed plants indicates clearly that woody stems evolved before herbaceous stems. For purely peda-

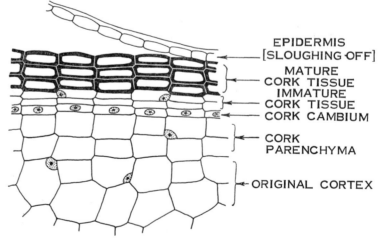

Fig. 6.35. Positional relationships of cork, cork cambium, cork parenchyma, epidermis, and cortex.

EPIDERMIS [SLOUGHING OFF]
MATURE CORK TISSUE
IMMATURE CORK TISSUE
CORK CAMBIUM
CORK PARENCHYMA
ORIGINAL CORTEX

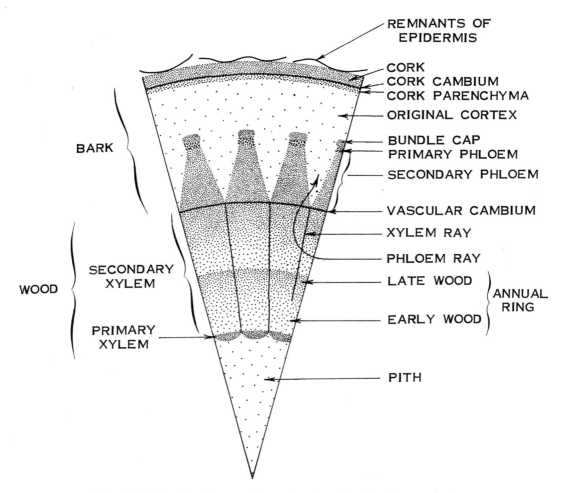

Fig. 6.36. Schematic diagram of a wedge-shaped section of a woody stem.

gogical reasons, it is preferable to reverse the natural order and discuss the apparently simple monocot stem and herbaceous dicot stem before the woody stem.

Very early in the first season's growth of a woody twig before any significant amount of secondary growth has occurred, the distribution of tissues is very similar to that of a herbaceous dicot stem. As secondary growth proceeds, however, all the primary tissues outside the cambium become distorted or lost. The only primary tissues which are not displaced are the primary xylem and the pith.

A woody stem may be divided into three major zones, the *wood*, the *bark*, and the *cambium*. The various tissues in each of

these are listed below in order as they occur from the outside to the inside of a stem in which secondary growth has begun (Figs. 6.36, 6.37, 6.38):

BARK
Broken remains of old epidermis
Cork
Cork cambium
Cork parenchyma
Remains of original cortex
Bundle cap
Primary phloem (if not already crushed)
Older secondary phloem
Younger secondary phloem

CAMBIUM

WOOD
{
Younger secondary xylem
Older secondary xylem
Primary xylem (metaxylem and protoxylem)
Pith
}

The vascular rays extend from xylem to phloem across the cambium, but in the progressively older and outermost phloem the rays are stretched laterally with the increasing circumference of the stem. Thus they appear as wedges with the narrowest point of the wedge touching the cambium zone.

In many trees, the bark is characterized by deep fissures which are natural results of the increasing girth of the stem. The bark is always under lateral tension

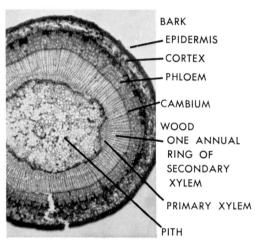

BARK
EPIDERMIS
CORTEX
PHLOEM
CAMBIUM
WOOD
ONE ANNUAL RING OF SECONDARY XYLEM
PRIMARY XYLEM
PITH

Fig. 6.37. Transverse section of a one year old basswood twig.

due to internal expansion pressures and this tension is relieved periodically by the formation of lengthwise splits which extend deeply into the living tissues of the bark. Each time this happens a new cork cambium layer develops internally to the fissure.

Cross sections of basswood twigs (Figs. 6.37, 6.38) are often used to illustrate the tissues of woody plants. In the phloem of this plant, small strands of sieve tubes and companion cells are surrounded by phloem fibers. This arrangement prevents much of the crushing of functional phloem which results from expansion

pressures. An examination of freehand sections of living basswood twigs is of considerable value as an aid to the interpretation of the standard prepared slides because there is a sharp color contrast between the brilliant white of the phloem fibers and the duller colors of the cortex and phloem rays.

In most trees of temperate regions there is a line of demarcation between successive annual increments of secondary wood and, as is widely known, the age of a tree can be determined by counting annual rings (Figs. 6.36, 6.38, 6.39, 6.41). With microscopic examination of wood sections it may be noted that the innermost cells of each annual ring are larger and thinner walled than the outer cells of the same ring. The inner portion is the *early wood* which is formed when the available supplies of water are high and the transpiration rate is low. The outer portion of an annual ring is the *late wood* formed when the leaves are fully out and the transpiration rate is high enough to reduce the availability of water to growing cells. The contrast between the late wood of one year and the early wood of the following year accounts for the apparent demarcation between successive annual rings.

Early wood and late wood are commonly termed spring wood and summer wood but these terms are somewhat inappropriate since the factors which operate to induce the formation of smaller, thicker-walled cells are in operation before the official calendar start of summer.

As a tree gets older, the central portion of the wood gradually becomes inactive in conduction. Cellular bubbles or *tyloses* grow from the living xylem parenchyma cells into the lumens (openings) of the vessels and tracheids (Fig. 6.40). Air penetrates into the tissue and oxidation of organic waste materials turns the wood dark. This nonfunctional xylem is called *heartwood* in contrast to the functional xylem which is the *sapwood*. There is no constant conversion rate of sapwood into heartwood but it gradually increases from year to year. The heartwood has no other

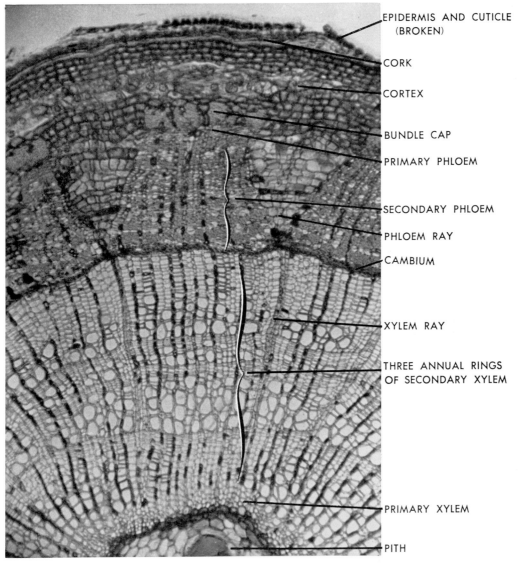

EPIDERMIS AND CUTICLE
(BROKEN)

CORK

CORTEX

BUNDLE CAP

PRIMARY PHLOEM

SECONDARY PHLOEM

PHLOEM RAY

CAMBIUM

XYLEM RAY

THREE ANNUAL RINGS
OF SECONDARY XYLEM

PRIMARY XYLEM

PITH

Fig. 6.38. Portion of a transverse section of a three year old basswood twig for comparison with Fig. 6.36.

function than its contribution to the mechanical strength of a tree. In many trees it is highly prized as a source of wood for furniture (Fig. 6.41).

THE NATURE OF THE ROOT

The growth of the root system and the growth of the shoot system are mutually interdependent. The root system is nonphotosynthetic and must depend on the aerial parts of the plant for supplies of organic food. On the other hand, stems and leaves require water and inorganic chemicals from the soil which must be absorbed and transported by the roots. The extent of the root system is seldom realized but, often, it is more spread out in space than is the stem system. The number of branch roots is very large and the health of a plant depends a great deal on the continued, active growth of these young roots. Such growth is, primarily, the result of two related activities: (1) the increase in number of cells due to cell

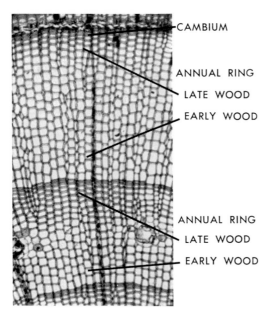

CAMBIUM

ANNUAL RING

LATE WOOD

EARLY WOOD

ANNUAL RING

LATE WOOD

EARLY WOOD

Fig. 6.39. Transverse section of a pine stem illustrating the contrast between late wood and early wood which makes the annual rings evident.

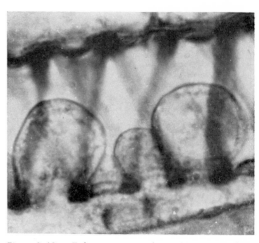

Fig. 6.40. Tyloses expanding into a xylem vessel.

Fig. 6.41. Transverse section of a tree trunk showing annual rings, xylem rays, and the color contrast between heartwood (dark) and sapwood (light).

Fig. 6.42. Root tips covered by root caps.

divisions in the root tip, and (2) the enlargement of cells in the region immediately behind the root meristem.

The tip of a root is covered by a conical mass of cells which are held together very loosely. This is the *root cap* (Fig. 6.42) and portions of it may extend a considerable distance back along the root. New root cap cells are formed constantly in the inner portion of the cap. Meanwhile the walls of the outer root cap cells become gelatinous and slough off in the soil. This sacrifice results in a slippery layer which protects the root tip from mechanical injury as it is forced through the soil.

Inside the root cap there is a meristematic region similar to that of a stem tip. A small group of cells in the apical meristem undergo mitosis at a relatively slow rate. However, the cells on the periphery of this promeristem begin to divide more rapidly. The planes of cell division of these cells are almost always perpendicular to the long axis of the root and, as a result, the root is made up of parallel, longitudinal rows of cells. There are no lateral primordia on the root tip and, as is obvious, the root tip does not give rise to leaves (Fig. 6.43).

As cells in the longitudinal rows become more and more remote from the tip the division rate slows down and eventually stops altogether. When cell division stops in these cells, they begin to absorb water rapidly and increase in size. The major dimensional increase is lengthwise, as may be observed by tracing a column of cells back from the tip and noting the size changes. In roots this region of cell elongation is not as extensive as it is in stems, seldom being more than 2 or 3 millimeters long. The increase in length results in a pushing of the root tip through the soil since the older parts of the root are firmly anchored in the soil and are not easily displaced.

Once any cell has finished elongating it begins to change in other ways until, eventually, it assumes its mature condition. Different cell types vary in the time and method of differentiation and there is no sharp boundary between the region of differentiation and the preceding one.

One of the important differentiation processes occurs in the epidermal cells. Some of them form long, tubular outgrowths called *root hairs*. They begin as small swellings in the epidermal cell walls but may reach a final length of several millimeters. Each root hair is, thus, an outgrowth of the epidermal cell from which it arises (Fig. 6.44).

Absorption by Roots

The number of root hairs is vast and they effectively increase the total surface area of root tissue in contact with the soil. This permits a more efficient intake of water and dissolved chemicals from the soil.

In order for all parts of the root, especially root hairs, to grow vigorously it is necessary that several environmental factors be properly balanced. The temperature of the soil must be suitable. The soil must be well aerated since the living cells of most roots require abundant supplies of oxygen for respiration. There must be adequate soil water but not enough to eliminate the air in the soil. Constant supplies of organic food must be made available by transport from the leaves.

The entrance of water into the root hairs is basically a diffusion phenomenon (osmosis). The relative water concentration inside the root hairs is less than that of the soil solution and the diffusion gradient is inwards. The effect of the transpiration pull on the water column in the xylem possibly increases the steepness of the diffusion gradient and thus increases the rate of water uptake.

The entrance of chemical substances (other than water) from the soil into the roots is a more complex matter involving several related phenomena. Entrance by simple diffusion of molecules or ions in solution undoubtedly occurs but it is not considered to be of major importance by most authorities.

Direct ion exchange is the term applied to situations in which ions of equivalent electrical charges are traded between cells and soil particles. Root hairs grow in

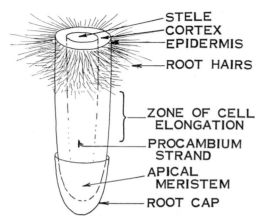

Fig. 6.43. Schematic representation of the nature of a root tip.

1. The outer layer of cells is the epidermis which matures from a protoderm (as in stems and leaves).
2. The inner core is made up of small elongated cells with dense protoplasm. This is destined to become the vascular cylinder, or stele. At this stage it is a procambium strand.
3. The wide zone of more or less nonspecialized cells between the epidermis and the future stele is the cortex which matures from the ground meristem.

Epidermal cells do not become cutinized as they do in stems and leaves. Furthermore, many of them give rise to root hairs as noted previously. When the root hairs grow old and die, they collapse and the epidermis ceases to be a functional tissue.

The cells of the root cortex remain relatively thin-walled and have a considerable volume due to absorption of water. Often

between soil particles and often become tightly adherent to them. This makes it possible for ion exchanges to occur without the substances actually diffusing in solution. Obviously, this brief statement barely touches on a concept which has had a great influence on modern soil management practices. The successful use of anhydrous ammonia as a fertilizer is largely dependent on the principle of ion exchange.

Active solute absorption is a term used to label a situation in which certain chemical ions are accumulated inside cells in far greater concentration than they occur in the soil solution. Such accumulations indicate movement of the ions against the normal direction of the diffusion gradient. Undoubtedly this accumulation requires the expenditure of energy. Since it has been demonstrated that active solute absorption occurs only in healthy, vigorous roots with high respiration rates, it has been postulated that some of the energy released by respiration is utilized in this way.

Differentiation of Root Tissues

In the region of differentiation various cells begin to take on characteristics of their mature conditions. In cross sections through this region, three concentric zones may be recognized (Fig. 6.45):

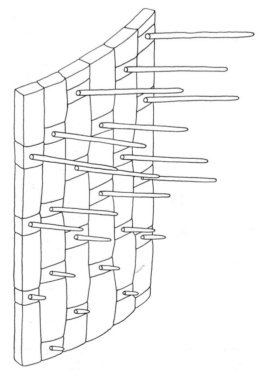

Fig. 6.44. Origin of root hairs from epidermal cells of a root.

they accumulate reserve foods. In many roots they comprise the largest volume of the root. Inward moving water and dissolved substances diffuse from cell to cell in the cortex in their passage toward the stele.

The innermost layer of cells in the cortex, immediately in contact with the stele,

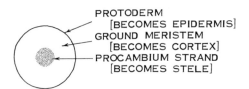

PROTODERM
  [BECOMES EPIDERMIS]
GROUND MERISTEM
  [BECOMES CORTEX]
PROCAMBIUM STRAND
  [BECOMES STELE]

Fig. 6.45. Transverse section of a root tip before differentiation of vascular tissues in the procambium strand.

is called the *endodermis*. Actually the endodermis is a single-layered cylinder of cells which separates the rest of the cortex from the stele (Figs. 6.46, 6.49, 6.51). A peripheral band in the radial walls of each endodermal cell becomes impregnated with a substance, possibly like suberin, which is relatively impermeable to water. This is called the *Casparian strip* (Fig. 6.50). Any substances which enter or leave the stele must pass through the living protoplasm of the endodermal cells since the Casparian strips bar intercellular radial movements. This insures that the whole of the endodermis functions as one continuous differentially permeable membrane surrounding the stele. In older parts of the root the endodermal cells may become completely thickened except for a few passage cells opposite the xylem.

The cells of the procambium strand grow in length but do not become laterally stretched as do cortex cells. They con-

tinue to be densely protoplasmic. At first all of these cells appear alike but as they begin to mature and differentiate into the vascular cylinder, several different tissue systems become evident.

The xylem of mature roots appears, in cross section, as a star-shaped core of thick-walled empty cells. The differentiation of protoxylem cells begins at the points of the star and progresses inward. In sections of young roots, mature protoxylem may be evident only at the points of the star while the inner cells are still living and thin-walled (Figs. 6.46, 6.48). Later, all of the cells in the center become differentiated into mature, metaxylem cells (Figs. 6.47, 6.49).

Exceptions exist in certain thick roots, such as corn prop roots and asparagus roots, in which a number of thin-walled, nonxylem cells remain in the center. This tissue resembles the pith tissue of stems (Fig. 6.51).

Root xylem may contain both vessels and tracheids. Parenchyma tissue is more extensive in roots than in stems and, usually, there are no conspicuous amounts of xylem fibers.

Most of the cells which lie in small masses between the points of the xylem star, and thus alternate with them, become differentiated into phloem tissue. This arrangement of primary xylem and primary phloem in an alternating fashion is one of the distinguishing differences between root anatomy and the anatomy of stems. Cells in the phloem remain thin-walled and do not stain as strikingly as do xylem cells but with practice they are readily recognized. (Figs. 6.47, 6.49).

The outermost layer or layers of cells of the vascular cylinder is the *pericycle*.

Fig. 6.46. Transverse section of a root in which some differentiation of tissues has occurred.

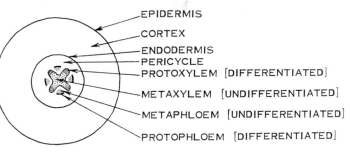

EPIDERMIS
CORTEX
ENDODERMIS
PERICYCLE
PROTOXYLEM [DIFFERENTIATED]
METAXYLEM [UNDIFFERENTIATED]
METAPHLOEM [UNDIFFERENTIATED]
PROTOPHLOEM [DIFFERENTIATED]

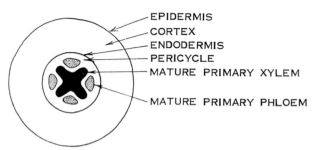

Fig. 6.47. Transverse section of a root after differentiation of all primary tissues has been completed.

It is in immediate contact with the endodermis to the outside and with the xylem and phloem on the inside. This seemingly insignificant tissue has three important functions:

1. The apical meristem of lateral roots forms in the pericycle opposite the points of the xylem star. When lateral roots begin to develop they force their way outward through the cortex (Fig. 6.52).

2. Part of the vascular cambium forms in the pericycle. This will be discussed further below.

3. The cork cambium also forms in the pericycle. This gives rise to a layer of cork cells similar to that in stems. When the cork is formed, all the tissues exterior to it, (endodermis, cortex, and epidermis) are sloughed off.

It should be noted that pericycle and

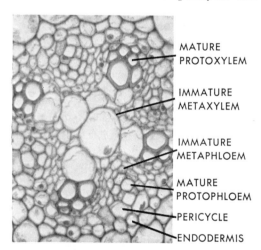

Fig. 6.48. Photomicrograph of the central portion of a buttercup root at a stage similar to Fig. 6.46. Note the differentiated protoxylem and the undifferentiated metaxylem.

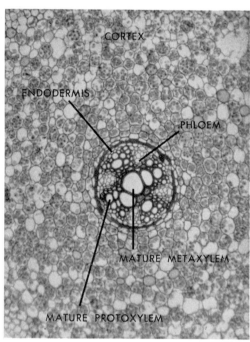

Fig. 6.49. Photomicrograph of a transverse section of a buttercup root at a stage similar to Fig. 6.47. Note especially the fully matured metaxylem, the endodermis, and the stored food in the cortex cells. The magnification is lower than that in Fig. 6.48.

endodermis may occur, also, in stems. However, they are very difficult to recognize and since they have no apparent special functions in stems, they are generally ignored in elementary treatments of stem structure.

Secondary Growth in Roots

All the tissues which grow and mature from cells laid down by meristematic activity in the apical meristem are called primary tissues, or tissues of primary origin. These include the root cap, epidermis, cortex, endodermis, pericycle, primary xylem, and primary phloem. As in

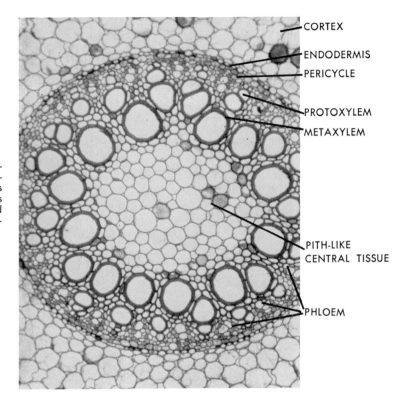

CORTEX
ENDODERMIS
PERICYCLE
PROTOXYLEM
METAXYLEM
PITH-LIKE CENTRAL TISSUE
PHLOEM

Fig. 6.51. Transverse section of the central portion of an asparagus root. Note the numerous protoxylem points and the well-defined endodermis.

stems, secondary tissues of dicot roots are formed by the activity of lateral meristems. One of these is the vascular cambium which is, at first, a lobed cylinder lying inside the phloem and outside the protoxylem points (Fig. 6.53). Its formation is due to the fact that residual procambium cells between the xylem and

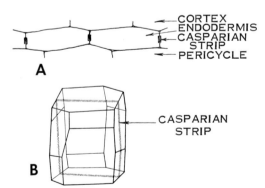

CORTEX
ENDODERMIS
CASPARIAN STRIP
PERICYCLE

A

CASPARIAN STRIP

B

Fig. 6.50. Nature of the endodermis. A. Transverse section of an endodermis showing position of Casparian strips in radial walls. B. Three-dimensional view of a single cell of the endodermis showing the Casparian strip as a peripheral band in the radial walls.

phloem, as well as the pericycle cells outside the xylem points, retain an ability to become meristematic. Usually the successive divisions of cambial initials are parallel to the outside of the root, resulting in the formation of radial rows of cells. The innermost cells of the cambial zone become secondary xylem and the outermost ones become secondary phloem while the layers in between remain as the cambium. The original shape of the cambium is lobed but, eventually, it becomes more or less uniformly cylindrical (Fig. 6.54). The essential details of cambial activity have been discussed previously.

Xylem tissue is never displaced in space by cambial activity but the phloem is continually pushed outward. Primary phloem and the older secondary phloem are crushed by this expansion and disappear. Also, as noted above the endodermis, cortex, and epidermis are sloughed off when the cork tissue is formed (Fig. 6.54).

As a root enlarges it comes to be more and more like a stem. Only the organiza-

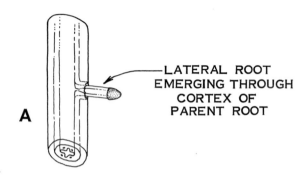

LATERAL ROOT
EMERGING THROUGH
CORTEX OF
PARENT ROOT

A

Fig. 6.52. Origin of lateral roots. A. Lateral root emerging through the cortex. B. Root primordium forming in the pericycle.

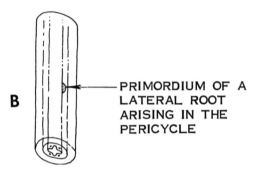

B

PRIMORDIUM OF A
LATERAL ROOT
ARISING IN THE
PERICYCLE

tion of the primary xylem remains as a clue to the original differences between young roots and stems.

The vascular rays in older roots are broader than they are in stems and, furthermore, there may be a much more extensive development of cork parenchyma.

Many kinds of plants, including almost all monocots, do not have the ability to form cambial tissues and thus their roots consist of primary tissues only.

TYPES OF ROOT SYSTEMS

When the primary root develops strongly and dominates the root system it is referred to as a tap root (Fig. 6.55).

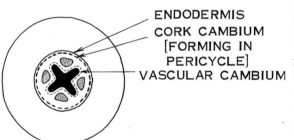

ENDODERMIS
CORK CAMBIUM
[FORMING IN
PERICYCLE]
VASCULAR CAMBIUM

Fig. 6.53. Transverse section of a root showing position of newly formed cambium and cork cambium.

Carrots, beets, turnips, etc., are examples of economically important tap roots in which large quantities of food are stored. The tap roots of dandelions whose tenacity in resisting removal from lawns makes them a well known example to home owners.

If the primary root dies, or does not become the dominant root several other roots may develop resulting in a fibrous root system (Fig. 6.56). This type of root system is well illustrated by cereal grains and other grass plants. In a few instances such as sweet potatoes, portions of the fibrous roots may become fleshy storage organs.

Root systems do not always arise by branching of the primary root. The seminal roots of corn develop from the embryo axis. The prop roots of corn arise at the basal nodes of the stem. Many plants may be rooted by placing cuttings or slips in the right environment. Such plants develop adventitious roots at the base of the cut stem.

SUMMARY OF ROOT FUNCTIONS

The main functions of the root system are considered to be *anchorage, storage of food, absorption,* and *conduction.*

The aerial parts of a plant are subjected to severe stresses due to the combined action of wind and gravity; a familiar example of such stress is the wild tossing of tree branches during a storm. Roots form a widespread network in the soil which effectively serves to anchor the plant so that the stem may grow erect.

The storage of food by roots has important economic aspects since the roots of carrots, turnips, sugar beets, garden beets, radishes, sweet potatoes, etc., are widely used in the human diet. As far as the plants are concerned the food stored in underground protected structures such as storage roots is utilized to promote rapid growth, flowering, and fruit development in a succeeding year.

A consideration of absorption by roots is a matter of prime economic as well as biological significance. Previously, in the discussion of root hairs, the entrance of water and inorganic chemicals into roots was outlined as was the importance of a healthy, vigorously growing root system to normal growth of the shoot.

ROOT-SOIL RELATIONSHIPS

The maintenance of proper soil conditions for good root growth is one of the primary aims of agriculture. Good soil structure permits easy entrance of water yet allows for drainage of excess amounts. In addition to holding water, good soil structure must allow for air circulation. Soils must have sufficient chemical substances for normal growth but these should be released slowly so that they are not rapidly leached out of the soil in drainage water. They must have abundant micro-organisms which are vital to the maintenance of soil fertility, yet should not be heavily infested with root-destroying organisms. In other words, a good soil has a delicately balanced and exceedingly complex mixture of physical, chemical, and biological factors. At the elementary level these can be considered only in brief form.

With the major exceptions of carbon dioxide and gaseous oxygen, all the essential chemicals for plant growth enter the plant through the roots from the soil. There are at least fourteen chemical elements required for plant growth. They are listed below with some indication of their major functions in metabolism.

Nitrogen (N) is an essential part of such compounds as amino acids, nucleic acids, and chlorophyll.

Phosphorus (P) is an essential part of nucleic acids. It also plays an important role in many enzyme reactions and in energy transfers.

Sulphur (S) is an essential part of some amino acids and numerous other important metabolic compounds.

Potassium (K) does not become bound in specific compounds. It remains mobile and enters into many essential reactions.

Calcium (Ca) forms part of the pectic compounds which cement plant cells together and also plays an important role in the functioning of cell membranes.

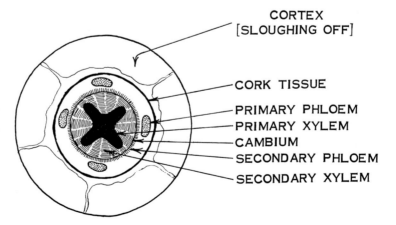

Fig. 6.54. Arrangement of primary and secondary tissues in a root after considerable cambial activity has taken place.

CORTEX [SLOUGHING OFF]

CORK TISSUE
PRIMARY PHLOEM
PRIMARY XYLEM
CAMBIUM
SECONDARY PHLOEM
SECONDARY XYLEM

Fig. 6.55. A tap root system.

on animals which feed on the plants. Others have no serious effects. Man has learned to use certain plants as collectors of specific chemicals. For example, iodine has been recovered from the cells of seaweeds which accumulated the iodine from ocean waters.

The evident relationship between roots and the soil makes a brief consideration of soil composition necessary. Rock particles occur in various sizes. The smallest particles are of colloidal size and have a special significance because of their enormous total surface area. Much of the inorganic chemical substance in the soil is bound tightly to the soil particles by adhesive forces. As noted previously, root hairs come into contact with the soil particles and, due to the large total surface areas involved, rapid absorption is made possible by direct ion exchange. Careless management of soil may result in the destruction of good soil structure and the concomitant decrease in the total surface area available to the root hairs.

Good soil normally contains a large

Magnesium (Mg) is an essential part of the chlorophyll molecule. It also bears an intricate relationship to calcium in membrane functions.

Iron (Fe) is not a part of the chlorophyll molecule but is essential to chlorophyll formation. Also, it plays an important role in oxidative enzyme systems and has a relationship to the availability of phosphorus.

Manganese (Mn), boron (B), copper (Cu), zinc (Zn), and molybdenum (Mb) are essential elements required in minute quantities. In many cases, these so-called micro-nutrients act catalytically as parts of enzyme systems. Other micro-nutrient elements may be added to this list as research proceeds in this field.

Carbon (C), hydrogen (H), and oxygen (O) enter into the activities of living matter in so many ways that no attempt to list them will be made.

Many nonessential chemical elements enter plants and accumulate. Some of them may have toxic effects on the plants themselves or, as in the case of selenium,

Fig. 6.56. A fibrous root system.

percentage of partially decayed organic matter called *humus* which is important in the maintenance of soil structure.

Microscopic examination of any fertile soil reveals a vast array of minute plants and animals which enter into complex relationships with each other, with the soil, and with plant roots. The source of food for most of them is the humus although some of them obtain their energy in other ways. Some of them are destructive in cultivated land but most of them are beneficial for they bring about a release of essential chemical elements bound up in the humus. It is apparent that biological processes in the soil are not separable from physical and chemical ones.

Carbon is locked up in organic matter by photosynthesis. When organic matter is burned or respired carbon is returned to the air as carbon dioxide. The supply of this gas in the air is essential to the continuance of all familiar forms of life on this planet since it is a raw material of photosynthesis. Although carbon dioxide is returned to the air in many ways, the most significant source is the respiration of the organisms of decay in the soil living on the dead organic matter of the soil.

Some of the carbon dioxide goes into solution to form a weak acid that has a "weathering effect" on soil particles. This is important in the gradual release of chemical elements in forms available to plant roots.

Some of the organic compounds in the soil, loosely referred to as humic acids, help to maintain other ions in solution. Iron often tends to form insoluble and thus unavailable chemical unions unless some of these complex organic acids are present in the soil.

Mycorrhizal relationships between soil fungi and roots are vital to the successful growth of some plants. In this type of relationship, fungus threads penetrate into, or between, the cells of the root. They may obtain all or a part of their nutrition from the root and, in return,

serve in a similar capacity to that of the root hairs. Mycorrhizae are found often in plants like orchids, heaths, and gymnosperms growing in acid soil, but they are not especially important to midwestern crop plants.

THE CONCEPT OF GROWTH

In the life cycle of all plants there are stages when the future plant body consists of but a single cell. One of these stages is the zygote and the diploid plant body or sporphyte develops from this single cell. As has been emphasized, the major subdivisions of this growth process are cell division including both mitosis and cytoplasmic division, cell enlargement, and cell differentiation.

Since all the cells in a plant are derived from the zygote they all have, theoretically, the same inherent potentialities, i.e., they all contain the same numbers and kinds of chromosomes and genes. Why then should one cell become a palisade parenchyma cell while another becomes a root hair when both are potentially alike? Why should one cell in a procambium strand become a xylem vessel while another, just a few microns away, becomes a sieve tube element? Why should a mature parenchyma cell in the cortex of a stem suddenly revert to the meristematic condition and form a cork cambium cell?

This general topic was discussed briefly in a preceding chapter in which the nature of chromosomes and genes was considered. Several questions similar to the above were raised and a conclusion was reached that the position of a particular cell in a mass of similar cells had a definite effect on its future development.

The shapes of cells can be cited as a case in point. Individual cells, free of restraint, tend to become spheres. Cells in masses, however, exert pressure against each other and become polyhedral rather than spherical. Cells in an apical meristem, for instance, have an average of fourteen faces per cell. Each face represents a contact with a neighboring cell. Immediately following a cell division, each of the two daughter cells has fewer than fourteen faces but, during the succeeding interphase, the number of faces gradually increases to more than fourteen because of divisions in neighboring cells (Fig. 6.57).

The walls of meristematic cells are not rigid and are subject to surface tension adjustments. New cell walls often contact existing walls at right angles. Such angles, however, are not stable in a system affected by surface tensions and they soon become readjusted to angles which are stable.

It is evident, therefore, that the shape of a particular cell in a meristem is subject to constant change due to division in neighboring cells and readjustments due to surface tensions, as well as to its own growth.

The position of the epidermal cells as the outermost layer of cells places them in an environment different from all other cells in the plant. Their direct exposure to the environment apparently fosters the chemical changes which result in the formation of the cuticle in leaves and stems.

The position of the cambium between a source of food in the phloem and a source of water and chemicals in the xylem, undoubtedly facilitates its function as a meristem.

Something about the position of an otherwise normal cell in the young ovule affects its nutrition in such a way that it becomes a megaspore mother cell and ultimately undergoes meiosis.

The supplies of food, oxygen, and water available to the epidermal cells of roots are undoubtedly affected by their position and these are important factors in the characteristic elongation of root hairs.

These, and numerous other examples which could be cited, indicate that the position of a cell in a mass of other cells has an effect on its immediate microenvironment. The relative availability of organic foods, water, oxygen, inorganic salts, etc., are all affected by position. Sometimes position also affects the ability of a cell to get rid of the products of its

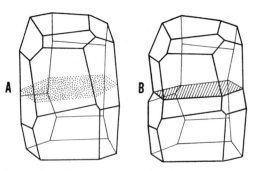

Fig. 6.57. Three-dimensional, schematic representation of the division process in a cell of an apical meristem. Based on the work of Prof. E. B. Matzke. A. Position of the cell plate as it is formed during cell division. B. Readjustment of newly formed cross wall and adjacent walls after completion of cell division.

own metabolism. The accumulation of some of these products is known to have an important effect on the ultimate nature of the cell.

It is known further that chemical substances produced in one part of a plant may influence the growth of other parts. A classical example of such an effect is the inhibition of the lowermost buds on a twig by substances transported downward from the buds above. This phenomenon is termed *apical dominance* and it plays an important part in the normal growth habits of plants. An understanding of apical dominance makes possible a certain degree of control over plant growth habits. Certain varieties of *Chrysanthemum*, for example, are most desirable if they are bushy. To achieve this aim the growth of branches of the main shoot is stimulated by pinching out the terminal bud, thus releasing the lateral buds from their normal inhibition.

The chemical substances which affect growth in such fashion are often called plant hormones or *auxins*. One of them has been isolated and identified as the relatively simple organic chemical, indoleacetic acid. The original discovery of this compound in plants stimulated a vast amount of research with both natural and synthetic growth regulating substances. A very significant result of this research was the discovery that certain of the synthetic compounds, when applied in excess, would kill many plants. One of the most notable of these compounds, which is widely known as 2-4-D, selectively kills dandelions and many other broad-leaved weeds while having no permanent effect on lawn grasses if applied in proper concentrations.

Another interesting aspect of the research program with growth regulating substances has been the investigation of their relation to changes in apical meristems as they shift from leaf production to flower production. In many plants there is a direct relationship between the length of days and flowering. Some plants flower when the days are short, others when the days are long. Still others are indeterminate. The relationship between the duration of days and nights which induces flowering is called the *photoperiod*.

It is quite possible that light has an effect on the production or distribution of growth substances and, in this way, influences the changes which lead to flowering. There is, also, a considerable body of evidence suggesting that specific flower inducing hormones may be involved.

Growth substances apparently are controlling factors in the upward growth of stems and the downward growth of roots. The production of these substances seems to be associated with new cell formation in meristems and they are known to be transported away from such meristematic regions. Neither the actual pathway nor the mechanism of movement is known but it is evident that the movement is affected by both light and gravity.

If a stem is held in a horizontal position, the growth substances accumulate along the lowermost side and stimulate the stem to grow more rapidly on that side than on the upper. This causes a stem to bend upward.

In roots, the effect of gravity is similar but the reaction is reversed. The accumulation of excess growth substances on the lower side of a root held horizontally inhibits the elongation of cells on the lower side. Cells on the upper side continue to grow at a normal, or possibly an accelerated rate, and thus the root bends downward.

When light shines on a stem from only one side it is known that the growth substances on the shaded side accumulate in excess of those on the lighted side. The shaded side is stimulated to grow more rapidly than the lighted side and the stem bends toward the light.

Explanations such as these which are based on scientific evidence are more acceptable explanations of the behavior of stems and roots than are the popular fallacies that the stems are reaching for light while the roots are reaching for water.

However, it is not yet known how it is that light and gravity affect the distribution of the growth substances. Nor is it known exactly how they affect the growth of plant cells. In a given cell there is a balance between the tendency of the protoplast to swell under the influence of osmotic absorption of water and the resistance of the cell wall to expansion. The growth substances might increase the first or decrease the second since either event would shift the balance toward greater cell enlargement.

Growth responses such as those which have been described are *tropisms*. The response to gravity is called *geotropism*. (Stems are negatively geotropic, while roots are positively geotropic.) The response to light is called *phototropism*.

In addition to the use of growth regulating substances as weed killers there are many other interesting applications of these compounds. For example, it was discovered early that if cuttings or slips are soaked in dilute solutions of indoleacetic acid before being placed in propagating benches they develop roots more rapidly and in larger numbers. The related chemical, indolebutyric acid, is even more effective in this regard and is widely used by commercial horticulturalists.

The loss of fruit from orchard trees by premature fruit drop has long been a problem to orchardists. Fruit fall is usually due to the formation of an abscission layer across the base of the stalk. Following the discovery that certain growth regulating substances such as napthaleneacetic acid prevent the formation of this layer it has become more or less standard practice to spray orchards with them.

Similarly, the use of such sprays is useful in preventing the sprouting of potatoes in storage. This is an interesting practical application of the results of studies into the nature of bud inhibition.

One of the applications of growth regulating substances which has been of great popular interest is the stimulation of certain plants to produce fruits without seeds. In the normal development of fruits, the growth of pollen tubes and meristematic activity in the developing ovules seem to stimulate the ovary to begin its enlargement into the fruit. Apparently the artificial application of appropriate growth regulators stimulates the ovary in a similar manner. If pollination has not occurred the resulting fruits are likely to be seedless.

The seedlessness is, in itself, of no great significance in commercial practice but the ability to accomplish "fruit set" in such plants as tomatoes when conditions for normal pollination are not satisfactory has been of great practical value.

The term *vitamin* applies to a group of growth regulating substances which are common to both plants and animals. Information concerning these important compounds has been accumulated intensively since the early part of this century. They occur in such small quantities that they cannot be considered significant as basic foods or building materials. In most cases where their functions have been elucidated, they facilitate many essential chemical reactions as parts of enzymes.

Two general groupings of vitamins are recognized. The water-soluble vitamins include the vitamin B complex and vitamin C (ascorbic acid), while the fat-soluble vitamins include vitamins A, D, K, and E.

In general, animals obtain their vitamins, directly or indirectly, from plants. However, the experimental feeding of animals with vitamin free diets is compli-

cated by the fact that the bacterial flora in the intestinal tracts of animals often accomplishes a synthesis of some of the deficient vitamins.

The recognition of the relation of vitamins to certain human diseases has been a dramatic part of medical history. Two horrifying diseases in particular, beri-beri and scurvy, were shown to be due to deficiencies of vitamin B_1 and vitamin C, respectively.

In the Orient where polished rice is a major ingredient of the diet a long term educational process is necessary in order to effect a realization that the polishing process removes the main natural source of vitamin B_1.

In days gone by, sailors on long voyages, where supplies of fresh fruits and vegetables were not practicable, often came down with scurvy. It was learned by empirical (trial and error) means that citrus fruits could be used to alleviate the symptoms of this disease. It has since been established that citrus fruits are outstanding sources of vitamin C and thus the empirical cure for scurvy has been given a scientific basis.

Deficiencies of vitamin D cause rickets in children. The discovery that radiation with ultraviolet light results in the formation of this vitamin from its precursor has made possible an inexpensive method for adding vitamin D to such common foods as milk.

Vitamin A is related to the night vision and color perceptive abilities of certain animals, including man. The precursor to vitamin A is beta carotene which is available from plants, particularly the green or yellow plant parts. The molecular structure of this vitamin is essentially that of a beta carotene molecule cut in half.

The necessity of vitamins for plant growth has been more difficult to establish, particularly since the green plants are able, for the most part, to make their own supplies.

Some years ago, investigators developed techniques for growing roots in culture without stems and leaves. In these experiments it was found necessary to add certain vitamins, particularly members of the vitamin B_1 complex, to culture solutions in order for the roots to grow normally.

For many years a vast amount of biochemical research has been carried on with micro-organisms such as bacteria and fungi. Many of these organisms synthesize certain vitamins in such quantities that they can be extracted commercially. Other forms have been shown to need certain vitamins or their precursors in order to grow normally. These have proved to be interesting organisms because they have enabled research workers to gain an insight into the biochemical reactions in which specific vitamins are concerned.

| # Life Without Chlorophyll

The primary advantage of chlorophyll to plants is based on its relation to the manufacture of simple foods during photosynthesis. In these simple foods the energy of sunlight is stored in such a way that it can be released in controlled amounts within the energy-demanding biochemical systems of living protoplasm.

It follows, then, that living organisms can survive without chlorophyll providing they have mechanisms for incorporating available and usable organic foods into their own protoplasm. This is true for the vast majority of animals and for a few higher plants such as the parasitic weed, dodder (*Cuscuta*) (Fig. 7.1). This plant obtains its basic food supply through absorbing organs (*haustoria*) which penetrate the tissues of a host plant. The dodder plant is normally yellow-orange in color but its seedlings have been observed to be green. The Indian pipe (*Monotropa*) (Fig. 7.2) is completely without pigmentation and is dependent for its basic nutrition on an association with a fungus which penetrates its roots.

While such plants are exceedingly interesting, they are not particularly important and the major emphasis of this chapter will be placed on a study of the fungi.

A fungus can be defined in a very general way as a simple plant without chlorophyll. Of course no living organisms are truly simple and when one attempts to draw a firm line between the plant kingdom and the animal kingdom, one finds that many of the simple plants without chlorophyll have apparent relatives on the other side of the line.

Such a broad definition of the fungi includes the bacteria, the actinomycetes, and the slime molds as well as the true fungi. The latter group includes the algalike fungi, the sac fungi, and the club fungi. Some of the differences between these groups are indicated in a brief, annotated outline of a classification of the plant kingdom which is included in Chapter 8.

In the following discussions examples from the various groups of fungi are used to illustrate the salient features of their growth, reproduction, and biological significance.

NATURE AND GROWTH OF THE FUNGUS PLANT BODY

The plant bodies of various fungi parallel, in many ways, the types of plant bodies found in the algae. They range from single cells which may be motile or nonmotile, to complex, densely intertwined masses of filaments in which the mass has a characteristic shape. Many of the filaments of

Fig. 7.1. Stem of a dodder plant twisted about the stem of a host plant.

fungi are septate, i.e., they have cross walls which divide the filament into a cellular series. Others generally lack septae and are, thus, without division into cellular units. None of the fungi, even those with highly complex plant bodies, have evolved vascular tissue.

The similarity in growth habits between many fungi and algae as well as certain similarities in mechanisms of reproduction (to be discussed later) have led many persons to suggest that the fungi evolved from the algae following a loss of the ability to manufacture chlorophyll. However, most modern mycologists (students of fungi) are of the opinion that the fungi had independent origins from those of the algae and that the similarities between the groups represent examples of parallel evolution.

The single-celled plant body is characteristic of many species of bacteria. Bacterial cells are so minute that their internal structure is not easily studied with the light microscope. They fall into the following three general shape categories: spherical (*coccoid*), rod-shaped (*bacilloid*), and spiral (*spirilloid*). A few species of bacteria move by means of flagella but most bacteria are nonmotile.

Bacteria are closely similar to the blue-green algae which are, however, photosynthetic organisms. In some modern classifications the bacteria and the blue-green algae are classified together as fission plants. Very possibly they represent the oldest forms of life on earth. Neither group is discussed at length in this text.

The cultivated yeasts frequently exist in the vegetative state as single, nonmotile cells (Fig. 7.3). They have been economically important fungi for centuries and the selection of strains for particular uses has favored forms in which cells separate readily after a division.

Most of the other forms of fungi have stages in which they exist as single cells for a period of time. The cells referred to are reproductive structures (spores and gametes) and they are not considered here as plant bodies.

Much emphasis is placed on the significance of single-celled motile plant bodies

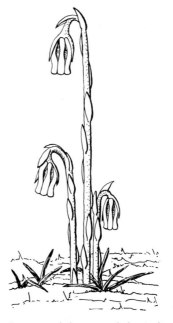

Fig. 7.2. Stems and flowers of the Indian pipe.

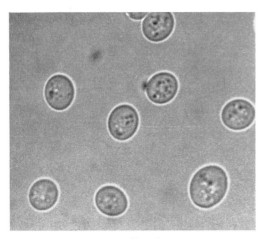

Fig. 7.3. Cells of yeast.

in the evolution of the algae and it is logical to speculate that certain groups of fungi had a similar ancestry. The type of ancestral cell envisaged would have been without chlorophyll but would have had cytoplasm, a true nucleus, and one or more flagella. It may or may not have had a cellulose wall. Many fungi produce reproductive structures (zoospores and gametes) which fit this description. Many protozoa (primitive animals) could be described in a similar manner. In addition, some unicellular, motile algae can be induced to develop without chlorophyll and grow in an otherwise normal manner provided they are able to obtain simple soluble foods. It is not clearly evident, however, that there are any living organisms, classified as true fungi, which exist only in the single-celled, motile condition. Possibly they did exist at one time but have been supplanted by more complex forms.

The slime molds constitute a relatively small and insignificant group of organisms which exhibit such a mixture of plant and animal characteristics that they have been classified in both the plant and animal kingdoms. They are very interesting organisms and have been the subject of considerable research in experimental biology.

At a certain stage in the life cycle of many slime molds they exist as simple cells without cell walls. These cells ex-

hibit an amoeboid type of motion in which parts of the cell are pushed forward or retracted in relation to a flowing motion of the cytoplasm. In a few species the major portion of the life cycle is passed in this condition.

In many others, however, the vegetative state consists of a multinucleate but noncellular mass of protoplasm which is called a *plasmodium*. Protoplasmic synthesis and nuclear divisions occur in the plasmodium which grows rapidly and spreads over the surface on which it is

Fig. 7.4A. Plasmodium of the slime mold, **Physarum polycephalum**, growing on agar.

Fig. 7.4B. Sporangia of a species of the slime mold genus, **Stemonitis.**

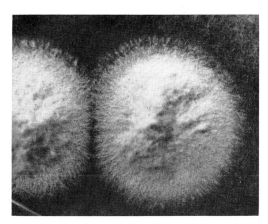

Fig. 7.5. Mycelium of a species of **Aspergillus,** growing on agar.

growing. It continues to exhibit a massive amoeboid type of movement throughout its vegetative existence and, in this way, engulfs its food supply. A plasmodium of the slime mold, *Physarum polycephalum*, grown under laboratory conditions, is illustrated in Figure 7.4A.

Commonly this vegetative phase is passed in protected places such as crevices in partially rotted woody stems and leaf mold. Prior to the reproductive phase (Fig. 7.4B) the plasmodium crawls into a position which is more exposed to light and desiccation.

In filamentous fungi, whether septate or nonseptate, the individual thread is called a *hypha*, and a mass of intertwined hyphae is referred to as a *mycelium* (Fig. 7.5). Fungi with unbranched hyphae do occur but, more commonly, they are profusely branched. The growth of a mycelium on a suitable medium is often extremely rapid. The mycelium of the common black bread mold, for example, can cover many square inches of a suitable nutrient medium in a few hours' time (Fig. 7.6A).

Hyphae may be modified in various ways to form specialized vegetative structures. The black bread mold mentioned above is organized into growth centers. At each center some of the hyphae form rhizoidal branches which penetrate the food substance and anchor the mycelium. From each center, as it matures, numer-

ous other hyphae spread laterally in a radiating pattern. When each of these *stolons* comes in contact with the surface of the food supply it establishes a new growth center (Fig. 7.6B). This development is analogous to the method by which strawberry plants are spread. When each center reaches a certain stage in maturity it sends other hyphae upwards into the air. These give rise to reproductive structures which will be discussed presently.

Many filamentous fungi which are dependent on living organisms for their food supply develop specially modified hyphae called *haustoria* which penetrate the living cells of the host. In the formation of a haustorium an ordinary hypha comes in contact with a host cell. At this point, a small hole is formed in the host cell wall as a result of the digestive activity of enzymes secreted by the fungus. Through this small hole a minute hyphal branch passes inward where it establishes an intimate contact with the host cell protoplasm. Sometimes the haustorium enlarges into a small, peglike protrusion, as in the case of *Albugo* sp. infecting the tissues of the weed shepherd's purse (Fig. 7.7A). In other cases it may enlarge into a rhizoidal system. This is true of the haustoria of *Erysiphe* sp., illustrated in Figure 7.7B, in the epidermal cells of a grass host.

In some species of a primitive group of fungi which are called chytrids the haustoria become more extensively modified into *rhizoidal mycelia*. In species of the genus *Rhizophidium* a zoospore swims to the wall of a host cell where a small pore is digested in the wall. Some of the protoplasm of the spore then passes through this opening into the host cell protoplasm where it proliferates into a finely branched system of nonseptate hyphae. This rhizoidal system presents a large total surface area in contact with the host protoplasm through which food is absorbed rapidly (Fig. 7.12).

Some mycelia have a diffuse organization with the branching hyphae being

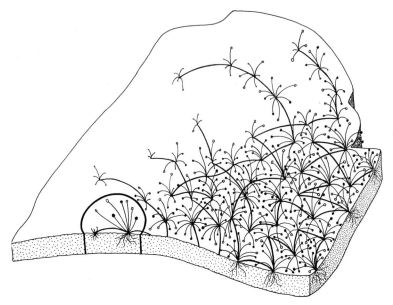

Fig. 7.6A. Mycelium of the black bread mold spreading across a grain of rolled oats.

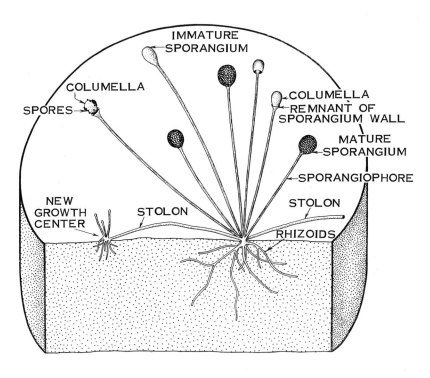

IMMATURE SPORANGIUM

COLUMELLA

SPORES

COLUMELLA

REMNANT OF SPORANGIUM WALL

MATURE SPORANGIUM

SPORANGIOPHORE

NEW GROWTH CENTER

STOLON

STOLON

RHIZOIDS

Fig. 7.6B. Detail of stolons, growth centers, rhizoidal branches, and sporangia of black bread mold.

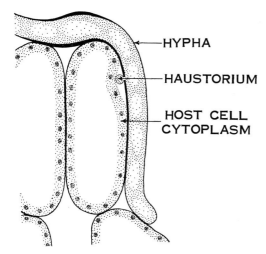

Fig. 7.7A. Haustorium from a hypha of **Albugo** penetrating a host cell.

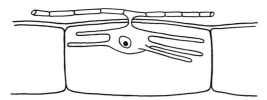

Fig. 7.7B. Haustorium of **Erysiphe** in the epidermal cell of a grass host.

loosely intertwined. Others may form felt-like layers of tightly woven hyphae. Growth conditions, particularly humidity, may cause the same species of fungus to react differently under different circumstances. In some fungi, there may be such a dense compacting of the mycelium that it takes on the characteristic appearance of a pseudoparenchyma. Frequently the interwoven hyphae form ropelike strands. Such strands are of common occurrence under the bark of rotting logs (Fig. 7.8). The complex fruiting bodies of many fungi are formed by highly modified mycelia. These are illustrated elsewhere along with a more detailed discussion of fungus fruiting bodies.

One very highly specialized group of plants is known as the lichens (Fig. 7.9). Their plant bodies consist of an algal component and a fungal component (Fig. 7.10). It has been demonstrated that each component can be grown separately but when this is done neither the alga nor the fungus resembles the lichen from which it came. The alga may be a green alga or a blue-green alga while the fungus is usually a member of the sac fungi. Lichens grow in many habitats from swamp forests to exposed rocky surfaces. In the latter case they hasten the weathering of

Fig. 7.8. Ropelike strands of mycelia of a fungus growing under the bark of a rotten log.

rock which leads eventually to soil formation. The mycelium of the fungal component is highly modified to resist desiccation and provides an internal environment which permits the algal component to carry on photosynthesis. Apparently the fungus obtains its basic food supply from the alga.

MODES OF NUTRITION AMONG THE FUNGI

Since plants without chlorophyll are unable to manufacture simple carbohydrates they must obtain them elsewhere and in the fungi evolutionary selection has fostered many different mechanisms for obtaining access to basic foods.

Many fungi lack only the photosynthetic mechanism and are able to synthesize the myriad other organic compounds which are essential to their existence from simple carbohydrates. However,

Fig. 7.9. Lichens growing on bark.

modern research has shown clearly that numerous species of fungi lack mechanisms for one or more other biochemical syntheses. Some of them are unable to synthesize essential vitamins. Others fail to manufacture one or more of the essential amino acids, etc.

The fungus *Neurospora* which gives rise to a red mold of bread has been used extensively for experimental purposes in such research. Wild strains of *Neurospora* are generally able to accomplish most of their own biochemical syntheses and will grow on simple media containing glucose. Research workers have selected several strains with deficiencies, i.e., inabilities to synthesize specific compounds essential to their metabolism. Other deficient strains have been developed as a result of mutations induced by such treatments as exposure to injurious radiation.

Frequently the loss of a specific gene has been correlated with the loss of the ability to form a specific enzyme. Such experiments have been largely responsible for the development of the modern concept that the probable function of a gene is related to the synthesis of a specific enzyme.

As mentioned previously, the process of respiration is known to involve a series of enzymatically controlled reactions in which the end products of one reaction become the raw materials of the next. Thus, if a cell is unable to synthesize one of the enzymes which control a given reaction, the whole process is interrupted and the respiration cycle ceases. If the end product of the missing reaction becomes available from another source, the series of reactions can continue.

It is also possible that some compound which limits the synthesis of the missing enzyme by its absence can be obtained from a source outside the cell. This, too, would permit the cycle to continue.

In many natural environments deficient strains disappear because of the difficulties involved in obtaining the compounds they are unable to synthesize. However, in biotic communities such as those which exist in the soil, there is a delicately balanced relationship between many organisms where each provides something that another needs. Also, many fungi have become adapted to growing as parasites on organisms which are able to manufacture the compounds which the particular parasite lacks.

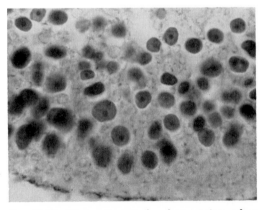

Fig. 7.10. Photomicrograph of a section of a lichen showing algal cells among the fungal hyphae.

Although many fungi require only simple, energy supplying foods, these foods often occur in forms which cannot be absorbed directly. For instance, much of the food manufactured by primary producers is converted to storage products such as starch and oil, or to building materials such as cellulose and protein. These compounds have large and complex molecules which are relatively insoluble and unable to pass through living cell membranes.

Many fungi have acquired mechanisms for secreting enzymes into such complex food materials. These enzymes accomplish an *extra-cellular digestion* which breaks down the complex molecules into simpler and more soluble molecules which can be absorbed through the living cell membranes of the fungus.

This process gradually alters the texture and other properties of the substance being digested. Woody tissues invaded by fungi with cellulose- or lignin-digesting enzymes gradually lose their mechanical strength and may be reduced, eventually, to a pulpy mass.

Much of the digested food is absorbed into the protoplasm of the fungus where it enters into diverse metabolic reactions. Some of it is used in respiration. The resulting carbon dioxide passes off into the air as a gas while the water formed during respiration may evaporate or accumulate. In the latter case a substance which was dry originally may become wet and soggy even though no water from other sources has been added.

The conversion of organic compounds to carbon dioxide and water results in a loss in dry weight of the total mass of both fungus and substrate. This accounts for the often observed fact that a rotted log is much lighter than a sound one of the same dimensions.

The soluble foods formed during the extracellular digestion process may benefit other organisms than the fungi which secrete the enzymes. The beneficiaries may be other fungi, plants of other groups, or members of various categories of animal life. Most animals lack the enzymes necessary to digest cellulose and the bacterial flora in the rumens of many herbivorous animals accomplishes the digestion of cellulose in the plants which have been ingested. This is an important function since herbivorous animals provide us with most of our meat and dairy products.

The destruction of wood as well as numerous other organic substances by fungi represents a serious economic loss but is, on the other hand, a vital part of various biological cycles. As has been pointed out, the carbon dioxide content of the atmosphere is constantly diminished by the process of photosynthesis. The respiration of fungi thus assumes significance as the major mechanism by which carbon dioxide is returned to the atmosphere. Furthermore the decay process gradually reduces the bulk of dead material on the surface of the earth and makes room for the growth of new organisms.

Environmental Cycles

All the chemical elements which are significant in living matter undergo cyclic patterns in their relationships with living matter. They exist in the environment, are incorporated into living matter, and are eventually returned to the environment. Without actually labelling them as such, both *carbon cycles* and *oxygen cycles* have been referred to frequently in this text. The *nitrogen cycle* is another example of a relationship which has been studied intensively because of the basic importance of nitrogen to all living matter.

Free nitrogen (N_2) is a gas which comprises the largest part of the atmosphere (almost 80 per cent). In this form, nitrogen is not available to green plants which, for the most part, require nitrates or salts of ammonia. Organic compounds containing nitrogen are not commonly absorbed from the soil by the higher plants but may be utilized by certain forms of algae as well as many of the fungi. Nitrites are generally toxic but this is not a serious matter since most nitrites are unstable in normal plant habitats.

The nitrogen compounds occurring in soil and in water are subject to constant change. These changes are of several types and are summarized in the following list:

1. Organic compounds can be broken down with an eventual release of ammonia.
2. Ammonia can be changed to nitrite.
3. Nitrite can be changed to nitrate.
4. Nitrate can be changed to nitrite.
5. Nitrite can be changed to free nitrogen.
6. Free nitrogen can be fixed as an organic nitrogen compound.

The breakdown of organic compounds to release ammonia is a decay or decomposition process.

The change from NH_3 to NO_2 to NO_3 is an oxidation series and is called nitrification.

The change from NO_3 to NO_2 to N_2 is a reduction series and is called denitrification.

The union of molecular nitrogen with other elements, particularly carbon, hydrogen, and oxygen, is called nitrogen fixation.

Each of the reactions in these series is carried on by different organisms. Some species of bacteria change NH_2 to NO_2 while entirely different species have the ability to change NO_2 to NO_3. In general, wet and poorly aerated soils foster the denitrification process which results in a net loss of nitrogen from the soil. Soils with well balanced conditions of aeration and moisture make possible the more beneficial changes.

Within the living plant nitrogen is used mainly in the form of NH_2 and is combined with carbohydrate derivatives in the synthesis of amino acids. If the nitrogen is absorbed as a nitrate (NO_3) this must first be reduced to NH_2 before such syntheses can be accomplished. Proteins are constructed by the union of numerous amino acid molecules in various combinations and the amino acids released by the digestion of one protein molecule may be used again in the construction of other protein molecules. In biological food chains where each member of a series of organisms devours the next one it is possible that a given amino acid might be a component, successively, of the proteins of each member of the series.

The fixation of nitrogen by certain micro-organisms is an extremely important part of the nitrogen cycle since it is the only significant biological process by which atmospheric nitrogen can enter the nitrogen cycle. (Considerable amounts of nitrogen are fixed by lightning and, in modern times, man has learned how to fix nitrogen by synthetic means.) The organisms which can fix nitrogen are a few species of blue-green algae, certain free-living soil bacteria, and the root nodule bacteria associated with leguminous plants.

The root nodule bacteria invade the roots of legumes (peas, beans, clover, alfalfa, etc.) and stimulate the root cells to divide abnormally. The swollen masses of cells are called *root nodules* (Fig. 7.11). Apparently they provide a suitable environment for the bacteria which increase in numbers rapidly. Certain strains or races of one species of bacteria have become specifically adapted to achieving their best development in specific kinds of legumes.

These bacteria are able to convert free nitrogen gas into organic nitrogen compounds. This process requires energy which comes presumably from the respiration of foods supplied by the host plant. The organic nitrogen compounds in the bacteria enter the nitrogen cycle when the bacteria themselves die and decay. It is not certain whether the legume host can utilize nitrogen compounds directly from the bacteria. In any event the

Fig. 7.11. Root nodules on the roots of a soybean plant.

total nitrogen fertility of the soil is enhanced by this process.

Nitrogen as well as certain other essential chemical elements such as iron and sulfur may exist in more than one chemical state and have different energy levels. Under certain circumstances such elements can shift or be shifted from one energy level to another. If the shift is towards a higher energy level, then energy must be supplied to the reaction. If the shift is from a higher level to a lower level, energy is released. Organisms such as iron and sulfur bacteria are able to use the energy released to reduce carbon dioxide to carbohydrate. This type of reaction is chemosynthetic rather than photosynthetic.

Utilization of the Metabolic Products of Fungi

While carbon dioxide and water are the most abundant substances released as end products of the respiration of fungi, other substances are released in significant amounts. In a previous discussion of respiration, it was pointed out that under aerobic conditions the carbon source is oxidized completely to CO_2 and H_2O while under anaerobic (without air) conditions the carbon source is incompletely oxidized and the end products are, in part, organic compounds with residual energy values. Such compounds are frequently utilized in the diet of other organisms.

A number of compounds produced during the respiration of fungi have important industrial uses. Among them are alcohol, citric acid, acetic acid, butyric acid, and many others. Techniques for growing fungi under controlled conditions with lowered oxygen tensions are important in several biochemical industries and much research has been done to improve the quality and production rate of such processes. This type of research involves experiments with growth conditions as well as genetical selections of strains with the ability to produce higher yields.

The discovery of the antibiotic chemical penicillin was the direct result of an observation that a substance secreted by a species of the common mold *Penicillium* caused an inhibition of the growth of certain bacteria in the same culture. This type of reaction had been known for a long time but Sir Alexander Fleming proceeded to extract the chemical in crude form. He was then able to demonstrate that it could be administered to human beings and that it would inhibit the growth of many bacteria causing serious diseases.

The search for other types of antibiotics has been carried on actively and has resulted in a whole arsenal of new wonder drugs for use by the medical profession in the unending fight against disease. Many of the organisms from which antibiotics have been extracted are soil dwellers belonging to a group of fungi called actinomycetes. Possibly the antibiotics play a natural role in the inhibition of competitors in the intense struggle for survival in the micro-environment of the soil. An ability to produce antibiotics would have a survival value and organisms possessing the ability to produce them would be favored in the process of natural selection.

The widespread use of antibiotics along with many other new techniques in medicine is having a phenomenal effect on the world's population. The numbers of mankind have always been subject to periodic decimation by plagues, floods, famines, and wars. Science and technology seem to promise a future in which the first three will be amenable to control, and it is to be hoped that a substitute for the fourth will be devised before the burgeoning population of the world overwhelms civilization.

Saprophytes and Parasites

From the preceding discussions it is evident that the fungi are extremely diverse in their growth habits and requirements. Their modes of existence may be grouped into two large categories. Those which exist only on dead organic matter are called *saprophytes* while those which exist only in a dependent association with a living host are called *parasites*. Yet the borderline between the two categories is not sharp. Some parasites can function as saprophytes while certain saprophytes can function as parasites. The common black bread mold has been known to be a weak parasite of strawberries and sweet potatoes and has been identified as the causal agent of one very painful type of ear infection in human beings.

Many of the fungi which exist only on or in living organisms actually kill the host cells in the path of the advancing mycelium apparently through the secretion of toxic substances. By altering the permeability of the host cell membranes in this way, substances within the host cells become more readily available by simple diffusion processes. Furthermore, living host tissues are often able to resist penetration by the infecting mycelium

and death of the host cells becomes a necessary prelude to growth of the fungus.

The invasion of host cell protoplasm by haustoria has been described previously. This is a very delicate relationship since the fungus is able, in this way, to absorb nutrients from the host without killing it. The general vigor and growth rate of the host are reduced by such infections but the fungus is often able to grow for much longer periods of time than if the host tissues were killed immediately.

One very common example of such a relationship is powdery mildew of lilac. The mycelium of the fungus which causes this disease covers the surface of the leaves while haustoria penetrate into many of the epidermal cells. However lilac leaves are rarely killed by the fungus which is universal on this plant. Apparently such fungi have a great many nutritional requirements as they are the most difficult types to establish in cultures on artificial media.

The mycorrhizal relationships between fungi and the roots of many plants was mentioned briefly elsewhere. This type of relationship should be considered as something other than strict parasitism. The fungus grows both within the root and externally in the soil and, apparently, this relationship increases the ability of the root to absorb necessary chemicals from the soil.

NONGAMETIC REPRODUCTION IN THE FUNGI

Since fungi are dependent organisms it follows that they can be successful only to the extent to which they are able to come in contact with and penetrate potential food supplies. The spread of a mycelium may permit coverage of an entire unit of the food supply such as a loaf of bread, a dead insect in the water, or a leaf on a tree; but the spread to another loaf, another insect, or another leaf frequently presents a barrier which the mycelium cannot bridge.

The rapid spread of many fungi is

actually accomplished by spores or spore-like structures produced by nongametic processes. Some of these swim in water, some are dispersed in air, others are carried on, or in, the bodies of various animals. In a number of cases special mechanisms of spore dispersal are characteristic of a particular type of fungus. The numbers of spores produced are large and this insures that any new and usable food sources in the vicinity are subject to infestation.

Production of Zoospores

The production of zoospores is limited to the algalike fungi and does not occur in all members of this class. The chytrids comprise one order of this class and they commonly occur in aquatic environments. In a previous discussion of a member of this group it was noted that when a zoospore came to rest on the wall of a host cell infection was accomplished by digestion of a small hole in the host cell wall through which the parasite entered the host protoplasm.

In many chytrids the orginal spore remains outside the host cell and gradually

enlarges as food is absorbed from the host. This enlarged structure is densely protoplasmic and, at maturity, becomes a sporangium (Fig. 7.12). Its contents become divided into a large number of small cells which are released as uniflagellate zoospores. Each one of these is able to swim to a new host cell and repeat the infection in the manner previously described.

The aquatic mold *Saprolegnia* frequently develops in the bodies of dead insects and other dead organisms in the water. After the infestation becomes established, many long hyphae grow outward in a radiate manner from the infested tissue (Fig. 7.13). These hyphae are without cross walls except at the tip where the terminal portion of each one becomes modified into an elongated zoosporangium. The hyphae which bear such sporangia are called sporangiophores.

The protoplasm of each of the zoosporangia becomes subdivided into many small cells which are discharged through an opening at the tip (Fig. 7.13). Each of these becomes a biflagellated zoospore which, after a brief period of activity, en-

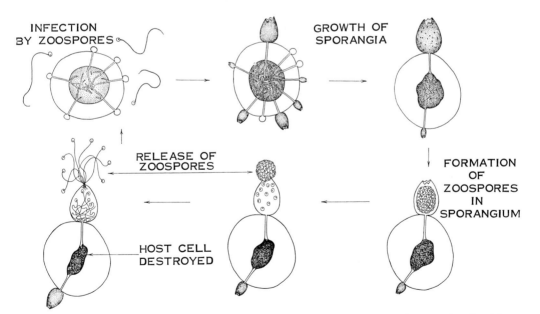

INFECTION BY ZOOSPORES

GROWTH OF SPORANGIA

FORMATION OF ZOOSPORES IN SPORANGIUM

RELEASE OF ZOOSPORES

HOST CELL DESTROYED

Fig. 7.12. Series of drawings showing the growth and nongametic reproduction of a chytrid and the simultaneous destruction of the blue-green algal host cell.

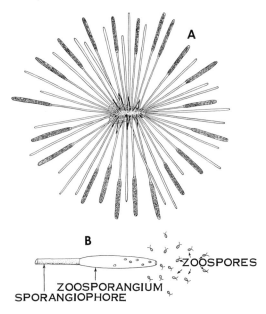

Fig. 7.13. Water molds. A. Dead fly infected with **Saprolegnia**. B. Discharge of zoospores from the zoosporangium of **Saprolegnia**.

ters a temporary nonmotile resting stage. When this structure becomes active again it gives rise to another zoospore which is able to initiate a new infestation.

Aerial Dispersal of Fungus Spores

The evolution of windspread spores has been as important a factor in natural selection among the fungi as it has among the higher green plants. Probably the ability to achieve aerial distribution of

spores or sporelike bodies evolved independently in various groups of fungi.

Spores of the Black Bread Mold

A very common example of wind dissemination is provided by the spores of the black bread mold. In a previous discussion of this fungus it was noted that the growth centers gave rise to erect hyphae with swollen tips (Fig. 7.6). These densely protoplasmic tips become modified into sporangia when delicate cross walls form to separate the tips from the rest of the erect hyphae which support them. Then cleavage begins in the protoplasm and a large number of spores is formed within each sporangium. These spores become pigmented and are so densely packed that light is not transmitted through the mature sporangium.

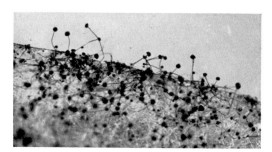

Fig. 7.14. Mycelium and sporangia of the black bread mold. Compare with Fig. 7.6.

As a result it appears black. When the spores are mature, the outer wall of the sporangium breaks and the spores float away in the air. A *columella* is left behind

Fig. 7.15. Series of photomicrographs showing maturation of the sporangia of black bread mold. Compare text description and Fig. 7.6.

as a central dome with a little collarlike rim at the base representing the broken sporangium wall (Figs. 7.6, 7.15).

Bread mold spores are produced in enormous numbers and are almost universally present in the atmosphere. Thus, any suitable medium which is exposed to air may become infested provided moisture and temperature conditions are satisfactory for the germination of spores and growth of the mycelium (Fig. 7.14).

The Sporangium of *Pilobolus*

The fungus *Pilobolus* is similar to the black bread mold in that it forms a sporangium at the tip of an erect sporangiophore (Fig. 7.16). However, the entire sporangium is distributed as a unit rather than as single spores. This sporangium is discharged in a most interesting manner which is related to the growth habits of the fungus.

The sporangiophore below the sporangium becomes highly turgid and inflated. This inflated portion is sensitive to light and through growth movements it bends in such a way that the sporangium is aimed towards a light source (Fig. 7.17). When the turgidity reaches a maximum, the sporangiophore explodes violently and hurls the sporangium towards the light.

Pilobolus is a dung fungus and, in grazing areas, the droppings of herbivorous animals are commonly infested with this organism. The aiming mechanism insures that the discharged sporangium will pass between the leaves of overhanging plants and come to rest on the surfaces of leaves at some distance away. These leaves are more apt to be ingested by another animal and, in this way, the continuous presence of this fungus in dung is assured.

Conidia

The *conidium* is a type of spore which is one of the most efficient means of asexual (nongametic) reproduction in the fungi. In a broad sense, a conidium is a fragment of a hypha which becomes adapted to survival during aerial dissemination before it breaks away from the parent hypha. Two of the evident modifications are a thickening of the wall and a dehydration of the protoplasm. In some species the conidium is unicellular, but conidia with two, three, or several cells are common (Fig. 7.18).

Conidia may be formed in a linear series as the direct result of fragmentation of a hypha or they may be formed

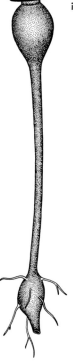

Fig. 7.16. Sporangium and sporangiophore of **Pilobolus**. Note inflation of the sporangiophore.

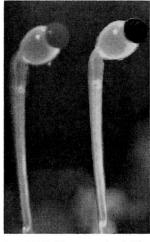

Fig. 7.17. Photograph of **Pilobolus** sporangiophores showing bending toward a light source.

at the tips of special branches called *conidiophores*. The tip of a conidiophore may become pinched inwards so that the conidium is formed by an abstriction process. In other cases the conidium is formed by a protrusion process in which a small droplet of protoplasm is forced out of the open end of the conidiophore. Both processes are frequently repeated so that conidia form in series at the tips of the conidiophores.

From the above discussion it is evident that there are at least three basically dif-

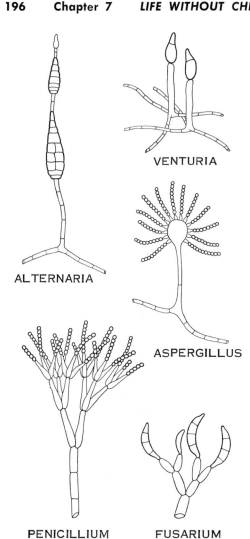

VENTURIA

ALTERNARIA

ASPERGILLUS

PENICILLIUM   FUSARIUM

Fig. 7.18. Examples of conidiophores and conidia of several common fungi.

these spores and they appear as a cloud of dust drifting away from the orange.

In the same way as the spores of bread mold are widely distributed, the conidia of *Penicillium* and the related genus, *Aspergillus* are everywhere present. Thus, infestation can occur wherever usable organic material is available and suitable growth conditions prevail.

Many diseases of plants become serious because of the efficiency of the method for spreading the causal agents by means of conidia. The gametic process, on the other hand, is often no more than a survival mechanism which results in the localized initiation of infections when the environment becomes favorable to the growth of the fungus. Once the disease is established the spread of the fungus from plant to plant is most commonly

Fig. 7.19. Orange infested with **Penicillium.**

ferent processes by which conidia are formed. Special names have been proposed for the spores resulting from each process but as yet they are not in common use.

The word conidium is derived from a Greek word meaning dust and the connotation is apt. For example, an orange infested with *Penicillium* will appear white as the mycelium grows and then blue as the conidia mature at the surface of the mycelium (Fig. 7.19). A slight puff of wind will displace vast numbers of

effected by spores such as conidia. Diseases like apple scab and the brown rot of stone fruits would be of little significance were it not for the mechanism of spreading the infection by means of conidia.

Uredospores of Stem Rust

In the life cycle of the fungus which causes the black stem rust of cereals, several types of spores are produced (as will be discussed in more detail below).

One of these spore types is the *uredospore* (Fig. 7.32). It resembles a conidium in being a spore produced by a nongametic process at the tip of a hypha and is the only means by which the infection can be spread from one plant to another in a field of susceptible cereal crop plants (wheat, barley, oats, etc.).

The Modified Sporangium

One structure which might be considered as an intermediate step in the evolution of a type of wind spread spore is the modified sporangium characteristic of an important group of phycomycetes. Usually it is formed by the abstriction of a multi-nucleated terminal portion of a special hypha called a *sporangiophore* (Fig. 7.20). In several species the modified sporangia are formed in a series at the tips of these hyphae. They develop thickened walls and their protoplasm becomes dehydrated. As a result they are able to survive in dry air as they are transported from one host to another.

To achieve infection of the new host it is necessary that a water film be present on the surface invaded. Depending largely on temperature conditions, the sporangium may germinate directly into a new hypha or its contents may become divided into zoospores which escape and swim in the surface water film. These zoospores may swim through an open stomate or may come to rest directly above an open stomate. It is also possible that they can form penetration hyphae

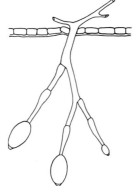

Fig. 7.20. Sporangiophore and sporangia of **Phytophthora infestans,** the organism causing late blight of potatoes and tomatoes.

which cause direct infections by perforating the cuticle.

It may be seen that weather conditions which induce the occurrence of water films on leaf surfaces (cool nights after humid days, for instance) will favor the spread of organisms which produce this type of sporangia. Diseases such as the late blight of potatoes and tomatoes, the blue mold of tobacco, and the downy mildew of cucurbits become serious under such conditions. So serious, as a matter of fact, that the U.S. Department of Agriculture maintains a warning service which predicts danger periods. These predictions are based on weather forecasts and records of local infection. The information serves as a guide for the timely use of expensive fungicidal sprays.

GAMETIC REPRODUCTION IN THE FUNGI

In the fungi, as in the algae, many variations of the basic cycle of gametic reproduction may be found. The examples which are discussed below serve to illustrate a few of these variations.

As has been mentioned elsewhere, reproduction which involves the fusion of motile isogametes is thought to be a primitive characteristic. The chytrids are considered to be a primitive group of fungi and the production of motile isogametes has been demonstrated in some of them. Occasionally observations have been made of the fusion of such gametes in pairs followed by the formation of motile zygotes which penetrate a new food supply before entering a resting phase. Presumably meiosis occurs during germination of such zygotes. Details of the gametic reproduction of a great many chytrids are unknown and the above description is not meant as a general one for the group as a whole.

It may be assumed that advanced forms of gametic reproduction such as oogamy evolved in many separate series in the fungi. Quite possibly the sequence of events in some of them followed the pattern of increasing size, loss of motility, decrease in numbers, and increased protection for the female gamete, while the male gamete retained many of the features of the primitive isogametes.

Oogamous Reproduction in *Saprolegnia*

The water mold *Saprolegnia* which belongs in an order of the algalike fungi provides a classical example of oogamous reproduction. The egg case (oogonium) consists of the swollen tip of a hypha with a cell wall across the base. Within the oogonium one to several eggs are formed (Fig. 7.21). Antheridia develop from the

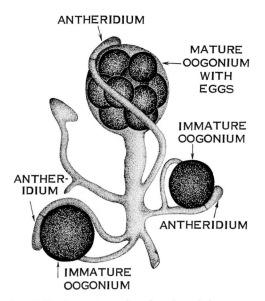

Fig. 7.21. Oogonia and antheridia of the water mold, **Saprolegnia.**

less prominently inflated tips of nearby hyphae. These may or may not be branches of the same hyphal system as that bearing the oogonia since *Saprolegnia* species may be homothallic or heterothallic.

When an antheridium comes in contact with an oogonium one or more very slender penetration tubes pass into the oogonium and come in contact with the eggs. These function as fertilization tubes through which small amounts of cytoplasm and a single nucleus pass into each egg. Nuclear fusions occur in each of the fertilized eggs and the diploid zygote becomes a thick-walled resting cell. In a

genus closely related to *Saprolegnia* it has been established that meiosis occurs in the germinating zygote.

Zygospore Formation in the Black Bread Mold

Gametic reproduction in the black bread mold (*Rhizopus nigricans*) resembles the conjugation of nonflagellated gametes which occurs in the green alga *Spirogyra*. *Rhizopus nigricans* is heterothallic and gametic reproduction will not occur unless mycelia of plus and minus strains grow close to each other. When this happens, slightly modified hyphae from one strain are stimulated to grow directly towards similar hyphae from the other. These hyphae are somewhat inflated and may be considered as either *progametes* or *progametangia*. When they come into contact, each one is stimulated to form a cross wall which delimits a multinucleate cell at the tip (Fig. 7.22).

The contents of these cells do not become further subdivided. For this reason they may be interpreted either as gametangia or as multinucleate gametes. The walls at the point of contact then dissolve and plasmogamy occurs. This is followed by the development of a very thick black wall and the zygote becomes a resting spore (*zygospore*).

The formation of the spectacular zygospores of *Phycomyces* is illustrated in Figs. 7.23A and 7.23B. The antlerlike spines arise from the supporting hyphae rather than from the zygospore itself.

When the zygospore of *Rhizopus* germinates it gives rise to a sporangium similar to the sporangia on the vegetative mycelia. In this species all of the spores produced in such a sporangium give rise either to plus strains or to minus strains. Details of when and where genetic segregation occurs are somewhat obscure but good evidence exists that nuclear fusions and meiosis are followed by degeneration of all but one of the haploid nuclei prior to germination of the zygote.

Asci and Ascospores

Gametic reproduction in the sac fungi is an elaborate process which terminates

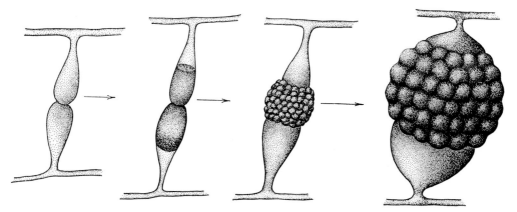

Fig. 7.22. Series of drawings illustrating gametic reproduction in the black bread mold, **Rhizopus nigricans.**

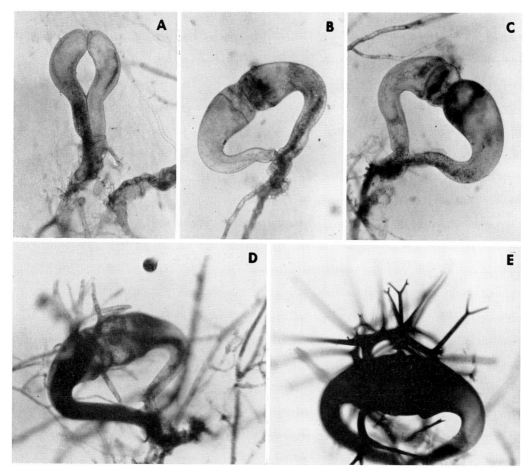

Fig. 7.23A. Series of photomicrographs showing gametic reproduction in another black bread mold, **Phycomyces blakesleeanus.**

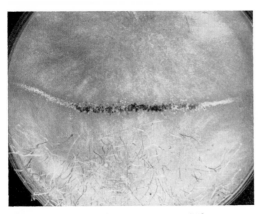

Fig. 7.23B. Plus and minus strains of **Phycomyces** growing on an agar plate with a line of zygospores forming at the juncture of the two strains.

in the production of a type of spore called an *ascopore* (Fig. 7.24). In most cases, the ascospores occur in groups of eight within saclike structures called *asci* (sing., *ascus*).

The female structure involved in the production of asci is called an *ascogonium*. While similar in basic function to an oogonium it does not contain egg cells as such. Instead, it contains a mass of noncellular protoplasm with several nuclei. The *antheridium* is, similarly, a multinucleate structure. In some of the sac fungi the antheridia and ascogonia are scarcely distinct from normal vegetative hyphae. In others, the ascogonium may be considerably larger and more elaborate than the antheridium.

The nature of the male gamete structure in some sac fungi suggests the possibility of an evolutionary reduction series in which the male gamete or possibly the antheridium has been modified into a minute, nonmotile, sporelike body. This is

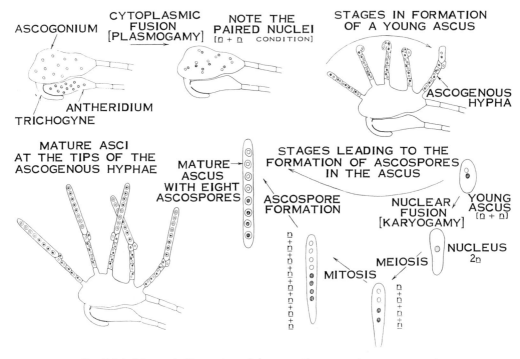

Fig. 7.24. Schematic illustration of the gametic process in an ascomycete.

called a *spermatium* and it is frequently adapted for dispersal in air or by insects.

With respect to the element of time, the three major steps in the gametic cycle, plasmogamy, karyogamy, and meiosis, are spaced differently in this group than in any other previously described. *Plasmogamy* occurs when the walls between the male structure and the ascogonium are dissolved at some point. The cytoplasms mix but nuclear fusions do not occur immediately. Instead, the nuclei come together in pairs, each one retaining its own identity throughout several succeeding mitoses. Each ascogonium may have several pairs of such nuclei. Eventually pairs of nuclei migrate into special hyphae which arise from the ascogonium. These are called *ascogenous* (ascusbearing) *hyphae* since each one gives rise, ultimately, to one or more asci (Fig. 7.24).

Each young ascus receives a pair of nuclei. Early in the further development of the ascus these nuclei fuse (*karyogamy*) and then go through the normal meiotic process immediately to form four haploid nuclei. In those species where the male and the female structures develop on sexually different strains, two of these haploid nuclei contain genes for femaleness and two for maleness.

Normally, one further mitotic division occurs in each of these nuclei so that eight haploid nuclei result. Each one of these becomes incorporated into an ascospore when the cytoplasm of the ascus is partitioned. In this manner, eight ascospores are formed within each ascus. Fig. 7.25 shows several mature asci of the soil fungus *Neocosmospora vasinfectans*.

It has been mentioned that the fungus *Neurospora* is used extensively in studies of biochemical genetics. This organism forms ascospores in a similar manner to the one described. Part of the reason for its value as a research organism is that the individual ascospores can be isolated one at a time in the order of their occurrence in the ascus. This enables research workers to relate experimental results ob-

tained from subsequent cultures with the genetic segregations which occurred during meiosis.

In many of the sac fungi, several asci occur together within the bodies of fruiting structures called *ascocarps*. The ascocarp develops from an intertwined and compacted mass of sterile hyphae which grows around the asci. The ascocarps are of various shapes, each of which has a

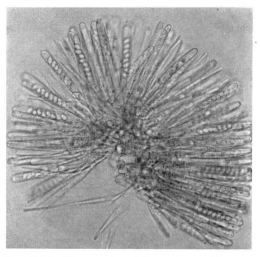

Fig. 7.25. Cluster of asci from the perithecium of **Neocosmospora vasinfectans**.

type name. The *cleistothecium* is rounded and completely encloses the asci; the *perithecium* has the shape of a flask with a small opening in the neck; and the *apothecium* may be either a disc or a shallow cup (Figs. 7.26, 7.27).

Ascocarps show considerable range in size. Many are small and inconspicuous, approximating the size of the head of a pin. Others are much larger and showy like the Scarlet Cup Fungus (*Plectania* sp.), and the Morel (*Morchella esculenta*). The latter fungus is highly prized as an edible mushroom (Fig. 7.28).

Among the numerous sac fungi which do not develop ascocarps of any type are the yeasts and species in the genus, *Taphrina*, which cause such diseases as peach leaf curl and plum pocket.

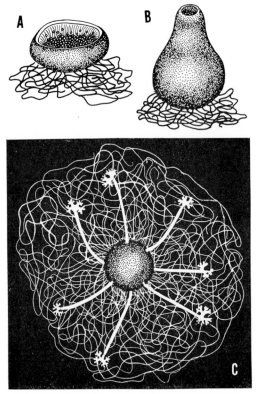

Fig. 7.26. Variations in ascocarp structure. A. Apothecium. B. Perithecium. C. Cleistothecium.

Fig. 7.28. The large and edible ascocarps of a morel.

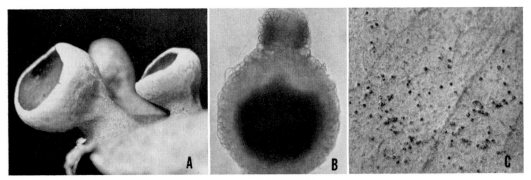

Fig. 7.27. Variations in ascocarp structure. A. Apothecium formed by the fungal component of a lichen. B. Perithecium of **Neocosmospora vasinfectans** (much enlarged). C. Minute cleistothecia of a powdery mildew growing on the surface of a leaf.

Basidia and Basidiospores

The club fungi are so named because a club-shaped structure, the *basidium*, bearing four externally maturing spores is formed at one point in the gametic cycle. The cells of the mycelium which give rise to basidia are all binucleate. Many authors refer to this condition as $n + n$ in order to emphasize that the two nuclei are separate and haploid. These nuclei may have come originally from sexually different mononucleate strains and, in such cases, they may be designated as plus and minus.

The basidium is a cell of the $n + n$ mycelium which becomes a somewhat inflated and club-shaped structure. In the young basidium the two nuclei fuse and then undergo meiosis to form four haploid nuclei. In those cases where the fusing nuclei were plus and minus then two of the four nuclei will be plus and two minus. Nuclear abortions or failures in the meiotic process may result in fewer than the normal four haploid nuclei in the young basidium.

Following meiosis, the basidium may become septate or remain without cross walls. In either event, delicate peglike structures grow out from the wall of the basidium. These are called *sterigmata* and, through each one, a drop of cytoplasm containing one of the haploid nuclei is extruded. This droplet then develops a wall and functions as a spore. Appropriately, it is called a *basidiospore* (see Figure 7.34).

The mechanisms by which the binucleate $(n + n)$ condition arises vary considerably in the group. In a number of species, each basidiospore gives rise to a mycelium whose cells each contain a single nucleus. Such mycelia seem to have rather limited growth potentialities. When fusions between hyphae of appropriately matched, mononucleate (n) mycelia occur, the resultant binucleate $(n + n)$ mycelium seems capable of a much more vigorous growth. It is evident, also, that in some species the $n + n$ condition can result

from a fusion between basidiospores or the fusion between a spore and a hypha.

Sporophores of the Club Fungi

Many of the club fungi live in humus and are especially significant in biological cycles such as the carbon cycle. A number of them grow in the woody tissues of trees and are thus responsible for serious economic losses in forest-related industries.

The mycelium of such organisms may grow for many years, accumulating food reserves which permit the formation of large and complex fruiting structures or *sporophores* (Fig. 7.29). The sporophore of a mushroom, for example, consists of two major parts, the *stalk* and the *cap*. On the under side of the cap there are a series of radiating plates which are called *gills*. Each gill is a compacted mass of my-

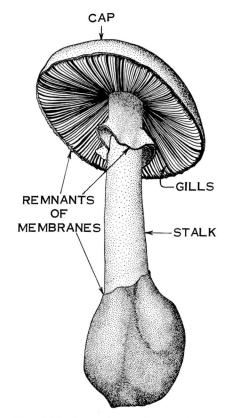

Fig. 7.29. Sporophore of a mushroom.

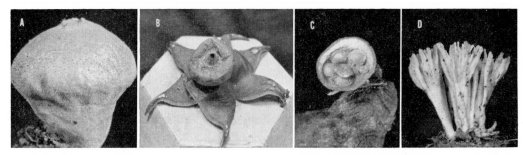

Fig. 7:30. Sporophores of some common club fungi: A. Puffball. B. Earth star. C. Bird's nest fungus. D. Coral fungus.

celium and its whole surface becomes lined with erect basidia standing side by side. The details of the formation of the basidiospores are essentially as described above.

The mycelium which produces mushroom sporophores is generally unnoticed since it grows in soil humus. With uniform soil and growth conditions this mycelium tends to grow in a radial fashion and to have a circular margin. The sporophores develop periodically near the perimeter of the mycelium. When first formed they are tiny, compacted, buttonlike masses just under the surface of the soil. Warm, humid weather conditions stimulate a very rapid growth of these buttons into mature sporophores. The growth may be completed in one night and this has resulted in many legends about mushroom growth. The discovery of a perfect ring of mushrooms appearing overnight in a pasture could well be a startling event and it is small wonder that such *fairy rings* have come to represent "evidence" of the conclaves of supernatural beings.

Although the edibility of mushroom sporophores has always fascinated mankind, some of them contain deadly poisons belonging to the class of true ptomaines and there is no safe field test by which the layman can predict the edibility of a strange mushroom. It is evident, also, that small and nonlethal doses of certain mushroom toxins result in severe psychological disturbances. Some of the visionary dreams induced by these compounds have a dramatic illusion of reality. In some instances, individuals go berserk and become physically dangerous. In fact,

it has been suggested that the leaders of certain peoples with a reputation for fearlessness and invincibility in battle fed their troops with mushroom toxins to induce this type of madness.

Many of the sporophores of the club fungi have unusual and interesting shapes. Among these are the puffballs, the earth stars, the bird's nest fungi, the coral fungi and many types of brightly colored mushrooms (Fig. 7.30).

The Rusts and Smuts

The rusts and smuts include most of the truly parasitic species of club fungi. They are of particular interest because many plants of economic importance such as wheat, corn, oats, barley, etc., are susceptible to diseases caused by members of these two groups.

Corn Smut

In corn which has been infected with the smut fungus *Ustilago zeae* cells are stimulated to grow abnormally and form distorted masses of nonspecialized tissues. This growth utilizes food which otherwise would contribute to the nourishment of the ear. Furthermore, if the grains themselves are infected they become enlarged and are eventually destroyed by the fungus which utilizes such abnormal tissues as a food supply. When the fungus has completely destroyed the abnormal tissues, cells of the mycelium became converted into thick-walled spores which are often referred to as *chlamydospores*. They are long-lived and are generally present in all areas where corn is grown.

When a chlamydospore germinates it gives rise to a basidium and basidiospores. The basidiospores are capable of initiating small, localized infections when transported to living corn plants. These infections are heterothallic and each of their cells contains a single haploid nucleus. Mycelia with binucleate $n + n$ cells are initiated by cellular fusions when plus and minus mycelia come in contact with one another. It is the binucleate mycelium which induces the severe symptoms in the host.

Black Stem Rust

One of the most critical plant diseases known to man is the black stem rust of cereal grains. It has been known ever since man began to cultivate these crop plants and its ravages have often affected the course of history. In addition to its economic importance it has additional interest in that the causal fungus *Puccinia graminis* must spend part of its existence in each of two entirely different host plants in order to complete its gametic cycle.

During the major part of the growing season, *Puccinia graminis* lives in the stem tissues of various grass type hosts including all of the cultivated cereal grains. When a particular mycelium has been growing for a week or ten days in the tissues of such a stem it begins to form a large number of *uredospores*. Each one of these is single-celled but binucleate $(n + n)$ as are all the cells of the mycelium. They are produced by a nongametic process.

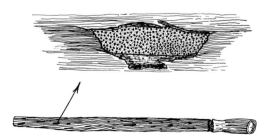

Fig. 7.31. "Red rust" stage on oats. Stem with evident pustules and enlargement of a pustule containing uredospores.

The uredospores develop just under the epidermis and their formation forces the epidermis to be raised somewhat forming a longitudinal blister or *pustule* on the surface. When the pustule cracks open large numbers of the reddish-colored uredospores are exposed for wind dispersal. This is the so-called red-rust stage which is familiar to grain farmers the world over as a sign of approaching disaster (Figs. 7.31, 7.32).

The uredospores are wind-spread among the plants of the field and each one is capable of initiating a new infection

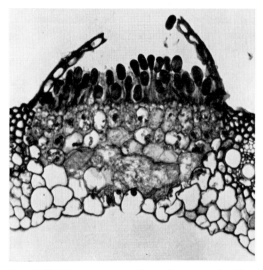

Fig. 7.32. Transverse section of a stem showing the production of uredospores by the infecting fungus.

provided environmental conditions are suitable for germination and growth of the newly formed hypha until it can penetrate the host. Within another week to ten days the mycelia in these new infections mature and begin to produce more uredospores. It takes but a few generations for a field of wheat to become so completely infected that the potential harvest of grain is seriously reduced in volume. Since the uredospore is the only mechanism by which this disease can be spread from plant to plant in the grain fields, this type of spore is responsible for most of the damage.

When the infected plants begin to mature, existing mycelia and any new ones begin to produce a somewhat different type of spore, the *teliospore* (Fig. 7.33), which plays an important role in the gametic life cycle. The teliospore is a two-celled spore rather than a single-celled spore as is the uredospore. Each cell, however, has two nuclei. The walls of the teliospore become very thick and the protoplasm becomes dehydrated. In this way the teliospore is able to withstand the desiccating effects of winter weather. In all localities where freezing is common during winter seasons, the teliospore is the only stage of *Puccinia graminis* which can survive. Both the mycelia and the ure-

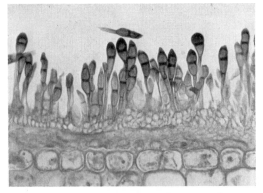

Fig. 7.33. Transverse section of a stem showing the production of teliospores by the infecting fungus.

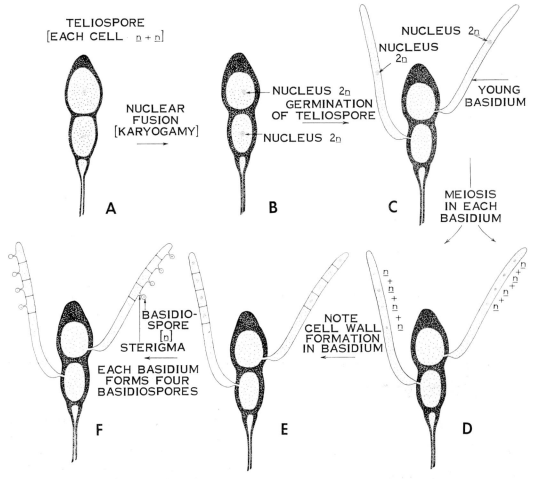

Fig. 7.34. Series depicting the germination of a teliospore, the formation of basidia, and the production of basidiospores.

dospores are eliminated by freezing weather.

The teliospore does not initiate any new infections directly. When it germinates in the following spring (Fig. 7.34) each of the two cells gives rise to a *basidium*. The plus and minus nuclei in each of the cells fuse and then migrate out into the basidia. Thus, each of the young basidia has a single diploid nucleus. This nucleus then undergoes meiosis and four haploid nuclei are formed, two of them being plus, and two minus. Sterigmata develop and *basidiospores* are extruded in the manner previously described.

These basidiospores cannot infect any of the grass type host plants. The only plant which they can infect is the common barberry, *Berberis vulgaris*. (This is not the familiar hedge plant which is the Japanese barberry.)

When a basidiospore lands on a barberry leaf it gives rise to a localized infection in which the mycelium has mononucleate cells. After a brief period of growth this mycelium forms flask-shaped structures just under the epidermis. These are called *spermagonia* (Fig. 7.35) and each one produces numerous, minute, sporelike bodies which are regarded as being homologous with male gametes. They are called *spermatia*. Also, several specialized *receptive hyphae* grow through the

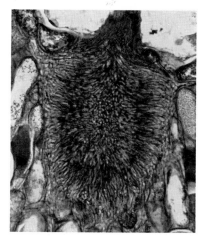

Fig. 7.35. Transverse section of a barberry leaf with a spermagonium.

spermagonia and protrude from their open necks. Each one of these is considered to be an outgrowth of the female structure described below.

A sugary solution is secreted and accumulates as a drop over each spermagonium. This solution contains many spermatia. Small insects are attracted by the nectar and crawl about the leaf feeding on it. In so doing they inadvertently transfer spermatia from one spermagonium to another.

Since the mycelia are heterothallic, spermatia will not fuse with receptive hyphae of the same strain. However, the activities of the insects sooner or later bring plus spermatia in contact with minus receptive hyphae, and vice versa. When this happens, the nucleus of the spermatium passes into the receptive hypha and moves downward until it reaches the vicinity of the opposite nucleus. The nuclei pair but do not fuse and the establishment of the binucleate $(n + n)$ condition is acomplished.

Meanwhile the framework of an entirely different type of structure has been formed just under the opposite epidermis from the spermagonia. Actually, several structures are "blocked out" in a cluster. When mature, each one of them will have a cup-shaped appearance and they are commonly referred to as *cluster cups* (Fig. 7.36). A more technical name for them is *aecia* (sing., *aecium*).

Before any one of them is recognizable as a cup it is called a *protaecium* and is considered to be the female gametangium from which the receptive hyphae originate. In a manner which is not clearly understood the pairs of nuclei in the fertilized receptive hyphae migrate into the protaecium.

Further development results in the production of long chains of spores in the aecium (Fig. 7.37). Each of these spores is single celled but has two nuclei. They are called *aeciospores* and upon their release they can infect only the grass type hosts. This is one important way in which the disease is initiated in grain fields in the spring.

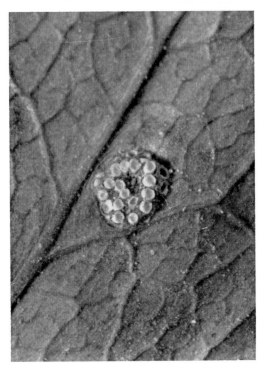

Fig. 7.36. "Cluster cups" (aecia) on the under surface of a barberry leaf.

Following the discovery of the basic facts of this alternation of hosts by *Puccinia graminis* it became evident that eradication of the barberry would break the cycle and possibly bring about some degree of control of this most serious of all plant diseases. Much effort has gone into this task and the barberry has been eradicated in many agricultural areas. Despite the distinct advantages of the eradication of barberry in the control of stem rust, the disease has not been eliminated completely. The reasons for this are based on geography as well as the biology of the fungus concerned.

In areas where freezing weather does not occur, such as many localities in the southern part of the United States and Central America, the fungus remains alive the year round in cultivated crops and wild grass hosts. Thus, the production of uredospores is never eliminated on the continent. In the spring, as the frost season passes, new crops are planted

in succession northwards. The uredospores spread the infection from one field to another and, in this way, the infection progresses slowly northwards each spring and summer. In some years this progression is so slow that many crops are well along in their development before infections begin. In such years losses due to stem rust are light.

Uredospores are spread more rapidly when large scale cyclonic disturbances cause air masses to travel hundreds of miles northwards in a few days' time. Uredospores float in these air masses and retain their viability. Eventually they drift down on fields throughout the agricultural regions of the continent and any susceptible variety of crop plant is liable to infection early in its growth.

Many years ago plant pathologists, working with agronomists, discovered that there were many different varieties of *Puccinia graminis*. Microscopic examinations of these varieties showed no

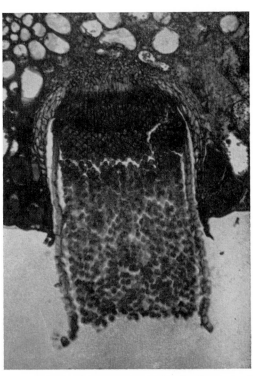

Fig. 7.37. Transverse section of a barberry leaf showing one aecium with aeciospores.

readily detectable differences between them but cultural experiments demonstrated that they had specificity for different species of cereal crop plants. Furthermore, within each variety there were shown to be many *races* of the rust; and some varieties of a specific kind of crop plant were found to be more resistant to one race of the rust than to another.

This information has been used widely in crop breeding programs and new varieties of crop plants with inbred resistance to many races of rust have been developed. Widespread use of resistant varieties is an effective means of control of the disease, but, ironically, this procedure seems to favor both the spread of previously insignificant races and the evolution of new ones.

Theoretically, the evolution of new races of rust would be slowed down by elimination of the barberry since the rate of recombination of genetic factors in the fungus could not be significant if the life cycle were broken. However, the complete elimination of the barberry on the continent is a practical impossibility and, thus, the evolution of new races continues.

Moreover, recent evidence indicates the distinct probability that an exchange of genes can take place between haploid nuclei in the $n + n$ mycelium. Such a bypass of the complete sexual cycle would abet evolutionary progress by the fungus.

Research workers in this area of science are taking a frank look at a rather grim future in which races of stem rust may develop for which there wil be no genetic sources of resistance to use in further plant breeding programs. This event could mean a tragic curtailment of the food supply in many areas of the world.

However, breeding for resistance to disease is not the only answer to the problem. Chemical control of plant disease has long been practiced but it is an expensive matter when applied to field crops. Such controls could be used, however, in cases of dire necessity. Research work with this aspect of disease control is being carried out at an increasing rate and it is almost certain that such research will result in less expensive chemical controls before the current techniques of breeding for resistance beome obsolescent due to successful evolution in the fungi.

CHAPTER 8

The Classification of Plants

Living organisms are generally classified in an ascending series of categories, each of which may be further subdivided. The major categories are listed below and a plant which has been used in the text is classified as an example.

Plant Kingdom	Example
Division (or Phylum)*	*Bryophyta*
Class	*Hepaticae*
Order	*Marchantiales*
Family	*Marchantiaceae*
Genus	*Marchantia*
Species	*polymorpha*

*The use of the term phylum in place of division is considered desirable by some authorities but is not permissible under the *International Code* which outlines the rules for plant nomenclature.

When a specific kind of living organism is discussed it may be referred to either by a common name or by a scientific name. However, common names vary from place to place and from language to language, and, furthermore, the same common name often applies to different plants in different localities.

On the other hand, the scientific name of an organism is the same in all lands and in all languages. Most scientific names are written in Latin and when a new species is described, a Latin translation of the description is included as a part of the publication no matter what the native language used in the publication may be.

Thus, one of the so-called dead languages has an important role in the transmission of scientific information across existing language barriers.

The scientific name is written as a binomial in which the generic name (*genus*) is listed first followed by the species name. The generic name of the maples is *Acer*, and the full binomial of the common silver maple is *Acer saccharinum* L. It is standard practice to include with the binomial an abbreviation of the name of the man who named the species. In the binomial cited above, the initial L. stands for Linnaeus who was one of the great biologists of the eighteenth century.

As far as the larger categories in the system of classification are concerned, we are living in an age when major changes are being made and others contemplated by plant scientists. As a result, the student who compares textbooks will find variations among them with respect to the systems of classification used.

For many years a standard classification was used almost universally which divided the plant kingdom into the following four divisions:

I — *Thallophyta* — Algae and Fungi
II — *Bryophyta* — Mosses and Liverworts
III — *Pteridophyta* — Ferns and Fern Allies
IV — *Spermatophyta* — All Seed Plants

This very simple and convenient classification had to be abandoned for several reasons, among them being:

1. The various groups of algae are no longer considered to be closely related to one another.

2. All the fungi are no longer considered to be degenerate algae. Also the various groups of fungi may have had independent origins.

3. The discovery of the fossil psilophytes resulted in a re-evaluation of the relationships of the vascular plants. One significant result of this process has been the realization that ferns are more closely related to the seed plants than they are to their so-called allies, the club mosses and horsetails.

Many of the current classification changes are top-level changes, i.e., changes are being made at the levels of the divisions, subdivisions, and classes of the plant kingdom. Despite these changes the major groups of plants remain well defined, and it is possible to discuss these groups without confusion by means of common names. In the following paragraphs each group will be discussed briefly. Then the common names will be linked to the scientific names as used in two of the contemporary classification systems.

Green algae contain chlorophylls *a* and *b* in addition to carotenoid pigments. They store starch and usually have cellulose in their cell walls. The plant bodies show a wide range from flagellated unicellular types to complex, nonmotile, branching systems. When flagellated cells occur, the flagella are alike and usually of equal length. Gametic reproduction ranges from isogamy to oogamy and from homothallism to heterothallism. Alternation of generations occurs in some species.

Stoneworts are algae of macroscopic size which are characterized by definite nodes and internodes. The major cell of each internode extends from one node to the next. The pigmentation and food storage products are similar to those of the green algae. Gametic reproduction is oogamous and involves unique multi-cellular fruiting bodies. Some species, as the name implies, become encrusted with lime.

Euglenoids are a group of animal-like plants (or plantlike animals) which have a pigmentation similar to that of the green algae. They lack cellulose, however, and their reserve food is a carbohydrate called *paramylum* rather than true starch. Some forms are incompletely autotrophic and require organic nutrients from the environment. Most of them are unicellular and motile.

Yellow-green algae contain chlorophylls *a* and *e* but the carotenoid pigments develop strongly to give the characteristic yellow-green color. Food reserves are said to be leucosin and oil rather than starch. The plant body types vary from motile unicellular forms to branching filaments. Gametic reproduction is not common involving only motile gametes in all known cases, except *Vaucheria* which is oogamous. In some genera, the wall consists of overlapping halves. Flagellated cells have two different kinds of flagella, one of which is usually shorter than the other.

Golden-brown algae owe their characteristic color to a strong development of carotenoid pigments which tend to mask the presence of chlorophyll *a*. Commonly, the pigments are located in two large chromatophores in each cell. There are only a few genera with the filamentous type of organization, and most forms are motile. A number of species are amoeba-like and may ingest solid food. Food reserves are said to be leucosins and oil. A special type of spore, the *statospore,* is common in the group. This structure has a silicified outer wall.

Diatoms also have a strong development of carotenoid pigments which tend to mask the chlorophylls *a* and *c*. Their wall structure is highly characteristic being composed of two overlapping halves which fit together like the two halves of a petri dish or a pillbox. The walls are silicified and ornamented in various ways. In one of the two major groups, the centric diatoms, these ornamentations are

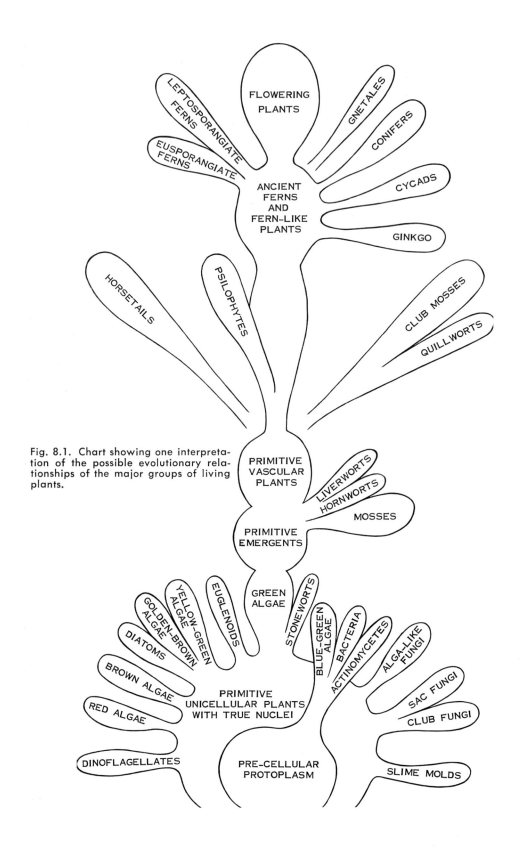

Fig. 8.1. Chart showing one interpretation of the possible evolutionary relationships of the major groups of living plants.

grouped about a point, while in the other group, the pennate diatoms, they are organized with respect to a longitudinal line. One of the chief food reserves of diatoms is oil. Diatoms grow in soil, creeks, rivers, ponds and lakes, and in the oceans where they are the most important primary producers of organic food.

Dinoflagellates comprise another group of organisms which are sometimes classified in the animal kingdom. Chlorophylls *a* and *c*, carotene, and certain unique xanthophylls give the chromatophores a brownish color. Food reserves are stored as starch or oil and cellulose may be present in the cell wall. All motile cells of this group are characterized by a transverse groove and two flagella, one of which lies in the groove while the other trails.

Brown algae owe their color to carotenoid pigments, especially certain brownish xanthophylls, which mask the presence of chlorophylls *a* and *c*. Food reserves in this group are polysaccharides which are more sugarlike than starchlike since they are water soluble. Brown algae are almost exclusively marine and most of them are macroscopic. The plant bodies of the more complex forms are parenchymatous or are made up of compact and intertwined filaments while the simpler forms are branched filaments resembling the green alga *Cladophora*. The occurrence of flagellated cells is restricted to zoospores and gametes. Gametic reproduction varies from isogamy to oogamy and alternation of generations is widespread in this group.

Red algae contain red and blue pigments in addition to carotenoids and chlorophylls *a* and *d*. Many of them are macroscopic but they are more delicate in appearance than the brown algae. Frequently they are gelatinous to the touch. A few of them occur in fresh waters but they are most abundant in marine habitats. Their gametic life cycles are complex and alternation of generations is a common feature. No motile cells are produced in this group. Even the male

gametes are without flagella and are carried by water currents to the female gametic structures.

Blue-green algae have red and blue pigments in addition to carotenoids and chlorophyll *a* only. As a group they are variously colored but many of them are actually blue-green. The more common food reserve is a carbohydrate which is sometimes referred to as *cyanophycean starch*. The pigments are distributed in the cytoplasm rather than in plastids. The chemical substances characteristic of nuclei in general are present in these plants but are not organized as in most other organisms. Chromatin granules can be demonstrated by appropriate chemical methods. They may be either diffusely arranged or densely clustered in the central region of the cell. True mitosis does not occur and cell division is accomplished by the inward growth of a ringlike furrow. There is no gametic reproduction of any kind and there are no flagellated cells. The most complex body type achieved in this group is the branching filament.

Bacteria are, for the most part, minute, single-celled plants whose internal structure is difficult to ascertain with the light microscope. Most of them are unable to manufacture their own basic foods and must function as either saprophytes or parasites. A few are able to carry on a type of photosynthesis and some others are chemosynthetic. Present-day research with the structure and physiology of bacteria is so intensive that it is difficult to make definitive statements concerning the organization of nuclear substances and the nature of the life cycle.

Actinomycetes are often referred to as higher bacteria. The cellular organization is bacterialike but the cells are joined in a filamentous organization. They are common inhabitants of the soil. Several important antibiotics including streptomycin are derived from species in this group.

Slime molds have a vegetative stage which consists either of a mass of separate amoeboid cells or of a multinucleate plasmodium. Details of the gametic life cycle vary considerably, but an intricate fruiting structure usually is formed in which spores adapted to wind dispersal are produced. These organisms have many animal-like characteristics and are classified as animals by most zoologists.

True fungi include the three major groups listed below. All true fungi lack chlorophyll and exist either as saprophytes or as parasites.

Algalike fungi exhibit a marked tendency towards the coenocytic growth habit, i.e., the plant body is generally without septae to divide it into cellular units. This is the only group among the true fungi in which flagellated reproductive cells occur. Gametic reproduction varies from isogamy to oogamy and from homothallism to heterothallism. In some forms the spores produced by nongametic processes are adapted to wind dispersal while, in more primitive ones, zoospores are produced. Many of the aquatic fungi (water molds) belong in this group.

Sac fungi have plant bodies composed of cellular units. Their gametic reproduction is complex and frequently involves a time lapse between plasmogamy and karyogamy during which the paired but not united nuclei from the male and female source are increased. Meiosis follows immediately after the eventual nuclear fusions. Then a mitosis occurs which increases the number of nuclei resulting from each diploid nucleus to eight. This group of eight nuclei is enclosed characteristically in a special cell called an ascus. The protoplasm of the ascus then becomes divided into a row of eight ascospores within the ascus. Nongametic reproduction is common in this group and frequently results in the production of such highly efficient, wind-dispersed spores as conidia.

Club fungi also have plant bodies composed of cellular units. They further resemble the preceding group in that the nuclei of the male and female gametes do not fuse immediately after plasmogamy. Commonly the binucleate (dikaryotic) condition lasts for considerable time.

In fact there are often two different types of plant bodies formed by the same species, one with mononucleate cells and the other with binucleate cells. Nuclear fusions occur within specialized cells called basidia and are followed by meiosis. Each of the four haploid nuclei within a basidium becomes incorporated into a basidiospore which is formed by an extrusion process on the outside of the basidium, rather than internally, as in the ascus.

Lichens are organisms consisting of an algal component and a fungal component. Each lichen has a characteristic appearance and structure which permits classification as a specific entity. The fungus and the alga can be grown separately and have specific identities of their own. However, these separate cultures bear no resemblance to the lichen from which they were isolated. The fungus is most commonly a member of the sac fungi, while species of both green algae and blue-green algae are found in various lichens.

Imperfect fungi include most of the fungi for which no sexual stage has been observed. This artificial group is necessary because the vegetative distinctions between the major groups of fungi, particularly the sac fungi and the club fungi, are not clear cut. Without the sexual or perfect stage a proper assignment of the fungus cannot be made. As research with the fungi continues and observations of sexual stages are obtained, species in this group are transferred to the appropriate category.

Liverworts are a group of nonvascular, green land plants in which the gametophyte is the dominant and independent generation. The sporophyte is epiphytic on the gametophyte and at least partially dependent on it. There are three series (among others) in the group: (1) the *Marchantia* series in which the plant body of the gametophyte has internal differentiation of tissues, (2) the *thallose* series in which the plant body is a simple, ribbonlike thallus without internal differentiation, and (3) the *leafy* series in which the plant body has an external differentiation into leaflike and stemlike parts. In all three series the sporophyte consists of a foot, a stalk, and a capsule. The capsule is simply constructed and the stalk does not elongate until after the spores have matured. As a significant exception it should be noted that the sporophyte of *Riccia* consists only of a capsule.

Hornworts are similar in many respects to the liverworts. The gametophyte is an independent land plant and is similar in structure to the gametophytes of the thallose liverworts. The sporophyte is also similar to the liverwort sporophyte in that it is epiphytic on the gametophyte. The major part of the sporophyte is a slender, green column which has true stomates in the epidermis. At the base of this cylindrical capsule there is a meristematic region which adds new tissues to the capsule. As the terminal part of the capsule matures it splits open in two valves and the spores are released. Between the terminal portion and the base of the capsule it is usual to encounter various stages in spore development.

Mosses are also nonvascular, green land plants in which the sporophyte is epiphytic on the independent gametophyte. The plant body of the gametophyte is leafy and bears some resemblance to that of a leafy liverwort. However, it is more robust and complex in its development. The moss sporophyte is also more complex in structure than the liverwort sporophyte. Furthermore, in contrast with the liverworts, the stalk elongates early, before the capsule tissues are fully differentiated. The whole sporophyte is green and true stomates may occur in the basal region of the capsule. The capsule tissues are organized as a series of concentric cylinders with one of the cylinders forming sporogenous tissue. The mouth of the capsule is covered characteristically by a lidlike structure, the operculum.

Peat mosses include all species in the genus *Sphagnum*. They are classified with the true mosses rather than the liverworts even though certain vegetative and reproductive structures are comparable with those of the liverworts. This is done primarily because the complexities of the sporophyte structure make it more readily comparable with the moss sporophyte. The occurrence of large water-storage cells intermixed with the smaller photosynthetic cells in the leaf is a characteristic feature of *Sphagnum*.

Psilophytes comprise a group of primitive vascular plants in which the plant body of the sporophyte consists primarily of a branching stem system. Psilophytes are rootless and for the most part leafless. Sporangia are borne terminally on the stems. Most members of this group are fossils dating back to the Lower Devonian and Upper Silurian. Two living genera, *Psilotum* and *Tmesipteris*, fit the above description with minor exceptions and are classified as psilophytes. The gametophytes of the fossil forms are unknown while those of the living forms resemble fragments of rhizomes of the sporophyte.

Club mosses and *quillworts* are vascular plants whose leaves are classified as microphylls. The sporangia are associated with modified leaves called sporophylls and these are often segregated from the vegetative leaves in cones (strobili). The gametophytes are reduced in size and inconspicuous. They are rarely green and usually depend on food stored in the spore or on an association with a fungus for their basic food supplies. This group contains many fossil genera which were conspicuous elements of the Coal Age swamp forests. Of the few living genera of club mosses, *Lycopodium* and *Selaginella* are best known. *Isoetes* is the generic name of the living quillworts. Club moss leaves are rather small, while quillwort leaves are longer and taper to a point. *Lycopodium* species are homosporous and their leaves are without ligules. Species of *Isoetes* and *Selaginella* are heterosporous and their leaves possess ligules. The quillworts differ from the club mosses in being aquatic plants. Also, their stems are very short and have a structural organization which is unique among living vascular plants.

Horsetails are sometimes called scouring rushes, or snake grass. The sporophyte is vascular and is characterized by stems which are jointed and ridged. The leaves are essentially without function and occur in definite whorls at the nodes of the stem. True roots arise from the nodes of underground portions of the stem. The spore-bearing structures are segregated into terminal cones. The spores give rise to minute, green, independent gametophytes. The single living genus, *Equisetum,* had many relatives in the Coal Age swamp forests.

Ancient ferns and *fernlike plants* were similar in many respects although it is unlikely that only one evolutionary line is involved. The dominant vegetative feature of such plants was the large, macrophyllous leaf. The macrophyll probably originated more than once as a result of the flattening and webbing of a psilophyte branch system. In some lines there was a segregation of fertile (sporangia-bearing) branch systems from vegetative-branch systems before the evolution of the leaf occurred. In other lines this prior segregation did not occur. In some of these ancient lines which are now extinct, the evolution of seed production occurred. The fossil remains of such plants are often fragmentary, and it is difficult for a nonspecialist to distinguish between the leaf of a fossil fern and the leaf of a fossil seed plant. In this brief discussion, the primitive, macrophyllous plants are grouped together under the artificial heading used above. From this group arose the several separate evolutionary lines which are discussed below.

Leptosporangiate ferns include the vast majority of living ferns. In this group the sporangia are often grouped in small clusters (sori) on the under surface of the leaf. The sporangia are delicate, thin-walled, and stalked. The number of spores in each sporangium is small (rarely more than 64) and definite. The leaves are the dominant vegetative organs and, in most cases, the stems a r e inconspicuous rhizomes from which the leaves as well as

the roots arise. Fern gametophytes are small, green, and independent.

Eusporangiate ferns comprise a rather small group of ferns which are older (in the evolutionary sense) than the group described above. Most of them have large compound leaves. One essential difference between the two groups of ferns has to do with sporangium development. In this group the sporangium is a masive structure which gives rise to an indefinitely large number of spores.

Gymnosperms include all seed plants in which the seed is not completely enclosed within the seed-bearing structure. In all gymnosperms the microspores mature into pollen grains which are wind-disseminated. Each pollen grain is able to form a pollen tube which penetrates the tissues of the nucellus and transports the sperms to the vicinity of the eggs. The whole group is admittedly a convenient but artificial complex of several independent evolutionary lines.

Cycads are the oldest living group of seed plants. Their leaves are large and fernlike. Their stems are thick, short, erect, and fleshy, with relatively poor development of vascular tissue. Pith and cortex tissues make up the larger part of the stem. The stems are clothed with the bases of dead leaves. Seeds are produced on megasporophylls which are segregated into strobili. Microsporangia are numerous on the surface of the microsporophylls which also are grouped into strobili. The two kinds of cones occur on separate plants.

Conifers are, for the most part, treelike forms with an extensive development of secondary vascular tissue and an outer corky bark. The pith and cortex tissues are relatively small. In most of them the leaves are highly modified as scales or needles. Conifers frequently retain their leaves during the winter season and are known commonly as evergreens. The strobilus (cone) is a basic reproductive structure in the group but is sometimes so highly modified that it no longer is identifiable as such. In many conifers the

In the following table two contemporary systems for the classification of living plants are outlined for purposes of comparison with the common names of each of the major groups listed in a central column between them.

The column to the left is a classification system based on one published by Oswald Tippo in 1942. It is used in many current textbooks including **College Botany** (Henry Holt & Co., 1949) written by Tippo in collaboration with Harry Fuller.

The classification system in the right hand column is one first presented in 1957 by Harold C. Bold in his text **Morphology of Plants** (Harper and Bros., 1957). This system represents a more extensive revision of the major categories than many botanists are ready to accept, even though the proposed changes are based on cogent arguments.

The chart on p. 212 shows possible evolutionary relationships between the major groups of living plants. The reader is cautioned that charts such as these are synthesized from many hypotheses and are speculative in nature.

A COMPARISON OF TWO CONTEMPORARY CLASSIFICATION SYSTEMS OF THE PLANT KINGDOM

Classification of Tippo (1942)			Classification of Bold (1957)
Sub-kingdom .... *Thallophyta*			
Phylum 1 ..... *Cyanophyta*	(Blue-green Algae)	Division 1	*Cyanophyta*
Phylum 2 ..... *Chlorophyta*			
Class ...... *Chlorophyceae*	(Green Algae)	Division 2	*Chlorophyta*
Class ...... *Charophyceae*	(Stoneworts)	Division 4	*Charophyta*
Phylum 3 .... *Euglenophyta*	(Euglenoids)	Division 3	*Euglenophyta*
Phylum 4 .... *Phaeophyta*	(Brown Algae)	Division 5	*Phaeophyta*
Phylum 5 .... *Rhodophyta*	(Red Algae)	Division 6	*Rhodophyta*
Phylum 6 .... *Chrysophyta*		Division 7	*Chrysophyta*
Class ...... *Xanthophyceae*	(Yellow-green Algae)	Class	*Xanthophyceae*
Class ...... *Chrysophyceae*	(Golden-brown Algae)	Class	*Chrysophyceae*
Class ...... *Bacillariophyceae*	(Diatoms)	Class	*Bacillariophyceae*
Phylum 7 .... *Pyrrophyta*	(Dinoflagellates, etc.)	Division 8	*Pyrrophyta*
Phylum 8 .... *Schizomycophyta*	(Bacteria and Actinomycetes)	Division 9	*Schizomycota*
Phylum 9 .... *Myxomycophyta*	(Slime Molds)	Division 10	*Myxomycota*
Phylum 10 .... *Eumycophyta*	(True Fungi)		
Class ...... *Phycomycetes*	(Algalike Fungi)	Division 11	*Phycomycota*
Class ...... *Ascomycetes*	(Sac Fungi)	Division 12	*Ascomycota*
Class ...... *Basidiomycetes*	(Club Fungi)	Division 13	*Basidiomycota*
	(Imperfect Fungi)		
	(Lichens)		
Sub-kingdom .... *Embryophyta*			
Phylum 11 .... *Bryophyta*			
		Division 14	*Hepatophyta*
Class ...... *Hepaticae*	(Liverworts)	Class	*Hepatopsida*
Class ...... *Anthocerotae*	(Hornworts)	Class	*Anthoceropsida*
Class ...... *Musci*		Division 15	*Bryophyta*
Order .. *Sphagnales*	(Peat Mosses)	Class	*Sphagnopsida*
Order .. *Bryales*	(True Mosses)	Class	*Mnionopsida*
Phylum 12 .... *Tracheophyta*	(All Vascular Plants)		
Subphylum .. *Psilopsida*	(Psilophytes)	Division 16	*Psilophyta*
Subphylum .. *Lycopsida*	(Club Mosses and Quillworts)	Division 17	*Microphyllophyta*
Subphylum .. *Sphenopsida*	(Horsetails)	Division 18	*Arthrophyta*
Subphylum .. *Pteropsida*			
Class ...... *Filicinae*	(Ferns)	Division 19	*Pterophyta*
	(Eusporangiate Ferns)	Class	*Eusporangiopsida*
	(Leptosporangiate Ferns)	Class	*Leptosporangiopsida*
Class ...... *Gymnospermae*			
Sub-class . *Cycadophytae*	(Cyads)	Division 20	*Cyadophyta*
Sub-class . *Coniferophytae*			
Order .. *Ginkgoales*	(Ginkgo)	Division 21	*Ginkgophyta*
Order .. *Coniferales*	(Conifers)	Division 22	*Coniferophyta*
Order .. *Gnetales*	(Gnetum, etc.)	Division 23	*Gnetophyta*
Class ...... *Angiospermae*	(Flowering Plants)	Division 24	*Anthophyta*

ovuliferous scales bear two ovules apiece and the microsporophylls have two microsporangia apiece.

Ginkgo is a large, profusely branched tree which bears simple, deciduous leaves with dichotomously branched veins resembling the vein system of the maidenhair fern leaf. The stem structure is more like that of a conifer than a cycad for it has extensive development of secondary xylem and a small pith and cortex. The stem has a characteristic arrangement of long shoots and spur shoots. The microsporangia develop in simple strobili while the ovules develop in pairs on slender stalks. As the ovule develops into the seed, the outer layer of the integument becomes fleshy and malodorous.

Ephedra, Gnetum, and *Welwitschia* are three genera with gymnospermous features but which seem to be quite separate from other gymnosperms and, quite probably, are not closely related to one another. Among their characteristics are compound, reduced microstrobili and megastrobili, and the presence of vessels in the xylem.

Angiosperms include all the flowering plants. The basic flower type consists of a shortened axis on which are borne sepals, petals, stamens, and pistils. The stamen is considered to be a microsporophyll and the simple pistil is a modified megasporophyll. A basic angiosperm feature is the enclosure of the ovules within the ovary portion of the pistil.

Index